The Breeding Birds of Hertfordshire

Edited by K W Smith, C W Dee, J D Fearnside,
E W Fletcher and R N Smith

PUBLISHED BY THE HERTFORDSHIRE NATURAL HISTORY SOCIETY

THIS BOOK IS DEDICATED TO THE HERTFORDSHIRE
BIRDWATCHERS WHO CARRIED OUT THE FIELDWORK AND
WITHOUT WHOM IT WOULD NOT HAVE BEEN POSSIBLE

ISBN 0-9521685-0-2

First published in 1993 by The Hertfordshire Natural History Society

Published with the support of:

Type services by Pre-Press Services, London SW4
Output by Diamond Graphics, Mitcham, Surrey
Printed and bound in Great Britain by The Bath Press, Avon.

Contents

Foreword

I expect most authors, confronted by a new book which renders one of their own to history, would feel regret and envy. However, with a county bird atlas, everyone involved knows that they are producing a freeze-frame of a constantly changing picture. This new book provides a snapshot, of excellent definition, of the distribution of Hertfordshire's breeding birds from 1988-1992, twenty years after the first Hertfordshire Breeding Bird Atlas. Far from regret, I feel pride in having been associated with the first atlas but I do feel envy, from my new county of Norfolk, because, like all other counties, we do not yet have two atlases to show how bird distributions are changing.

Bird atlas work is exciting and interesting and the army of volunteers involved in the fieldwork will have found it enjoyable – almost addictive – and will without doubt be delighted by this, the outcome of their efforts. As a working document it will enable birdwatchers, over the next few years, to put their records into an accurate county context. This, by itself, might seem sufficient reason for the observers and organisers to have devoted all the time and effort the production of such an atlas devours. However as an inventory of the avifauna of Hertfordshire, and a record of the changes since the first atlas, it will immediately become a vital tool for conservation. The current distributions and recorded changes, taken in conjunction with the environmental data will highlight all sorts of problems, and some successes.

Every species is of interest – some indicate worrying losses of birds once familiar in the county – but others show clearly the resilience of bird populations when given the opportunity to recover from losses. During the fieldwork for the first Hertfordshire Breeding Bird Atlas it was a real surprise to come across a Sparrowhawk in the county. They had suffered, as the top bird predator, appalling losses from the effects of persistent pesticides and their population was close to its all time low. The old atlas map showed records from just 9% of the tetrads in the county. Not for a moment did we imagine that only twenty years later this exciting bird would be recorded from 74% of the county's tetrads.

Now you have read the foreword read the book! The organisers and observers have every cause to be proud of it. All birdwatchers interested in Hertfordshire should now make use of it.

Chris Mead
Hilborough, Norfolk, June 1993

Preface

This book is the culmination of six years effort by members of the Herts Bird Club. When in 1987 the Bird Club Committee agreed that we should go ahead with the project, none of us realised just how much work would be involved. Having now completed the job we hope all of those who have contributed will feel that this book does justice to their efforts.

Unlike previous county avifaunas (Sage 1959, Gladwin & Sage 1986) this book concentrates solely on breeding birds. We are fortunate that Hertfordshire was one of the first counties to complete an atlas of breeding birds (Mead & Smith 1982) and we have maintained our leading position by being the first county to publish the results of a repeat survey.

The great strength of this book is that we have been able to make direct comparisons between the distributions of breeding birds now and 20 years ago. In evolutionary terms, 20 years is a very short period but it is remarkable how many changes there have been. Some are due to factors outside Hertfordshire whilst others are the direct result of changes of habitats and land-use within the county. With much talk in recent years of biodiversity and sustainable development it is important to realise that in future years it is the data in books such as ours which will be used to judge how well our national and local biodiversity have been managed. Our results for the last twenty years give no grounds for complacency, although some species have increased, many are in decline.

Throughout this book we have tried to maintain a scientific approach, both in assessing changes in bird distributions and interpreting the reasons for them. Some readers may be surprised that, in spite of detailed analyses of bird distributions against agricultural and other land-uses, we have been unable to come up with explanations for many of the changes. You should not be surprised; the reasons for such changes are often extremely complex and, if anything, ornithologists have been guilty of giving the impression that the reasons for changes are well understood when in fact they have only made informed guesses. We hope that this book will provide the stimulus to others to get on with some of the detailed investigations needed to provide explanations for the changes.

One of the key motivations for completing this survey was our belief that bird conservation should be based on sound facts. We are sure that the data we have presented will lead to a better targeted bird conservation strategy for the county. We look forward to learning how many of the currently declining species have recovered when the atlas is repeated in twenty years time.

ACKNOWLEDGEMENTS

The collection of data for an atlas such as this would not be possible without the enthusiastic help of the fieldworkers and local organisers. They are listed in Appendix 1.1 and we thank them all. It is an indication of the depth of ornithological expertise that exists in the county that many of the same people have also written the texts for the species accounts. Their initials appear against the texts they have written and are listed here in alphabetical order: Jeff Davies (JD), Chris Dee (CWD), Trudie Dockerty (TD), John and Carol Dowling (J & CD), Richard Drew and Jol Mitchell (RD & JM), Gary Elton (GE), Ted Fletcher (EWF), Mike Harris (MH), Martin Ketcher (MK), Tom Kittle (TK), David McKee (DM), John Melling (JM), Colin Shawyer (CRS), Ken Smith (KWS), Linda Smith (LMS), Robin Smith (RNS), Bruce Taggart (BT), Johne Taylor

(JET), Jim Terry (JHT), John Tomkins (JNT), Graham White (GJW), Peter Wilkinson (PJW), Adam Wilson (AW), Rob Young (RY).

The illustrations have been drawn by the following, mainly local, artists: Nik Borrow, Andrew Chick, Gary Clayden, Hugh Coe, Keith Colcombe, Jack Fearnside, Alan Harris, Ernest Leahy, Mike Pollard and Jan Wilczur. The line drawings for which each artist was responsible are listed in Appendix 1.1 and we thank them all for their enlivening contribution to the book.

We have received help from many organisations and individuals; in particular the Bedfordshire and London Natural History Societies have co-operated in the exchange of records in the overlap areas and the British Trust for Ornithology kindly allowed us to use their national population estimates derived for the new national atlas. The Hertfordshire Bird Recorders, Peter Walton and Rob Young, extracted additional breeding records from their files.

We thank the Royal Society for the Protection of Birds for financial help in acquiring the agricultural statistics used in this book. We also thank Hertfordshire County Council and English Nature for financial support for the publication of this atlas.

Finally we wish to thank Linda Smith for assistance with proof reading and Paula Fearnside for organising the pre-publication offer for this book.

KWS, CWD, JDF, EWF, RNS
August 1993

I: Introduction

The publication of the first atlas of Hertfordshire's breeding birds by Chris Mead and Ken Smith in 1982 was a major event for all interested birdwatchers (Mead & Smith 1982). It brought together for the first time maps showing the actual distribution of all the birds breeding, or suspected of breeding, in the county. The fieldwork for the atlas covered the period 1967-73 and was prompted mainly by pilot fieldwork undertaken in Hertfordshire for the national 'Atlas of Breeding Birds in Britain and Ireland' which was carried out between 1968 and 1972 by the British Trust for Ornithology and the Irish Wildbird Conservancy (Sharrock 1976). The publication of the local atlas allowed Hertfordshire to join the elite band of counties who had, by then, published a definitive account of their own breeding birds (the others being London, Bedfordshire and Kent (Montier 1977, Harding 1979, Taylor *et al* 1981)). Prior to this time the main sources of reference regarding the county's birds were the annual reports published by the ornithological section of the Hertfordshire Natural History Society (now known as the Herts Bird Club) and Bryan Sage's detailed book 'A History of the Birds of Hertford-shire' (Sage 1959). However, neither of these sources provided a comprehensive range of detailed distribution maps, due chiefly to the lack of birdwatchers able to undertake the necessary dedicated fieldwork and a lack of systematic coverage of the whole county.

In 1986 Tom Gladwin and Bryan Sage produced their book, 'The Birds of Hertford-shire' (Gladwin & Sage 1986). This updated Sage's earlier work and was a review of the distribution and status of all the species recorded in the county between 1958 and 1982, with some records of interest for 1983 and 1984. It also described the geography, the variety of habitats, the salient meteorological data and reproduced the maps from the original breeding atlas.

In the meantime many other counties and administrative areas have produced their own local atlases – the list is now well into double figures. This tally will certainly grow, reflecting the healthy interest during the last decade in conservation generally and birdwatching specifically and the concomitant quest for information.

In Hertfordshire the next logical step was to repeat the atlas fieldwork to update the information already published. Every active observer is generally aware that there have been significant changes in certain bird populations nationally – the welcome increases in Peregrine *Falco peregrinus* and Sparrowhawk numbers are often quoted along with the less welcome growth in the distribution of Canada Geese. On the debit side people have noticed fewer Nightingales and Nightjars and the decrease in many seed-eating birds is an accepted and worrying trend.

In 1988 the British Trust for Ornithology launched a second, updated breeding bird atlas project for Britain and Ireland based on the period 1988-91. In Hertfordshire it was realised that, if the correct local administration could be organised, it would be possible to capitalise on the fieldwork for the new national atlas and thereby to produce an update to the 1967-73 local tetrad atlas. There was thus a possibility of becoming the first county to produce a comprehensive comparison of the distribution of its breeding birds over a twenty year interval. Accordingly the Herts Bird Club endorsed the proposal and in 1988 initiated the fieldwork, the majority of which overlapped and augmented that being performed for the BTO project.

The methodologies followed were essentially those used during the first atlas and which have been adopted throughout Europe as standard by the European Ornithological Atlas Committee. All Ordnance Survey maps carry a regular grid at one kilometre intervals which allows the location of any point using the National Grid Reference system. Four one kilometre squares form a larger square with boundaries two kilometres long. This two kilometre square, aligned to the even numbered kilometre lines of the National Grid, is known as a tetrad, from the Greek word 'tetra' meaning four. Thus each ten kilometre square comprises 25 tetrads. Conventionally these are identified by the letters A to Z, omitting O, as recommended by the Ray Society. Individual tetrads are identified by a combination of the four-character ten kilometre square identifier plus the tetrad letter (e.g. Hatfield Aerodrome is in tetrad TL20E). Figure 1.1 shows two maps: an outline of Hertfordshire with its ten kilometre squares and tetrads superimposed, along with a diagrammatic explanation of the tetrad lettering system, and a similar outline with the locations of the main towns.

During the fieldwork each species was categorised as possible, probable or confirmed breeding using the standard definitions of the evidence of breeding developed by Sharrock (1976):

Possible breeding

This category comprised any birds seen during the breeding season in a suitable habitat. There were commonsense exclusions such as loafing gulls and birds resting prior to moving on to their final nesting locations (e.g. Dotterel *Charadrius morinellus*).

Probable breeding

This category included birds present in the tetrad and showing evidence of the intention to breed:

S   Singing male or breeding calls heard on more than one occasion.
T   Bird (or pair) apparently holding territory.
B   Nest building or excavation.
N   Birds visiting probable nest site.
D   Birds showing courtship display or behaviour.

It is possible that some singing males would not stay to breed but in most cases such behaviour was still considered a reasonable indicator of probable breeding so long as the song was heard on at least two separate occasions.

Confirmed breeding

This category was reserved for those cases where there was definite evidence of breeding, but note that it was not required to prove that the breeding attempt was successful:

NE   A nest was located which contained eggs.
NY   A nest was located which contained young.
FY   Adult birds were seen carrying food for the young.
FS   Adult birds were seen carrying a faecal sac.
FL   Recently fledged young were seen, not necessarily in the company of
            their parents.
UN   A nest used in the current year was found.
ON   Adult birds were seen visiting or leaving a nest site in circumstances
            indicating that the nest was in use.
DD   Birds were observed performing a distraction display.

It was recognised that there might be some cases where birds carrying food could be flying to a nest in an adjoining tetrad, particularly in the case of raptors hunting large

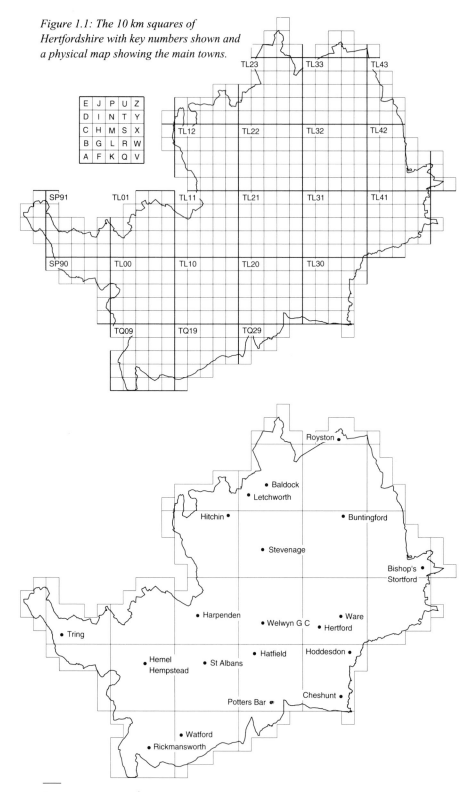

Figure 1.1: The 10 km squares of Hertfordshire with key numbers shown and a physical map showing the main towns.

E	J	P	U	Z
D	I	N	T	Y
C	H	M	S	X
B	G	L	R	W
A	F	K	Q	V

TL23 TL33 TL43

TL12 TL22 TL32 TL42

SP91 TL01 TL11 TL21 TL31 TL41

SP90 TL00 TL10 TL20 TL30

TQ09 TQ19 TQ29

Royston

Baldock
Letchworth

Hitchin Buntingford

Stevenage

Bishop's
Stortford

Harpenden Ware
Welwyn G C Hertford

Tring

Hemel
Hempstead St Albans Hatfield Hoddesdon

Cheshunt

Potters Bar

Watford
Rickmansworth

territories or when a sighting was close to a tetrad boundary. Additionally, recently fledged young could have moved from other tetrads.

Fieldwork for the atlas involved over 250 birdwatchers organised by co-ordinators who were each responsible for supervising one or more ten kilometre square (See Appendix 1.1 for details). Each observer was asked to cover a number of tetrads during the breeding season with the aim of detecting all species breeding in the square and attempting to find the best evidence of breeding under the three categories noted above. The main fieldwork season was from April to July, but care was taken to ensure that species which nested outside these periods, such as owls, Mistle Thrush and Crossbill in the earlier months and pigeons, doves and buntings, which could still be breeding into August and beyond, were not overlooked. Similarly, fieldworkers were requested to make special visits to search for species active at dawn and dusk. Standard recording cards (Figure 1.2) were provided for use by observers in the field and for the submission of records. Extra records collected by casual observations were submitted on supplementary record sheets.

In order to achieve a good standard of coverage, visits in each month from April to July were desirable. If this was not possible, visits later in the breeding season, when the sight of parents carrying food or the actual evidence of fledged young provided confirmation of breeding, were preferable. No guidance was given regarding the duration or number of visits as it was suggested that individuals should survey at a pace at which they were relaxed. Observers were asked to record the number of hours spent in each tetrad. It is estimated that, overall, 7600 hours of fieldwork were carried out. After assessment of the initial results, a target of at least ten hours fieldwork in each tetrad was set.

The overall concept of the fieldwork was that it should be enjoyable and not seen to be a drudge. Fortunately, most helpers found it so, remarking how much pleasure they had derived from the project. There was a personal challenge and peer pressure to prove

HERTFORDSHIRE BREEDING BIRD ATLAS   10 KM SQ .... TETRAD

OBSERVER .... LOCATION ....

19 ..   DATE ....   TOTAL TIME ......   VISIT/SUMMARY

Little G	01		Turtle D	26		Mistle T	51		Carrion C	76	
*G C Grebe	02		Cuckoo	27		G'hopper W	52		Starling	77	
*Heron	03		Barn Owl	28		Sedge W	53		House Sp	78	
*Mute Swan	04		Little Owl	29		Reed W	54		Tree Sp	79	
*Canada G	05		Tawny Owl	30		Lesser Wh	55		Chaffinch	80	
Mallard	06		Long-E Owl	31		Whitethr	56		Greenfinch	81	
Tufted D	07		Swift	32		Garden W	57		Goldfinch	82	
Sparr'hawk	08		Kingfisher	33		Blackcap	58		Linnet	83	
Kestrel	09		Green Wood	34		*Wood W	59		Redpoll	84	
Hobby	10		Great S Wp	35		Chiffchaff	60		Bullfinch	85	
Red-Leg P	11		Lesser S W	36		Willow W	61		Hawfinch	86	
Partridge	12		Skylark	37		Goldcrest	62		Yellowh	87	
Pheasant	13		Sand M	38		Spotted F	63		Reed Bunt	88	
Moorhen	14		Swallow	39		Long-T Tit	64		Corn Bunt	89	
Coot	15		House M	40		Marsh Tit	65				
*LR Plover	16		Tree Pipit	41		Willow Tit	66				
*R Plover	17		Meadow Pip	42		Coal Tit	67				
Lapwing	18		Yellow Wag	43		Blue Tit	68				
*Snipe	19		Grey Wag	44		Great Tit	69				
Woodcock	20		Pied Wag	45		Nuthatch	70				
*Redshank	21		Wren	46		Treecreep	71				
Fer Pigeon	22		Dunnock	47		Jay	72				
Stock Dove	23		Robin	48		Magpie	73				
Woodpigeon	24		Blackbird	49		Jackdaw	74				
Collared D	25		Song T	50		Rook	75				

Please return to your 10 km square organiser by August 31st.

Figure 1.2: The standard recording card used throughout the survey.

that a bird had bred rather than it be categorised as 'possible' or 'probable'. Also, the fieldwork appealed to the basic collecting instinct in most birdwatchers. Even the most common birds could not be taken for granted and had to be searched for. This was illustrated in the later years of the survey when a review of the cumulative records revealed the absence of records of common birds such as Dunnocks and Robins in squares where they were known to exist.

The human population in Hertfordshire is concentrated in the south, middle and west and this tended to be mirrored by the numbers of fieldworkers able to work in the respective ten kilometre squares. Co-ordinators in the north and east viewed the plethora of assistants in other parts of the county with some envy as they cajoled their own handful of helpers to undertake an extra tetrad or two. Nevertheless, coverage of the county was total – all tetrads were surveyed and, with the special treatment noted later, the organising panel are fully satisfied that the final results reflect accurately the distribution of the county's breeding birds.

Although the large majority of fieldwork could be undertaken from footpaths and other public areas, there were some instances when it was necessary to seek permission for access to private land in order to achieve the best coverage of a tetrad. It was stressed to observers that in such cases the wishes of the landowner should be strictly adhered to and that crops and private premises should be treated with total respect. No observers reported meeting any difficulty with these sensible guidelines, neither were there any complaints regarding behaviour.

The information held by the county bird recorder was also searched for records of the less common species. This was deemed sensible as some of the records submitted to the recorder would come from people not involved with the atlas fieldwork.

The cumulative results of the 1988-91 fieldwork were reviewed by the atlas organis-ers in late 1991 and certain tetrads where the quality of coverage was considered to be below an expected guideline (less than ten hours fieldwork or a high proportion of 'present' or 'probable' breeding records) were targeted for extra work in 1992. These represented around 7% of the total and were usually those where insufficient time had been spent, resulting in either fewer species than expected or a smaller percentage of confirmed breeding when compared with the average for the county overall.

The results of the fieldwork comprise the major part of this book. They are presented in two formats. The 111 main species – those for which the editorial panel considered that sufficient data are available – are each represented by a double page spread. One page describes the characteristics of the bird along with relevant breeding information plus an analysis of any changes between the atlas periods. The second page contains two maps showing the distributions of the species during the original atlas period of 1967-73 and the new atlas 1988-92. For two species, Shelduck and Feral Pigeon, insufficient data were available to prepare maps for the old atlas – Shelduck did not breed and Feral Pigeon was not included in the project. The distribution maps for 1988-92 for three species, Barn Owl, Long-eared Owl and Nightjar, are presented in a fashion which conceals actual tetrad locations to avoid drawing attention to the exact breeding places of these locally threatened birds. A further 25 species are treated separately at the end of the section. These are either birds which have now become extinct as breeding species in Hertfordshire or birds which have bred or attempted to breed on so few occasions that the inclusion of a map is unnecessary.

The county boundary shown on the maps was established in April 1965, when the South Barnet and East Barnet Urban Districts were lost from Hertfordshire, and Potters Bar Urban District included. At the same time there was a small exchange with Bedfordshire of mainly rural land in the north-west. Hertfordshire was unaffected by the subsequent local government re-organisation in April 1974, so in fact the county boundary is unchanged between the two atlas periods. However, for historical reasons these parts of old Hertfordshire, and an area to the south of Luton, were included in the fieldwork for the old atlas. In the early stages of this project it was decided to discontinue this practice and survey only tetrads containing part of the existing county, so 16 tetrads included previously were discarded. However, three tetrads which should have been surveyed before but were inadvertently missed (TQ09A, TL30Y and TL42X) have been included. This accounts for the differences in outline between the pairs of distribution maps.

Each species map has dots of three sizes in each tetrad which relate to the breeding definitions described earlier:

- *Possible breeding*
- *Probable breeding*
- *Confirmed breeding*

A blank in a tetrad indicates that the species was not detected at all throughout the atlas fieldwork. The records are cumulative across the period 1988-92 and therefore do not always mean that a species was present in a tetrad in every one of the five years, although this will surely be the case for all the common birds. In some instances the distribution shown will be more widespread than that in any single year. Also, it is considered that the maps for some species which are known to be declining (e.g. Corn Bunting) will paint an over-optimistic picture as they do not reflect any losses in more recent years.

The atlas organisers did consider whether the new atlas should attempt to collect data on breeding densities within a tetrad in addition to breeding status, but concluded that this was too ambitious a task, even in a small county such as Hertfordshire. The method of representing such extra information, which might fluctuate from year to year, posed further problems. An estimate of the Hertfordshire breeding population during the survey period has been made for each of the 111 main species and this is given, along with the most recent view of the national figure, together with an assessment of the current population trend. We are indebted to the BTO for allowing us to use their latest national population estimates.

The maintenance of all of the records was computerised, using a package written by D J Price for use in the 'Tetrad Atlas of the Breeding Birds of Devon' (Sitters 1988). As well as producing a relief from the manual labours involved in compiling the old atlas the use of this program enabled on-going feedback to be made available during the course of the fieldwork. The opportunity was taken to use computer facilities to produce statistics and comparisons with the old data and to produce the distribution maps. However, in order to so do, all the old atlas data (some 25,000 records) were entered into the current database. Open circle records from the old atlas (either probable or possible breeding) have been classified for the maps in this book as probable breeding. Appendix 1.2 provides further details of the computer processing facilities used to store data and generate the maps.

II: Hertfordshire landscape and land-use

Human geography

Situated immediately to the north of Greater London, and bordering Buckinghamshire, Bedfordshire, Cambridgeshire and Essex, the county of Hertfordshire has an area of 163,415 hectares. Several major and ancient communication routes radiating from London pass through the county and the main centres of habitation are concentrated along these. Over 30% of the human population of 975,829 is concentrated in the four largest towns, each with populations of over 60,000 (Watford, Hemel Hempstead, Stevenage and St Albans) and almost 90% of the total population is in urban or suburban areas of over 5000 occupants. With this geographical bias, much of the county, particularly in the north-east, consists of thinly populated and less developed areas, based around villages (Figure 2.1).

Rapid population growth, at an average rate of 3.5% per annum, occurred during the 1950s, largely as a result of the development of new towns at Stevenage, Hemel Hempstead, Welwyn Garden City and Hatfield. Further urban expansion is now limited by Green Belt policies and land designated as such now comprises 40% of the county and envelops all the main towns except Royston (Hertfordshire Environmental Forum 1992). The rate of population increase is now much lower and the average annual growth rates for the three decades since 1961 have fallen successively and dramatically. Over the twenty-year period since the old atlas there has been an average annual population increase of less than 0.3% (about 2500 people per year).

The building of new roads and widening of existing ones continues to have an impact upon the environment as demand for greater mobility and ease of travel increases. Hertfordshire has the second highest level of car ownership per person in south-east England and traffic in the county has doubled between 1975 and 1990. The completion of the M25 London orbital motorway has had a major effect on the Hertfordshire landscape and is now creating new and different development pressures.

Physical geography

Hertfordshire is located on the northern rim of the London Basin, with the chalk ridge of the Chiltern Hills extending along the north-western boundary. From 245 metres above sea level, the highest point in Hertfordshire on the Buckinghamshire border near Hastoe, the Chilterns decrease in altitude towards the north-east where a lower, but still significant, scarp slope reaches Royston. The main gaps in these hills, at Tring and Hitchin, form important communication corridors, the former being used by the Grand Union Canal and the main-line railway from Euston, the latter by the A1(M) trunk road and the railway from Kings Cross. Figure 2.2 shows the altitude map of the county.

The dip slope of the Chiltern ridge falls south-east towards central Hertfordshire and forms the catchment of the main river systems in the county. With the exception of those draining the small amount of the county on the north-west face of the Chilterns, the rivers of Hertfordshire flow into the Thames via the Colne or Lee. The River Colne, with its tributaries the Ver, Gade and Chess, drains the land south-west of a minor ridge between Redbourn and Hatfield. Flowing through Watford and Rickmansworth, the Colne forms part of the boundary with Greater London before joining the Thames at Staines. East of Hatfield a more extensive river system, comprising the Lee, and its

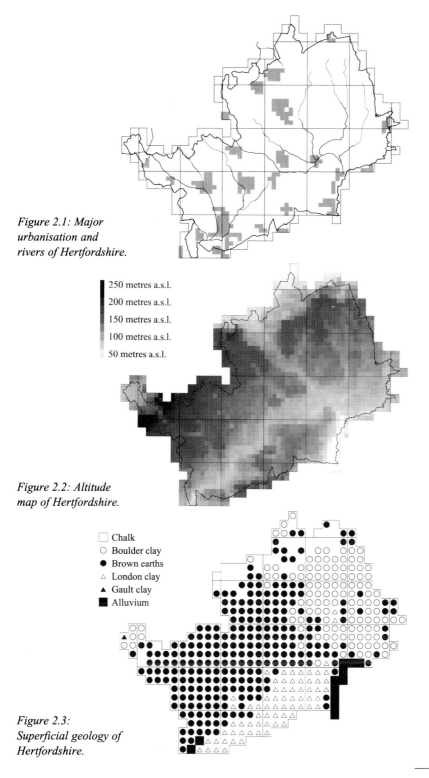

Figure 2.1: Major urbanisation and rivers of Hertfordshire.

250 metres a.s.l.
200 metres a.s.l.
150 metres a.s.l.
100 metres a.s.l.
50 metres a.s.l.

Figure 2.2: Altitude map of Hertfordshire.

☐ Chalk
○ Boulder clay
● Brown earths
△ London clay
▲ Gault clay
■ Alluvium

Figure 2.3: Superficial geology of Hertfordshire.

tributaries the Mimram, Beane, Rib and Ash, flows south and east to the county boundary near Hoddesdon. Here the Stort, which north of this point forms much of the boundary with Essex, joins the Lee which flows south along the county boundary to Cheshunt, the lowest point in the county at 15 metres above sea level, from where it continues until it joins the Thames at Poplar. The river systems are shown in Figure 2.1.

GEOLOGY

The underlying geology of Hertfordshire consists of the chalk beds of the London Basin overlying gault clay, both formed during the Cretaceous period. These slope down from the Chiltern scarp towards the south-east, extending under London and appearing again in Surrey as the North Downs. In the south of the county these chalk beds are overlaid with Eocene deposits of the Reading beds and London clay. Over these simple formations lies a much more complex mosaic of more recent deposits. During the rapid climatic changes of the Pleistocene period, several different types of glacial deposit were laid down over different regions of the county and these form the majority of the superficial geology of today (Figure 2.3). In the north and east is found the boulder clay, whereas much of the soil of the west comprises brown-earths. Extensive gravel beds are present in the Vale of St Albans and the valleys of the Lee and Colne and their tributaries.

WEATHER DURING THE ATLAS PERIOD

During the period of this atlas annual rainfall, as measured at Rothamsted, near Harpenden, averaged around 650 millimetres, consistently lower than the twenty-year average of 705 millimetres. The results of this drought upon the Hertfordshire landscape were all too obvious with streams, and even rivers, drying up completely and low water flows affecting many wetland habitats. Prolonged periods of severe weather late in the winter can have dramatic effects on the populations of resident birds, with recovery often taking several years. During this atlas period the only significant cold spell was in February 1991 and winters were in general very mild.

In 1988, the first year of fieldwork for this atlas, weather during the early part of breeding season was favourable and many species started to breed earlier than average, but nationally July was the wettest for 50 years. The whole of the 1989 breeding season was hot and dry resulting in another early start. In 1990, May was unusually warm and dry and the breeding season started even earlier. A very wet June undoubtedly affected nesting success, but drought conditions returned in July and August. May 1991 was again dry with northerly winds dominating the weather. Migrant birds arrived later than usual or not at all and, together with resident species, were badly affected by another wet June, the coolest for 300 years. After an unsettled July, August was very warm. The weather in the early part of the 1992 breeding season was changeable, but from mid-May onwards conditions were very warm. Many species began nesting early.

LAND-USE

Land-use data collection

In order to relate bird distributions to land use, data for each tetrad were extracted from the 1:25,000 Ordnance Survey maps. Fourteen different parameters were measured for each of the 491 tetrads surveyed for the atlas.

The nine area parameters (Table 2.1) were measured by superimposing a transparent overlay, containing 100 regularly spaced dots, onto each one kilometre square of the map and counting the number of dots falling within each land-use category. The categories were identified by the conventional mapping symbols used on the maps. For

	Area (hectares)	%	Tetrads	%
Derived from maps:				
Broad-leaved woodland	9972	5.1	466	94.9
Coniferous woodland	863	0.4	136	27.7
Mixed woodland	6310	3.2	346	70.5
Parkland	3540	1.8	276	56.2
Golf courses	1550	0.8	61	12.4
Mineral workings	574	0.3	36	7.3
Open water	1022	0.5	125	25.5
Marsh	131	0.1	33	6.7
Built-up areas	32,385	16.5	485	98.8
Derived from MAFF census:				
Farmland	104,895	53.4	438	89.2
Other open country	35,157	17.9	339	69.0

Table 2.1: Total area of each land-use category and number of tetrads in which these habitats are found for the 491 tetrads of this atlas. The data were derived from measurements from 1:25,000 Ordnance Survey maps using a grid of 100 points per square kilometre and 1988 MAFF census returns.

	Length (kilometres)	Tetrads	%
Rivers	259.8	148	30.1
Streams	998	379	77.2

Table 2.2: Total length of rivers and streams and number of tetrads in which these habitats are found, for the 491 tetrads of this atlas. The data were derived from measurements from 1:25,000 Ordnance Survey maps using a grid of 100 circles per square kilometre, covering 32% of the square. Each segment of river or stream has been taken to represent 127 metres of true length.

	Total number	Tetrads	%
Ponds	3086	434	88.4

Table 2.3: Number of ponds and number of tetrads in which ponds are present, for the 491 tetrads of this atlas. Counted from 1:25,000 Ordnance Survey maps.

the purposes of this analysis, points not falling within any of the designated categories were ignored and the land assumed to be in agricultural use. This is shown in Table 2.1 as farmland or other open country.

The lengths of rivers and streams (Table 2.2) were estimated in a similar way, but using an overlay containing 100 regularly spaced circles of known diameter. Watercourses shown on the maps with double blue lines were classed as rivers, those with single lines counted as streams. The length was derived from a count of the number of circles through which a watercourse passed on the basis that, for the size of circle used, on average each intersection represented 127 metres of watercourse. The minimum and maximum contour in the tetrad and number of ponds (Table 2.3) were also extracted from the maps.

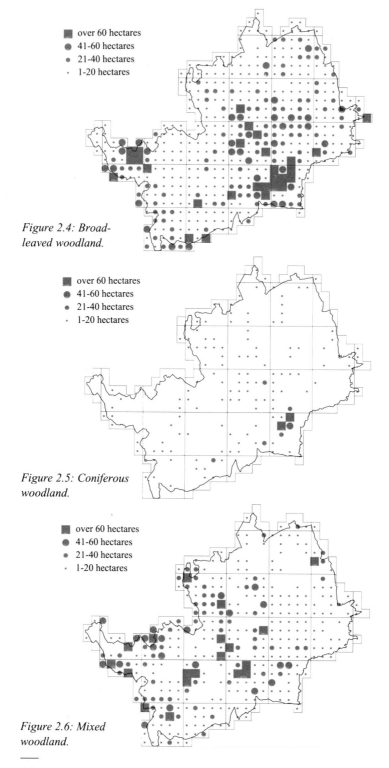

■ over 60 hectares
● 41-60 hectares
● 21-40 hectares
· 1-20 hectares

*Figure 2.4: Broad-
leaved woodland.*

■ over 60 hectares
● 41-60 hectares
● 21-40 hectares
· 1-20 hectares

*Figure 2.5: Coniferous
woodland.*

■ over 60 hectares
● 41-60 hectares
● 21-40 hectares
· 1-20 hectares

*Figure 2.6: Mixed
woodland.*

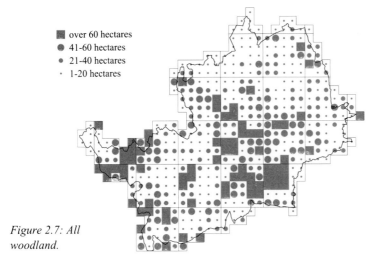

over 60 hectares
● 41-60 hectares
• 21-40 hectares
· 1-20 hectares

Figure 2.7: All woodland.

Land-use changes

The main survey dates for the latest published 1:25,000 scale maps are between 1960 and 1980, so measurements have been assumed to be representative of the old atlas period. In extracting the data from the maps, the 10-kilometre square co-ordinators were asked to use their local knowledge of the area to indicate any major differences between the maps and the status of the land in 1992. In fact, in only a few instances were changes of sufficient scale to warrant mention. The values shown in the tables represent the new atlas period.

Major changes in land-use between the old and new atlas periods were only identified for 28 one kilometre squares affecting 21 tetrads (4.3% of the total). The area of golf courses increased by 10.3% from 1546 hectares to 1705 hectares. A net increase in open water (927 hectares to 1022 hectares) was identified, representing worked out gravel pits which have been flooded. A somewhat smaller decrease in the area of land under active mineral extraction was recorded (625 hectares to 574 hectares). Changes for the other parameters were no more than 1%, although for urbanisation this amounted to an estimated increase of 386 hectares across the county. This represented only major changes and extensions of built-up areas and did not identify the in-filling by small housing developments that has taken place. No attempt was made to measure the area taken up by new roads, but the M25 alone will have covered at least 100 hectares with concrete and taken even more land for embankments and verges.

As a rough check of the accuracy of the figures, the 16.5% of land categorised as built-up compares well with the figure of 17% recognised by Hertfordshire County Council's Planning Information Service (PLANIS) in 1990 (Hertfordshire Environ-mental Forum 1992). The figures for woodland are less close; 8.7% from the atlas measurements, 6.7% from PLANIS. For this atlas, data are relative to a total of 196,400 hectares comprising the 491 tetrads surveyed, whereas the PLANIS figures relate only to the 163,415 hectares within the administrative boundary of Hertfordshire, so these comparisons need to be treated with some care.

Land-use distribution

Figures 2.4 to 2.15 show the distributions of the major land-use types at the time of the fieldwork for this atlas.

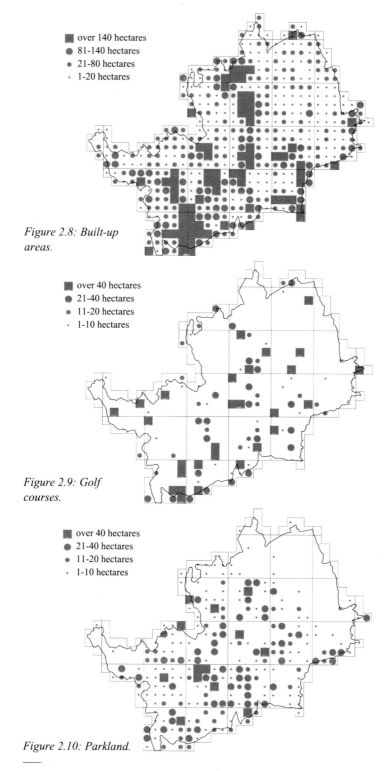

over 140 hectares
81-140 hectares
21-80 hectares
1-20 hectares

Figure 2.8: Built-up areas.

over 40 hectares
21-40 hectares
11-20 hectares
1-10 hectares

Figure 2.9: Golf courses.

over 40 hectares
21-40 hectares
11-20 hectares
1-10 hectares

Figure 2.10: Parkland.

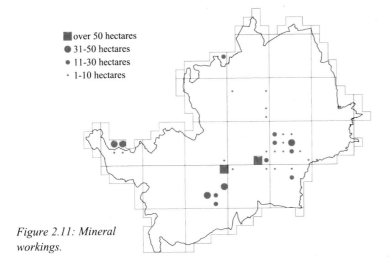

over 50 hectares
31-50 hectares
11-30 hectares
1-10 hectares

Figure 2.11: Mineral workings.

Some broad-leaved woodland (Figure 2.4) is present in 95% of the atlas tetrads, although there are obvious concentrations. The main centres are the Ashridge Estate in the west and the extensive complex on the London clay south of Hertford, extending south-west from Box Wood to Northaw Great Wood and Nyn Park. Another area between Welwyn Garden City and Stevenage, includes Sherrardspark Wood, Bramfield Forest, Hitch Wood and the Knebworth complex.

There are small amounts of coniferous woodland scattered across the county (Figure 2.5) but only eight out of 491 tetrads contain more than 20 hectares of this habitat. Over 25% of the coniferous woodland in Hertfordshire is contained in just three tetrads in Broxbourne Wood, Cowheath Wood, Highfield Wood and Box Wood. Indeed, these tetrads also contain considerable amounts of broad-leaved woodland. There is a problem in identifying pure coniferous woodland from the Ordnance Survey maps so those figures may be an underestimate.

The planting of mixtures of coniferous and broad-leaved trees has been a far more widespread forestry practice in recent decades and mixed woodland is far more common than pure conifers (Figure 2.6). It is generally absent from the north-east of the county and the main concentrations are Home Park, Hatfield Park and Millward's Park around Hatfield, Brocket Park and Symondshyde Great Wood west of Welwyn Garden City, and Prae Wood and Potter's Crouch between St Albans and Hemel Hempstead.

Combining the areas of all woodland (Figure 2.7) demonstrates that there are at least 60 hectares in 76 out of 491 tetrads (15.5%) in the county.

Figure 2.8 shows the distribution of built-up areas, comprising urban and suburban housing and industrial, commercial and retail premises. The largest populated area is around Watford in the south-west, with Hemel Hempstead and St Albans further north. There is a band of development along the route of the A1 trunk road including Hatfield, Welwyn Garden City, Stevenage, Hitchin and Letchworth. In the east there is a fairly narrow band of urbanisation along the Lee valley from Hertford to Cheshunt.

Golf courses have become an increasingly familiar part of the Hertfordshire landscape over the past two decades. Their extent is not always easy to determine from the maps and, with the recent spate of new enterprises, it is possible that this habitat has been under-recorded. Figure 2.9 shows that 28 tetrads have more than 10% of their land

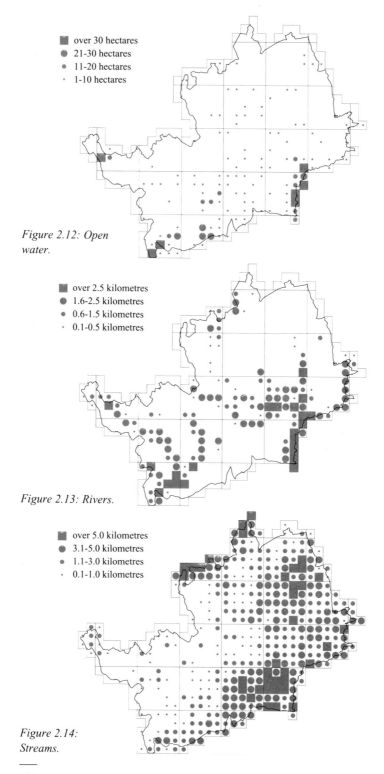

over 30 hectares
21-30 hectares
11-20 hectares
1-10 hectares

Figure 2.12: Open water.

over 2.5 kilometres
1.6-2.5 kilometres
0.6-1.5 kilometres
0.1-0.5 kilometres

Figure 2.13: Rivers.

over 5.0 kilometres
3.1-5.0 kilometres
1.1-3.0 kilometres
0.1-1.0 kilometres

Figure 2.14: Streams.

18

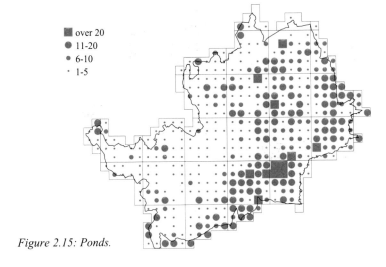

over 20
11-20
6-10
1-5

Figure 2.15: Ponds.

area being put to this use. As might be expected, the distribution matches fairly closely that of urbanisation.

An assessment from the Ordnance Survey maps of the area of parkland is not easy and such land is not necessarily outside agricultural use. The way in which the overlap between these measurements and the agricultural statistics has been dealt with is explained in Appendix 2.1. Figure 2.10 shows parkland to be evenly spread across the county.

Much of the gravel extraction at the time of the old atlas was in the lower Lee and Colne valleys. These workings have now been largely exhausted and the resulting gravel pits have either been in-filled or flooded. The continued demand for aggregate has encouraged the establishment of new workings further up the valleys, and the main regions of gravel extraction are now around Hertford and Ware and in the Vale of St Albans. Figure 2.11 shows the distribution of all mineral workings and includes, in addition to gravel, the chalk extraction near Tring.

All the large areas of open water (Figure 2.12) in the county are man-made. The oldest are associated with landscaped country estates such as Brocket Park, Woodhall Park and Hatfield Park. Provision of water for the Grand Union Canal led to the construction of the Tring Reservoirs and Aldenham Reservoir, and, in the 1950s, Hilfield Park Reservoir was built to supply drinking water. The flooding of worked out gravel pits has produced substantial areas of open water in the lower valleys of the Lee and Colne. Time has allowed banks and islands to become substantially vegetated, to the benefit of wildlife and leisure interests.

The distribution of rivers in the county has already been described and is illustrated in Figure 2.13. The importance of the Colne and Lee valleys is shown, as is the area around Ware and Hertford, where most of the tributaries of the Lee converge. The underlying geology is clearly shown in the distribution map for streams (Figure 2.14). On the chalk and brown-earths, streams are scarce. In contrast, on the boulder clay and London clay, such watercourses feature in almost every tetrad. A very similar pattern is shown by ponds (Figure 2.15) with many more on the poorly drained clay soils in the south and east. Marshland makes a very minor contribution to the Hertfordshire landscape and its distribution is highly correlated with that of rivers.

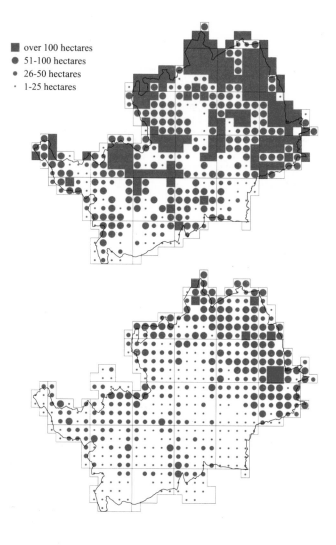

■	over 100 hectares
●	51-100 hectares
•	26-50 hectares
·	1-25 hectares

Figure 2.16: The distribution of wheat in 1988 (above) and 1969 (below).

AGRICULTURE

Agricultural data collection

A census of all registered agricultural holdings, known as the 'June returns' is conducted by the Ministry of Agriculture, Fisheries and Food (MAFF) each year to provide up-to-date information on the areas of crops planted and numbers of animals on holdings. The results of these censuses are generally available, summarised by parish. The Computer Services Department of Edinburgh University has devised a system to manipulate this information from parish summaries to totals based upon squares of the

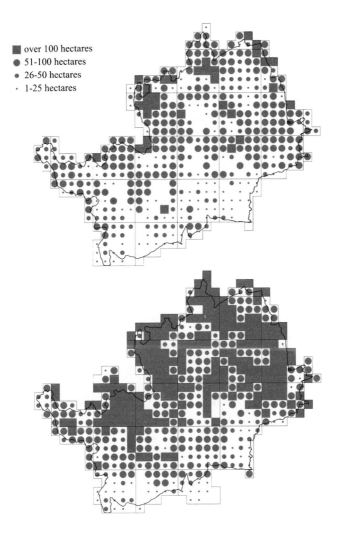

Figure 2.17: The distribution of barley in 1988 (above) and 1969 (below).

Ordnance Survey grid. Although designed initially to work at the 10 kilometre square level, this method has been used to provide data for each one kilometre square, although care is needed in its use. In the analyses data have been grouped by tetrad for the years 1969 and 1988, to represent each of the two atlas periods.

There are inevitably a number of anomalies in converting parish level agricultural statistics into grid based data. These have been dealt with in a consistent manner to arrive at the datasets used in the analyses. The methods used to ensure that the total area described by the measured land-use parameters and the agricultural statistics add up to 400 hectares in each tetrad are explained in Appendix 2.1.

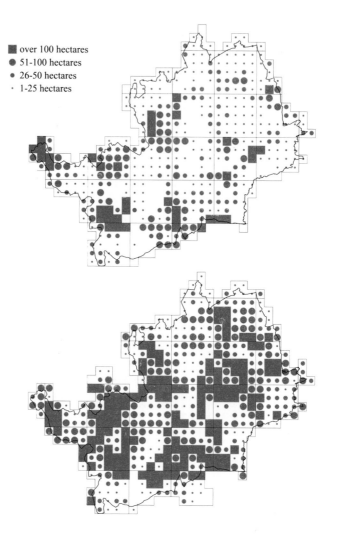

■ over 100 hectares
● 51-100 hectares
• 26-50 hectares
· 1-25 hectares

Figure 2.18: The distribution of temporary grassland in 1988 (above) and 1969 (below).

Agricultural changes and distribution

Tables 2.4 and 2.5 show the agricultural data for the two years. There have clearly been significant changes in the use of agricultural land and cropping patterns over the last twenty years. These changes have largely been stimulated by government policy, market forces and technical developments. These are likely to have had a profound effect on wildlife, particularly as agricultural land forms over 70% of the county area.

Table 2.4 and Figures 2.16 to 2.25 show the MAFF census variables which accounted for more than 1% of the agricultural land area in either 1969 or 1988 and their distribution in the county.

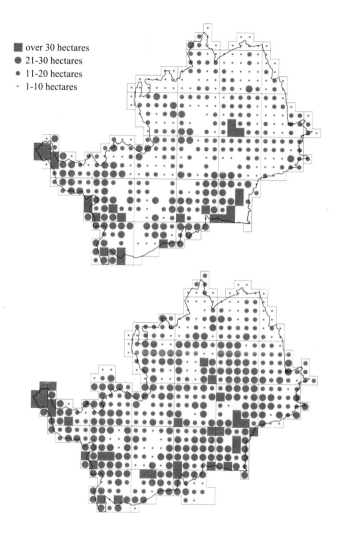

Figure 2.19: The distribution of permanent grassland in 1988 (above) and 1969 (below).

Across the county, the overall area of land cultivated for cereals has changed little, declining only 4% from 63,234 hectares in 1969 to 60,785 hectares in 1988. However, there has been a major decrease in the area of barley and oats, balanced by a two-fold increase in the amount of wheat. Figures 2.16 and 2.17 show the pattern of distribution of wheat and barley in Hertfordshire in each of the two periods. The actual distribution of each crop has changed little. Wheat is still concentrated on the boulder clay in the north-east although at a greater density, whereas barley is grown on the better drained soils in the west.

What is not clear from the MAFF statistics is the extent of the switch from spring-sown to winter-sown cereals. In the 1969 census there was no requirement to report

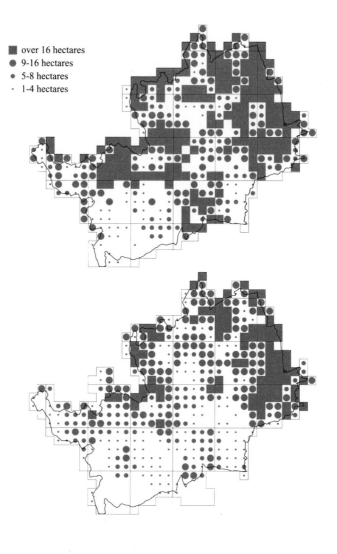

Figure 2.20: The distribution of field beans in 1988 (above) and 1969 (below).

separately the barley area by sowing season, although this was recorded in the 1988 census. In England and Wales in 1980 only 61% of barley was spring-sown and by 1983 this had fallen further to 50% (O'Connor and Shrubb 1986). Hertfordshire appears to be lagging the national pattern as in 1988 56% of the barley area was still spring-sown. Even if we conservatively estimate that 60% of the barley area in 1969 was spring-sown, there has still been a loss of over 12,000 hectares of this crop type, some 13.7% of the total arable area.

Since 1969 there has been a net loss of over 5500 hectares of temporary grassland (defined as including clover leys), and over 7000 hectares of permanent grassland, as

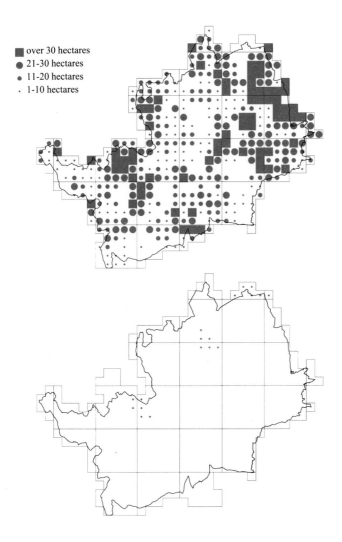

over 30 hectares
21-30 hectares
11-20 hectares
1-10 hectares

Figure 2.21: The distribution of oilseed rape in 1988 (above) and 1969 (below).

measured by the MAFF census. In reality the loss of permanent grassland is somewhat less than this as a result of the expansion in leisure provision, especially golf courses. Figure 2.18 shows the pattern of loss of temporary grasslands. Although some grass and clover leys do remain on the valley floors, there has been a retraction from these regions to the higher ground. The main areas of permanent grassland (Figure 2.19) are now confined to the south and west, when previously they were fairly evenly spread, except for the extreme north.

In 1969 field beans were the major non-cereal crop in Hertfordshire but comprised less than 4% of the agricultural area. The distribution (Figure 2.20) has changed little in

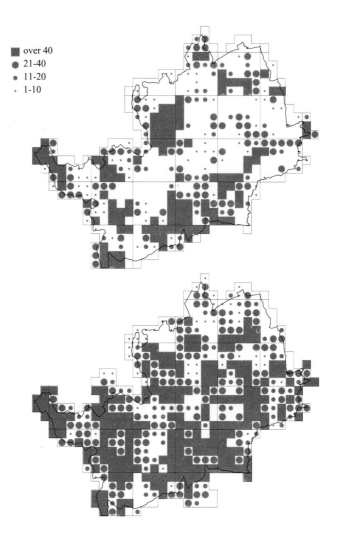

over 40
21-40
11-20
1-10

Figure 2.22: The distribution of dairy cattle in 1988 (above) and 1969 (below).

the intervening period although there has been an increase in area to almost 6%. This reflects a spread from the crop's former stronghold on the boulder clay in the east to the lighter soils of the west.

In contrast, the growing of oilseed rape has increased substantially, encouraged by government subsidies, and has usurped field beans as the most widespread crop after wheat and barley. From a rare and insignificant crop in 1969, the bright yellow fields of oilseed rape in flower are now a common sight across the county in early summer (Figure 2.21). There is no clear pattern of distribution except away from the major towns, which lack farmland.

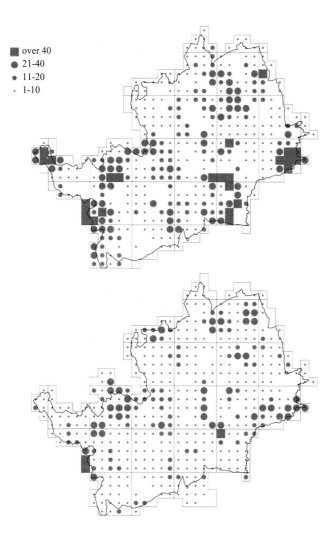

Figure 2.23: The distribution of beef cattle in 1988 (above) and 1969 (below).

Table 2.5 shows the major livestock variables from the MAFF census results. Overall, the number of breeding cattle has fallen but there is a clear difference between the patterns for beef and dairy livestock. Numbers of breeding dairy cattle (Figure 2.22) have decreased by 44% and this type of farming has disappeared from over 130 tetrads in the centre and east of the county. The farming of beef cattle is still widespread in Hertfordshire (Figure 2.23) but is possibly becoming more intensive. Although the number of breeding animals increased by 43% between the two atlases, the number of tetrads in which they are present has fallen.

Pig farming has declined drastically (Figure 2.24) and the majority of pork production

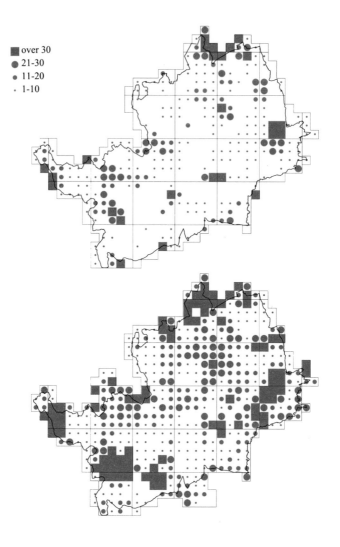

over 30
21-30
11-20
1-10

Figure 2.24: The distribution of pigs in 1988 (above) and 1969 (below).

is now concentrated in a few areas, mainly on the county boundary. Sheep farming, however, is a growing trend (Figure 2.25) despite the decrease in grassland, with the number of ewes increasing by 58% between 1969 and 1988.

In combination the statistics show a trend away from traditional mixed farming methods towards specialisation in cereal and brassica monocultures and a switch from grass-based livestock production to short-cycle arable rotations. The improvements in crop quality have necessitated regular and high input levels of chemical fertilisers and fungicides. Pesticide applications have also replaced the ecologically balanced interactions between predator and prey. Improved crop varieties and harvesting machinery

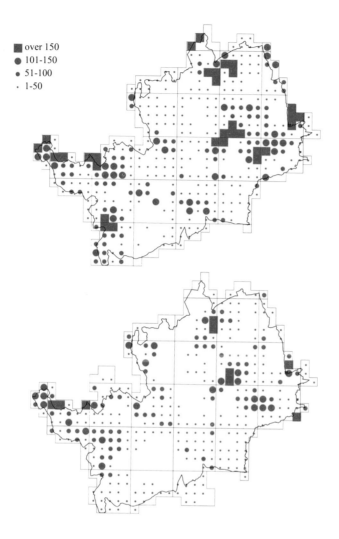

Figure 2.25: The distribution of sheep in 1988 (above) and 1969 (below).

have reduced wastage and, until very recently, stubble burning and immediate plough-ing returned the land to production soon after the harvest. All these factors have reduced the diversity of habitat and variety of food available to our wildlife.

	Area (hectares)			Number of tetrads		
	Old	New	Ratio	Old	New	Ratio
Bare fallow	2699	699	0.26	464	366	0.79
Potatoes	1649	457	0.28	406	254	0.63
Horticultural crops	2277	696	0.31	459	366	0.80
Oats	3873	1206	0.31	472	304	0.64
Temporary grassland	11,155	5484	0.49	481	411	0.85
Barley	41,491	23,120	0.56	483	435	0.90
Permanent grassland	25,646	18,464	0.72	487	438	0.90
Rough grazing	1478	1698	1.15	349	322	0.92
Beans	4380	6257	1.43	418	404	0.97
Wheat	17,739	36,364	2.05	474	437	0.92
Oilseed rape	17	7389	433.41	18	398	22.11

Table 2.4: Areas of selected agricultural crops and numbers of tetrads in which the crop type was found for the old and new atlas periods for the 488 tetrads common to both surveys. Information derived from MAFF census returns for 1969 and 1988. Crop types selected are those exceeding 1% of the total agricultural land in either year.

	Count			Number of tetrads		
	Old	New	Ratio	Old	New	Ratio
Pigs						
Gilts in pig	1930	494	0.26	421	210	0.50
Sows in pig	7054	2775	0.39	468	277	0.59
Hens for laying						
Growing pullets	204,176	63,125	0.31	435	175	0.41
In flock <12 months	569,383	144,988	0.25	466	293	0.63
In flock >12 months	109,048	95,117	0.87	477	368	0.77
Dairy cattle						
Heifers in calf	3434	2121	0.62	438	271	0.62
Cows in calf	2328	697	0.30	439	219	0.50
Cows & heifers in milk	14,810	8702	0.59	443	300	0.68
Beef cattle						
Heifers in calf	489	1044	2.14	349	312	0.89
Cows in calf	623	898	1.44	357	309	0.87
Cows & heifers in milk	2496	3224	1.29	441	369	0.84
Sheep						
Two-tooth ewes	1369	3722	2.72	155	303	1.95
Ewes for breeding	12,460	18,093	1.45	325	375	1.15

Table 2.5: Numbers of animals in major livestock categories and numbers of tetrads in which the livestock was farmed for the old and new atlas periods for the 488 tetrads common to both surveys. Information derived from MAFF census returns for 1969 and 1988.

III: Main species texts

This chapter contains the species accounts and compares the results of the 1988-92 atlas work with those for 1967-73. For each of the 111 main species, a standard format is followed; a page of text alongside a pair of maps representing the results of the fieldwork for the two atlas periods. At the end of the chapter, short accounts are provided for a further 25 rare, extinct or colonising species.

For the main species, the current national breeding population (Gates *et al* 1993) is provided together with an estimate of the county breeding population (see Appendix 3.1) and a statement of the local population trend over the past 20 years. The main body of the text gives a brief description of the species including its habits and relevant ecology. The distribution maps are interpreted, possible reasons for changes are discussed, and the significant habitat associations are presented. Where appropriate, comment is also made on the accuracy of the maps in relation to fieldwork problems peculiar to the species. The authorship of each species account is indicated by initials at the foot of the text. The artists responsible for each illustration are identified in Appendix 1.1.

The facing map page presents the cumulative distribution data for each atlas period, superimposed on an outline of the current county boundary and the tetrad borders used to delimit the fieldwork. Each dot represents one tetrad and the size of the dot indicates the breeding category (possible, probable or confirmed). Alongside each map a table is provided showing the numbers of tetrads in which the species was recorded, sub-divided by breeding category. These counts are also shown as percentages of the total tetrads surveyed, 491 for the new atlas and 504 for the old. The percentages for the three separate categories are rounded to the nearest whole number and will not necessarily sum to that for the total.

To avoid unwanted disturbance at recent breeding locations, the new atlas results for three species (Barn Owl, Long-eared Owl and Nightjar) have been placed convention-ally in the centre of the map and not in the actual breeding tetrads.

Little Grebe

Tachybaptus ruficollis

National population 5000-10,000 pairs, Hertfordshire 90-200 pairs, increasing.

More catholic in its requirements than the Great Crested Grebe, this tiny grebe can be found in almost all wetland habitats where luxuriant vegetation is present within the water and as a dense emergent growth. Such sites include gravel pits, reservoirs, canals, streams, ponds and watercress beds. Although the Little Grebe's skulking behaviour makes birds difficult to observe, their presence is usually betrayed by their loud, vibrant trills. Pairs can often be heard trilling in a cheerful duet and it is thought that this distinctive vocalisation has been developed to compensate for the relative lack of visual stimuli during courtship. Their reaction to disturbance is to dive, often only to re-emerge within cover. Little Grebes appear to be able to adapt to even the most disturbed sites.

The nest is a heap of floating vegetable matter raised above the surface level of shallow water. It is usually located near the water's edge in the cover of marginal vegetation. Breeding takes place between late March and July with most pairs raising at least two, occasionally three, broods. Between four and six eggs are normal and breeding success is chiefly affected by water level variations and predation by other birds and pike. Nest building, incubation and the feeding of the young are carried out by both parents.

It is possible that odd pairs of Little Grebes could have been overlooked at some bodies of water in less intensively covered tetrads but, given the species' specific habitat requirements, this is unlikely to have altered the distribution map significantly.

A small but significant increase in the number of occupied tetrads has taken place since the original atlas. The bird is still largely confined to the river valleys but, interestingly, there has been a decrease in the lower Lee valley and an increase through the middle of the county. This increase has probably been due to the excavation of new gravel pits and the progressive growth of vegetation at some sites and, perhaps, more sympathetic management of rivers (Raven 1986). Nationally, the trend is not clear with increases in the 1970s followed by more recent declines. These are thought to be related to the series of cold winters in the 1980s and it is possible that the recent run of warm winters has benefited the species.

Positive associations are evident with parkland, mineral workings, open water, marsh, rivers and streams. As these habitats have not changed significantly in extent between the atlases they cannot be used to explain the increase in the distribution of Little Grebes. It is more likely that changes in the quality of the habitat and winter conditions are involved.   AW

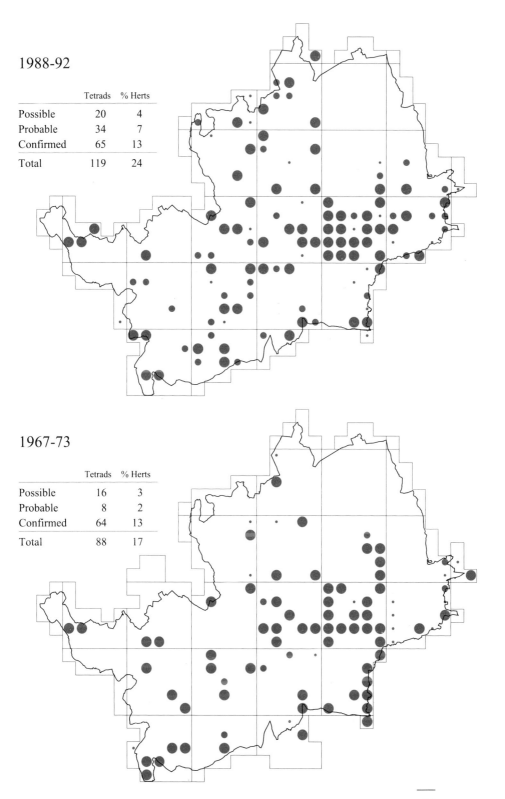

1988-92

	Tetrads	% Herts
Possible	20	4
Probable	34	7
Confirmed	65	13
Total	119	24

1967-73

	Tetrads	% Herts
Possible	16	3
Probable	8	2
Confirmed	64	13
Total	88	17

Great Crested Grebe

Podiceps cristatus

National population 8000 birds, Hertfordshire 70-120 pairs, increasing.

The Great Crested Grebe is the largest British grebe and feeds almost entirely on fish and some aquatic invertebrates. Around the middle of the 19th century, the under-pelts of this species fell foul to fashion in the form of 'grebe furs'. Persecution of the British population began in 1857 and the ensuing massacre left the country with possibly as few as 42 pairs by 1860 (Harrisson & Hollom 1932). Bird protection acts subsequently came to the rescue and Great Crested Grebes were eventually awarded full breeding season protection in 1880. Hertfordshire is of great significance in the history of this bird. A single pair at Tring Reservoirs in 1866 built up to a considerable breeding stock in the following 20 years and it was from this nucleus that the re-colonisation of southern England occurred.

An attractive and enigmatic species, Great Crested Grebes can now be encountered on all the larger water bodies in Hertfordshire. They favour gravel pits, reservoirs and large ponds where the depth of the water is less than five metres and where ample emergent aquatic vegetation is present.

Great Crested Grebes have a courtship display that is unsurpassed by any other species in Hertfordshire; in particular, the 'weed dance' is one of the most delightful sights that can be experienced within our county boundaries. The nest, which usually contains three to five whitish eggs, is a fairly low, shapeless accumulation of aquatic vegetation that is normally built in branches overhanging the water's edge or among growing reeds, though it is sometimes found in other types of aquatic vegetation, floating or resting on the bottom in shallow water. The breeding season normally extends from April to July but can last until September. Records of birds incubating in December and January, although distinctly unusual, indicate that this species is able to breed at any time of year providing mild conditions prevail. Great Crested Grebes can be single or double brooded and incubation is carried out by both parents.

Being birds of open water, Great Crested Grebes are easy to locate, their nests are usually obvious and their young are vociferous to the point of irritation. It is thus assumed that the maps provide an excellent distributional record.

The bird was counted in Hertfordshire in 1965 (129 birds) and again in 1975 (157 birds) (Hughes *et al* 1975). The distribution of this species has increased by over 80% from 24 to 41 tetrads since the original atlas when an absolute maximum of 69 pairs were recorded. This increase has been primarily due to the excavation of new gravel pits across the southern half of the county. Birds are very quick to find and colonise new sites and often fly at night, presumably searching for new breeding areas.

As to be expected for a wetland species, there are associations with open water, rivers, built-up areas and parkland.   AW

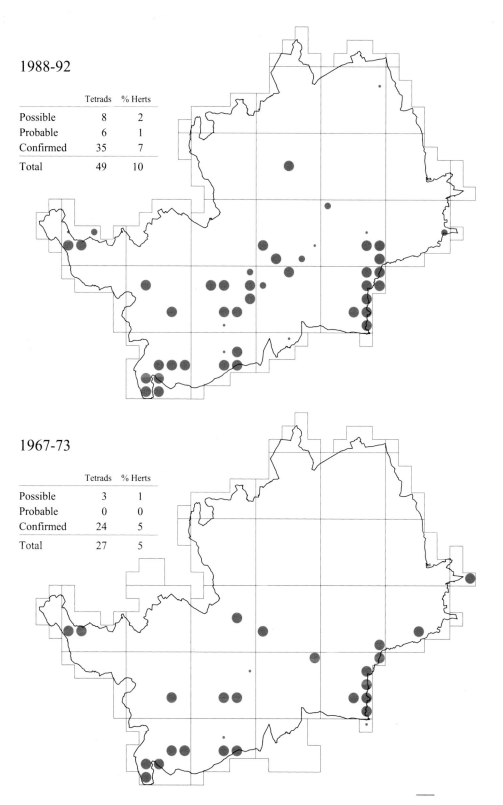

1988-92

	Tetrads	% Herts
Possible	8	2
Probable	6	1
Confirmed	35	7
Total	49	10

1967-73

	Tetrads	% Herts
Possible	3	1
Probable	0	0
Confirmed	24	5
Total	27	5

Grey Heron

Ardea cinerea

National population 10,330 nests, Hertfordshire 71 nests in 1992, increasing.

Like a tall grey sentinel, a Grey Heron standing motionless beside a river or wading slowly in the water is a familiar sight. Equally recognisable is the Grey Heron's slow flapping flight reconnoitring ponds or returning to roost with its broad rounded wings, kinked neck and long trailing legs. Frequenting fresh-water sites their diet comprises fish (especially eels), frogs, small mammals and birds.

The breeding range extends throughout Europe and Asia as far north as the Arctic. Although there are migratory populations elsewhere, British Grey Herons are sedentary and nest in small colonies, often at traditional sites. At the heronries males advertise with a yelping call and a flighting display. The nest, usually in a tall tree, is a large untidy pile of sticks and reeds. Exceptionally in England nests are at ground level, like those in the reedbed at Marsworth Reservoir, Tring from 1956-84. The three to five eggs are laid in late February to March.

The conspicuous nests at traditional sites make Grey Herons easy to census, although isolated nests may be overlooked. In Hertfordshire the Grey Heron is the most accurately recorded of all our regular breeding birds. The number and location of occupied nests in each of the last 40 years has been reviewed by Smith (1990) and are shown in Appendix 3.2.

At the time of the first atlas numbers were low following the severe winter of 1962/63. Apart from single nests at Goldings, Batchwood and Knebworth, the only heronry was at Marsworth until the colonies at Panshanger and Brocket Park were established in 1972 with three nests each.

Since then numbers have increased steadily, the new map shows regular heronries at Wilstone, Brocket Park (straddling two tetrads), Panshanger and Stockers Lake, this one started in 1977 had attracted 35 nesting pairs in 1991. The other breeding records were an isolated nesting attempt at Verulamium in 1991 and the heronries at Fishers Green and Waltham Abbey in the Lee valley which are actually just over the border in Essex. Although the observer was convinced that breeding had occurred, the record from SP91G (Marsworth) was of a recently fledged juvenile with no actual evidence of a nest. In addition there were more widespread sightings throughout the county.

Traditionally heronries were regarded as sacred, but this did not protect the Grey Herons from persecution by gamekeepers and others until they were given statutory protection in 1954. They are severely affected by prolonged freezing conditions, such as the winters of 1946/47 and 1962/63 and the slow rate of recovery in the 1960s may have been exacerbated by poor adult survival and lower reproductive success due to debilitation caused by organochlorine pesticides in the food chain. The recent sustained increase in numbers is likely to have been assisted by a combination of mild winters, controls on environmental contamination by pesticides, and improvements in water quality and fish stocks. LMS

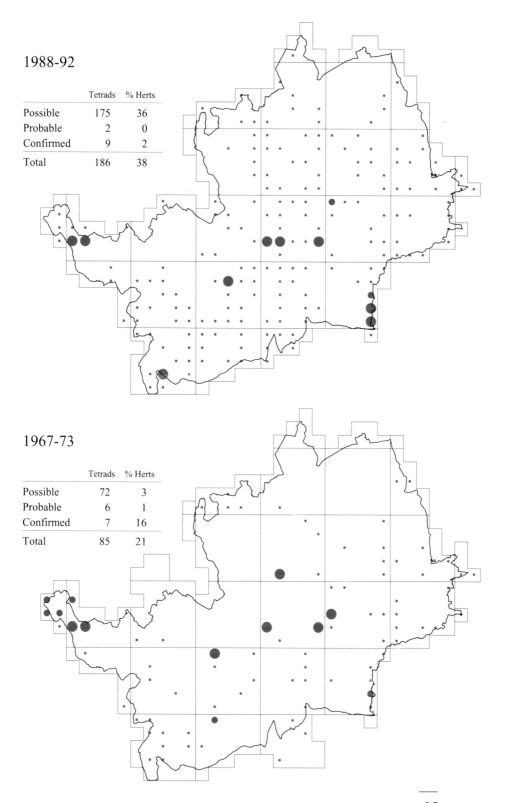

1988-92

	Tetrads	% Herts
Possible	175	36
Probable	2	0
Confirmed	9	2
Total	186	38

1967-73

	Tetrads	% Herts
Possible	72	3
Probable	6	1
Confirmed	7	16
Total	85	21

Mute Swan

Cygnus olor

National population 5138 pairs and 15,422 non breeding adults, Hertfordshire 76 and 200 respectively, increasing.

The Mute Swan is one of our most familiar and popular water birds, found on rivers, lakes and estuaries throughout lowland areas of Britain, including public parks close to human habitation. It is the largest of the three species of swan recorded in this country, weighing up to 15 kilogrammes. The Mute Swan has a long association with man, providing an important food for the gentry between the thirteenth and fifteenth centuries. On water, its pure white plumage, arched neck and down-pointed bill give it a graceful appearance but on land it is ungainly and thus is seldom found far from water. Its diet consists largely of pond weeds but it will also graze on the roots and stems of grasses and feed on spilt grain.

During early spring pairs may be found aggressively defending their territory in any suitable freshwater habitat. However, in some parts of the country colonial nesting has been noted, Abbotsbury in Dorset being the most famous site. The nest is a large mound of dead and green vegetation, often very obvious but sometimes well hidden amongst island scrub or in reed beds. On average six eggs are laid, incubated solely by the female for a period of 36 days.

The presence of birds in an area is easy to detect, making the collection of atlas records relatively simple. In addition, the Wildfowl and Wetlands Trust and the British Trust for Ornithology undertook a national Mute Swan survey in 1990 when full coverage was achieved in Hertfordshire. Thus the distribution maps for both periods are likely to be very accurate.

In the period between the two atlases there was a well-documented decline of Mute Swans due to the ingestion of lead shot, and a subsequent recovery to former levels. A comparison between the old and new maps shows little change, with pairs continuing to be associated with open water and rivers. However, the new map shows a much higher incidence of possible breeding, particularly in central and northern parts of the county and it may be that these birds are settling in new sites as the population expands from the all time low in the 1970s and early 1980s It will be interesting to see if these localities regularly hold territories in the years to come. There are also some notable losses, particularly the River Stort north of Bishop's Stortford, the River Lee south-west of Hertford, around Brookmans Park and the Rib valley. These declines may be attributed to the spread of urbanisation in the case of the former sites (Mute Swans prefer seclusion when breeding) but in the case of the River Rib, the current practice of arable cultivation up to the river's edge and lower water levels are likely to be significant. These sites probably lost birds during the national decline and are now unsuitable for pairs seeking new territories.   BT

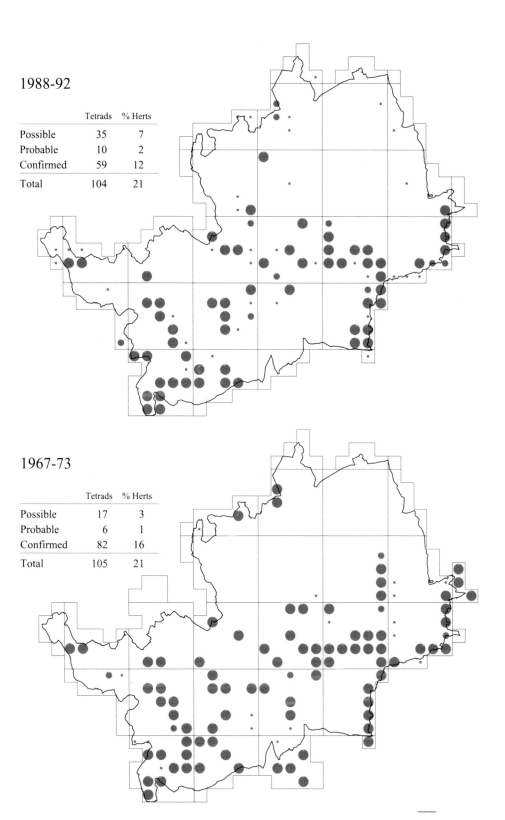

1988-92

	Tetrads	% Herts
Possible	35	7
Probable	10	2
Confirmed	59	12
Total	104	21

1967-73

	Tetrads	% Herts
Possible	17	3
Probable	6	1
Confirmed	82	16
Total	105	21

Greylag Goose

Anser anser

National population circa 22,000 including non-breeding adults and juveniles, Hert-fordshire 1-5 pairs and up to 100 non-breeding individuals, increasing.

Largest of the 'grey geese' and the only goose indigenous to the British Isles, the Greylag Goose may have bred in the county in former times when wild populations extended as far south as the Cambridgeshire fens. However, during the last two centuries these have declined and are now restricted to the north-west Scottish Highlands and the Western Isles, with the Hertfordshire stock, as in many other parts of Britain, consisting entirely of feral birds. It is a gregarious species, groups varying from family parties to flocks of several thousands in other parts of its range. During the breeding season it is highly territorial, the gander driving off rival males with the familiar, loud, three-note honking of the domestic farmyard goose of which the Greylag is the ancestor.

Feral birds occupy a wide range of wetland habitats from upland lochs in Scotland to lowland reservoirs, gravel pits, marshes and suburban parks, where they become quite tame. The nest is frequently on an island where the birds are comparatively safe from predators such as foxes. Normally four to six eggs are laid, hatching after 27-28 days, when the female soon leads the young to a suitable feeding area. This is invariably marshy, aquatic vegetation with nearby grassland but later in the season the birds will take advantage of cereal stubble and root crops such as potatoes.

The feral population in Hertfordshire results mainly from birds released or escaped over the past 30 years. The first breeding in the county was at Tring Reservoirs in 1963, believed to be by birds which originated from Whipsnade Zoo and returned there to winter. The old atlas recorded breeding at this site in each of the survey years but numbers have significantly reduced in recent years and Greylags were absent between 1988 and 1992. Elsewhere in the county there has been a general increase, although confirmed breeding was found in only one more tetrad than in the old atlas. This is likely to be a reasonably accurate picture because the Wildfowl and Wetlands Trust 1991 survey of introduced geese enabled a concentrated effort on this species. The stronghold in the county is centred around Stockers Lake in the Colne valley, although breeding is not an annual occurrence at any one site.

The new map shows 50% of occupied tetrads within the 'possible breeding' category. It may be that these birds are part of the nationally expanding population seeking out suitable new breeding areas or merely escaped individuals which have become resident at a locality which offers suitable feeding. At these sites, hybridisation with Canada Geese is a distinct possibility. BT

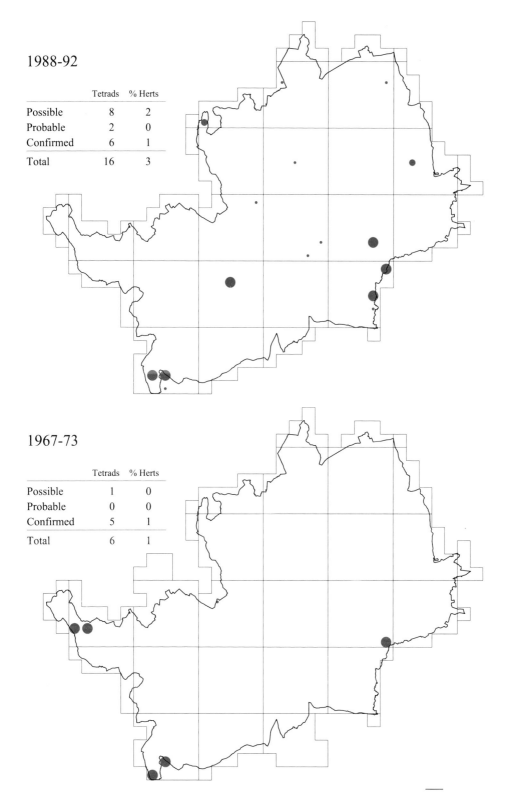

1988-92

	Tetrads	% Herts
Possible	8	2
Probable	2	0
Confirmed	6	1
Total	16	3

1967-73

	Tetrads	% Herts
Possible	1	0
Probable	0	0
Confirmed	5	1
Total	6	1

Canada Goose

Branta canadensis

National population 60,834 birds, Hertfordshire 156 pairs and 909 non-breeders, increasing.

A native of North America and the world's most numerous goose, the Canada Goose was introduced to this country during the reign of Charles II to enhance the grounds of large estates. These introductions, and subsequent escapes, enabled many feral populations to establish, but until the 1950s it was still very much a bird of private grounds and parkland. At this time birds were transported to many new locations, primarily due to agricultural pressures and for wildfowling purposes. This coincided with the creation of many new freshwater habitats in the form of gravel pits and reservoirs and thus provided the nucleus for a population explosion.

The British geese do not undergo the long-distance migrations of their North American counterparts and tend to remain within 100 kilometres of their natal area. They may make short feeding flights but often prefer to walk from the water to graze on neighbouring fields or feed on autumn stubble. Many flocks can be found in public parks where they become tame and in recent years there has been growing pressure to control numbers owing to problems with fouling by droppings.

Male Canada Geese are very territorial during the breeding season, aggressively defending sites from March onwards. The nest is frequently on an island, eggs being laid in April or May. The average brood of four is reared on the spring growth of grass and thus most nest sites require nearby grassland.

The atlas maps should, on the whole, be accurate since the birds are large and relatively conspicuous, are often vocal and frequent regularly watched sites. In addition, the 1991 survey of introduced geese, organised by the Wildfowl and Wetlands Trust, enabled a detailed assessment of the county's population to be made.

The two maps show one of the most remarkable distribution changes in the atlas with birds found in 35% of tetrads in the new atlas compared with 3% in the old. As with the national population, local releases were initially responsible, particularly in the Tring area, but a natural spread is now thought to be the primary cause for expansion. Of the occupied tetrads, 28% are in the 'possible breeding' category and it is apparent that Canada Geese are continuing to expand within the county, taking advantage of the creation of habitat such as new gravel pit complexes and increasing their tolerance of the urban environment. They can now be found on all the major river systems, gravel pits, lakes, farm ponds and even newly-created golf course waters. The habitat analysis shows the species to be associated with all wet habitats. During the 1991 survey, 460 birds counted at Stockers Lake make this the thirteenth most important site nationally for moulting Canada Geese (Delaney 1992).   BT

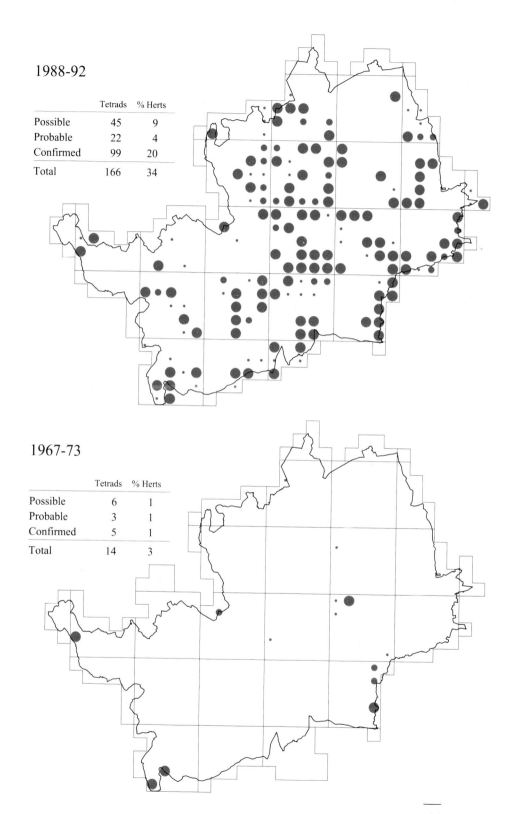

1988-92

	Tetrads	% Herts
Possible	45	9
Probable	22	4
Confirmed	99	20
Total	166	34

1967-73

	Tetrads	% Herts
Possible	6	1
Probable	3	1
Confirmed	5	1
Total	14	3

Shelduck

Tadorna tadorna

National population 10,600 pairs, Hertfordshire population four pairs, increasing.

The Shelduck is a large, goose-like species with a preference for coastal habitats, especially sheltered estuaries with extensive mud and sandbanks and shallow bays. It is gregarious outside the breeding season but becomes highly territorial prior to nesting, the male defending favoured feeding areas. These territories are abandoned soon after hatching when the ducklings are taken to the nearest available water, where they feed on a variety of crustaceans, molluscs and other invertebrates. After a couple of weeks the broods are tended in crèches by a few adults whilst the majority undertake a moult migration to the German Wadden Sea. In the 1950s a moulting flock was discovered in Bridgewater Bay, Somerset and more recently moulting flocks have been found on the Firth of Forth, the Wash, Humber and Cheshire Dee.

The national waterfowl index for Shelduck has gradually risen since the early 1960s and there is a growing tendency for birds to breed inland, away from traditional estuarine sites.

The nest is often in a rabbit burrow, occasionally a considerable distance from water, but haystacks and buildings are also frequently used. In Hertfordshire, where the breeding population is small, it is difficult to predict where breeding will occur due to the presence of non-breeding individuals. Usually the first sign of success is the appearance of newly hatched ducklings on site. The situation is also complicated by the birds breeding at one locality and moving the young to another site within a few days of hatching (G J White *pers comm*).

Shelducks were absent in the previous atlas and first bred in Hertfordshire in 1983 at Rye Meads, when five young were raised. The second breeding record was in 1985 at Cole Green landfill site near Welwyn Garden City. The following year pairs bred again at Rye Meads/Amwell and Cole Green and birds have subsequently summered and/or bred in the county each year. The new distribution map reflects the increased use of inland sites. The reason for this increase is unclear but the series of mild winters since 1962/63 may be a contributing factor since this species is particularly vulnerable to severe weather. Although a few pairs breed each year, these have all been, apart from Rye Meads, on or near gravel pits, most of which did not exist in 1968-72. Thus, a high national population, combined with increased habitat availability, may be the reason for the establishment of a small but regular breeding population in Hertfordshire. One aspect that each of the sites have in common is that they are relatively free from human disturbance and this may be a limiting factor for the expansion of the population.   BT

1988-92

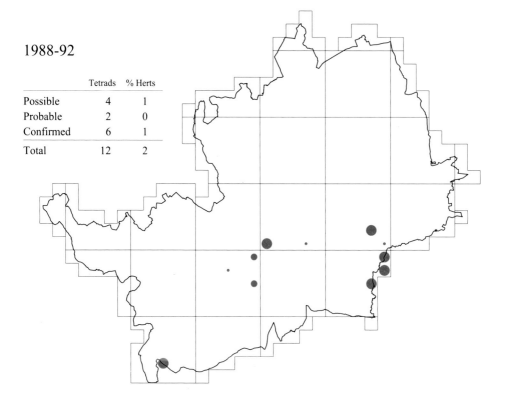

	Tetrads	% Herts
Possible	4	1
Probable	2	0
Confirmed	6	1
Total	12	2

Mandarin

Aix galericulata

National population <7000 birds, Hertfordshire 10-15 pairs, increasing.

The male Mandarin must be one of the most visually stunning birds. It is for this very reason that it has been kept in many wildfowl collections throughout the country. A significant self-supporting feral population was initially based around the Surrey and Berkshire border and on the strength of this the Mandarin was admitted to the British List in 1971. Whether the Hertfordshire birds result from the spread of the Surrey population, or from an alternative source, is unclear. Whatever their origin, Mandarins have seemingly established a viable population in the centre of the county. The Hertfordshire birds form part of an increasing national population which is fast growing in international importance because of intense pressure in its natural range, largely due to habitat destruction.

Secluded waters with well spaced, mature deciduous trees offer an ideal environment. Here the birds find both suitable nest sites and a supply of both summer and winter food. The summer diet is largely aquatic insects and in winter typically acorns, nuts and beech mast. Because of this diet they tend not to mix with other species of duck (Madge & Burn 1988) but have been known to be attracted to the feeding of Mallard with bread (*pers obs*). Some ground cover, such as that offered by rhododendrons, is also required. The Mandarin usually nests in holes, although it will occasionally resort to nesting under a bush or log at ground level. Cavities in mature trees are preferred, often between seven and eight metres from the ground. Nest boxes have been successfully utilised and their provision may assist in the spread of the species. Competition for nest boxes from Jackdaws has been recorded and in one instance this resulted in a Jackdaw hatching a Mandarin chick (Davies 1990). Between 9 and 12 eggs are laid and shortly after hatching the chicks will free-fall from the nest hole; the female leads the ducklings to their first meal, often some distance away.

During the breeding season the adult birds become retiring and elusive and even the flamboyantly plumaged male can become difficult to locate. Concealed and remote nest sites, and the careful approach of the adults to the site, result in breeding being unlikely to be confirmed until the chicks have hatched. Unlike the migratory Asian population, British birds are largely sedentary and, as most suitable sites are well known, it is unlikely that breeding goes undetected. Broods can be moved soon after hatching and this habit can conceal the actual breeding location.

The maps illustrate the establishment of a small but significant population in the centre of the county during the last 20 years. Gladwin & Sage (1986) described the Mandarin as a 'scarce visitor' but a general increase in records reported in the recent Hertfordshire Bird Reports suggests that the population in and around the county is continuing to rise and that further colonisation is possible.   RY

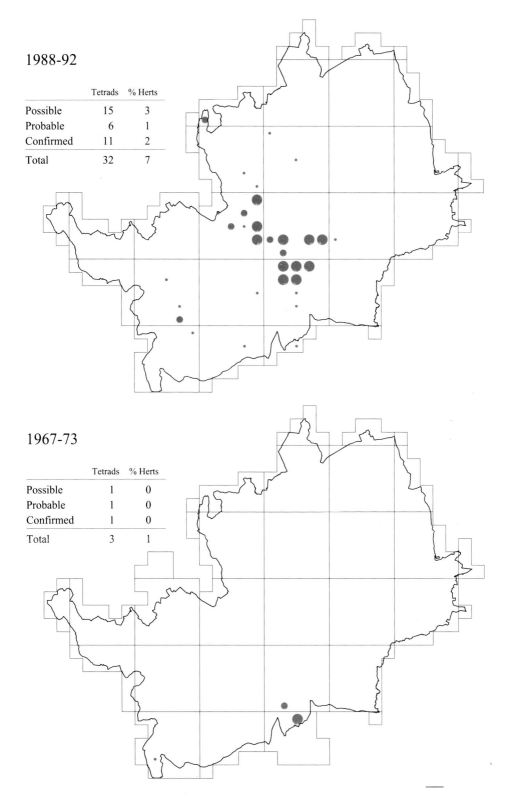

1988-92

	Tetrads	% Herts
Possible	15	3
Probable	6	1
Confirmed	11	2
Total	32	7

1967-73

	Tetrads	% Herts
Possible	1	0
Probable	1	0
Confirmed	1	0
Total	3	1

Gadwall

Anas strepera

National population 770 pairs, Hertford-shire 24 pairs, increasing.

The change in status of the Gadwall in Hertfordshire over the last 20 years has been remarkable. It has followed the national trend of steady increase (Fox 1988). The Gadwall is now a common winter visitor to well-vegetated gravel pits and reservoirs with the county supporting a highly significant percentage of the British population. It typically feeds in association with Coot, surface feeding and up-ending but also making use of the wastefulness of the latter as it brings up beakfuls of aquatic weeds following dives. This behaviour has earned the

Gadwall the nick-name 'Coot-mugger'. More recently a corresponding rise has been seen in the local breeding population and this species looks set to become a significant part of the county avifauna.

The Gadwall breeds near shallow water, marshes or slow-flowing rivers with abundant marginal aquatic plants. It nests in rank vegetation such as sedges, nettles or willowherb, under grass tussocks or brambles where the female lays and incubates the 8 to 12 eggs for 27-28 days. The nest site may be some distance from water. In Hertfordshire breeding Gadwalls are associated principally with the gravel pits of the Lee and Colne valleys, but additionally it can be found along river valleys where shallow open water and marsh exist.

Summering drakes are easily observed but, as with most duck, solitary broods can be very secretive. However, due to the limited number of sites, which are mostly well-watched, a good estimate of the population has been achieved by combining data from the atlas and the broods recorded in the county bird report. At present between 20 and 35 pairs summer annually.

During the old atlas colonisation had barely begun, with only one confirmed breeding record during the period. The present distribution shows that most of the major open waters in the county are now occupied by at least one or two pairs. Rye Meads is by far the most important site, with up to 50% of the Hertfordshire population. The shallow nutrient-rich effluent lagoons provide a major food source for ducklings and ensure a high survival rate.

In Britain, the Gadwall first became established as a breeding bird with the expansion of feral populations, initially in Norfolk and Suffolk (Fox 1988). In recent years a general increase across western Europe has included this country. The reasons for the increase are unclear (perhaps climatic) but in Britain there is no doubt that the increasing availability of permanent fresh water in the form of gravel pits and reservoirs has been a major factor.   GJW

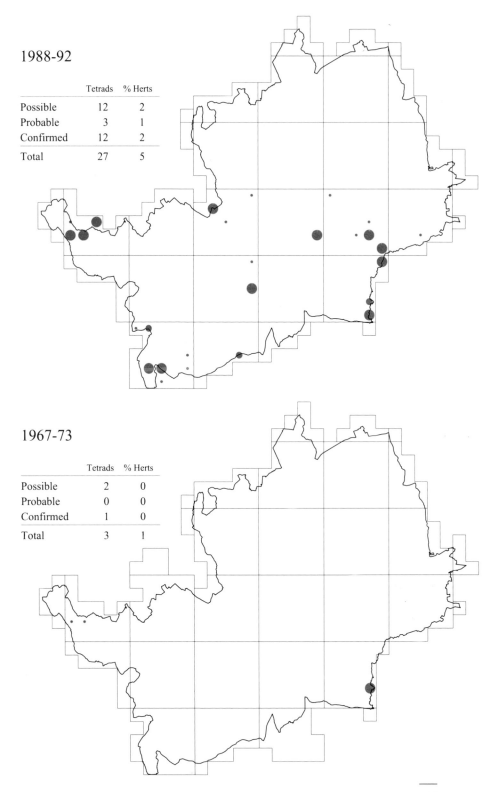

1988-92

	Tetrads	% Herts
Possible	12	2
Probable	3	1
Confirmed	12	2
Total	27	5

1967-73

	Tetrads	% Herts
Possible	2	0
Probable	0	0
Confirmed	1	0
Total	3	1

Teal

Anas crecca

National population 1500-2600 pairs, Hertfordshire nil, no change.

The Teal is the smallest of our dabbling ducks, feeding in very shallow water over soft substrates. It specialises in feeding on small food items, mainly seeds in the winter and invertebrates, especially midge larvae, during the summer months. It is a widespread bird in winter, favouring both fresh and brackish waters.

Although less tolerant of disturbance than Mallard, the Teal is found as a winter visitor across Hertfordshire in wetlands of all sizes. Pairs or small flocks may be found in marshes, lakes or along rivers, while the largest concentrations are centred on the more open gravel pits, sewage works and reservoirs. These birds roost mainly by day and flight into the surrounding countryside to forage by night. Wintering birds originate predominantly from Scandinavia, although work by the Rye Meads Ringing Group has shown that at least some reach us from well into Russia.

Teal nest most frequently in north and west Britain. Favoured habitats include moorland pools, bogs and peatlands. They also nest in lowland marshes and river valleys where there is abundant cover but overall numbers are small. The nest is a hollow, lined with dark brown down, well hidden in dense, riparian vegetation but can be up to 150 metres from water. The eight to ten eggs are incubated by the female for 21-22 days. Even in favoured areas, breeding densities are low. There is little evidence to show any major trends in the national breeding population although some local decreases have been noted, both here and abroad. This conflicts with the trend of increasing wintering numbers throughout north-west Europe over the last 30 years.

Breeding in Hertfordshire is best described as sporadic. However, the occasional pair may be present but very unobtrusive and, as broods are always well hidden in vegetation, the recording of confirmed breeding would be fortuitous. Despite this the maps almost certainly show an exaggerated picture of distribution, many records referring to late spring migrants. Little change is apparent over the 20 years; a thin spread of summer records but with less than one confirmed breeding record annually.

There is no evidence that breeding was regular anywhere in the county during recorded history other than at Tring Reservoirs. A lack of suitable habitat and increasing disturbance are likely to be limiting factors. With the increasing number of gravel pits there is perhaps the potential, particularly through habitat management, to retain one or two breeding pairs in the county.   GJW

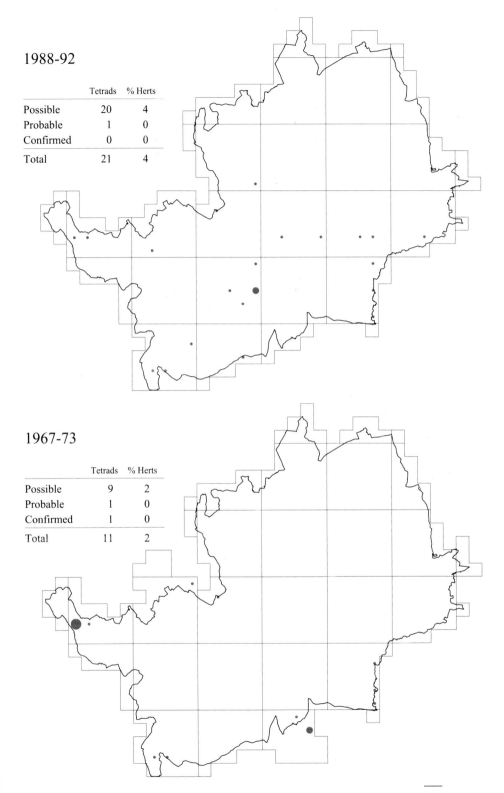

1988-92

	Tetrads	% Herts
Possible	20	4
Probable	1	0
Confirmed	0	0
Total	21	4

1967-73

	Tetrads	% Herts
Possible	9	2
Probable	1	0
Confirmed	1	0
Total	11	2

Mallard

Anas platyrhynchos

National population 100,000 pairs, Hertfordshire 4000-6600 pairs, some increase.

This highly adaptable and tolerant duck is the most widespread of our wildfowl. It is a familiar bird of park ponds, lakes, rivers and estuaries, in fact just about every wetland habitat. With its close association with humans through domestication and hunting it has become a well-studied species. Resident breeding birds are augmented both by local releases of artificially reared birds for shooting and, during the winter months, by many more from further north and east.

As with other dabbling ducks the Mallard favours shallow waters for feeding. It has a variable diet, from all kinds of vegetable matter to a greater percentage of invertebrate items during the summer. It flights out widely from wetlands to feed on crop residues. Larger, deeper waters are used as daytime roosts during the autumn and winter months.

A large variety of nest sites is used. Typically the nest is on the ground, concealed amongst rank, herbaceous vegetation. However, they may use nest boxes, the crowns of pollarded trees, and many artificial sites have been recorded, sometimes some distance from water.

Mallard have a long breeding season with broods most frequent from April to July. Early breeders can suffer high losses due to predation of eggs and young but repeat attempts through the summer boost the overall success.

The atlas results present a good picture of the county distribution; summering birds are obvious and broods usually easily observed. Both surveys show a wide distribution but there is a marked increase in occupancy of tetrads from 64% to 82%.

Over the same period the national CBC index for farmland has shown an increase and then stabilisation. Although farmland is not the key habitat for Mallard, this suggests an overall high population causing overspill into non-optimum habitats. Reports from further afield also suggest an increasing population. Bearing in mind the improved coverage of the new atlas, there seems little doubt that there has been some increase in Mallard in the county in recent decades. The reasons for this are not clear. The growing habit of releasing captive reared birds for shooting has been suggested but a general improvement in the condition and availability of suitable habitat is a more feasible explanation.

The distribution maps tie in closely with available wetland habitats. In both atlases there were positive associations with open water, rivers, streams and ponds – even the smallest wetland is likely to be occupied by Mallard. Sparse distribution on the chalk and clay-with-flints to the north and west of the county reflects the scarcity of ponds and streams there. The river corridor of the Grand Union Canal and River Bulbourne can clearly be seen through this area. GJW

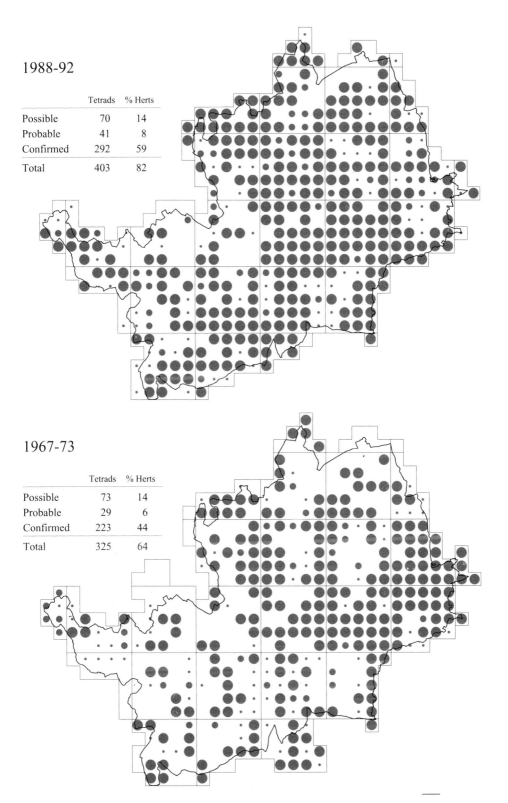

1988-92

	Tetrads	% Herts
Possible	70	14
Probable	41	8
Confirmed	292	59
Total	403	82

1967-73

	Tetrads	% Herts
Possible	73	14
Probable	29	6
Confirmed	223	44
Total	325	64

Garganey

Anas querquedula

National population 40-111 pairs, Hertfordshire one-five pairs, increasing.

The Garganey is a small, slightly built,
slender necked, dabbling duck unique
amongst British wildfowl in being almost exclusively a summer migrant,
spending the winter in sub-Saharan
Africa. The first birds arrive in late March
and April with final departure during
September.

Britain is on the extreme north-west
edge of the breeding range of Garganey
and the numbers tend to vary from year
to year with high numbers in years following wet winters and warm early
springs. The former results in plenty of
shallow pools to attract and hold birds and the latter ensures that there are plenty of
migrants to find the sites. Over the last ten years between 40 and 111 pairs have bred in
Britain (Spencer *et al* 1993).

The Garganey requires small, freshwater pools with substantial fringing vegetation
for breeding, the nest itself being lined with distinctive white-tipped down and well
concealed amidst tall grass, usually within 20 metres of the water's edge. Incubation of
the 8 to 11 eggs is carried out entirely by the female and they hatch after 21-23 days. The
young are normally accompanied by the female only.

Garganey is a difficult species to locate in the breeding season, remaining well hidden
in vegetation for much of the time and not always staying in the vicinity of the nest site.
The situation is further complicated by non-breeding birds which can continue to arrive
into late May or early June. The usual confirmation of breeding is when the female
appears with young, often in a totally unexpected place. Return migration can start as
early as mid-June, making summer occurrences not necessarily those of breeding birds.

In Hertfordshire, the Garganey is mainly a regular but scarce spring and autumn
passage migrant. Breeding had only been confirmed on five occasions up to 1987.

During the fieldwork for the new atlas, breeding was confirmed in one tetrad,
probable in another and Garganeys were present and possibly breeding in three more.
This compares with just three possible breeding records in the old atlas. Given such
small numbers it is impossible to determine any particular trend in the distribution or
habitat associations.   RD & JM

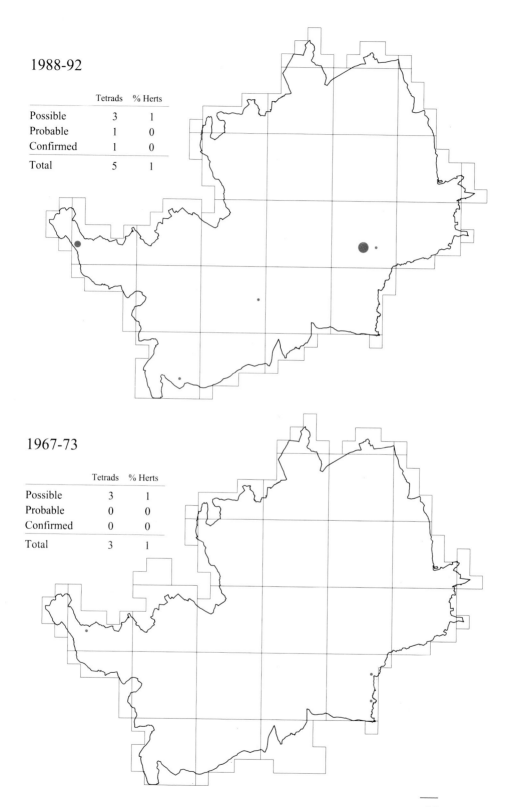

1988-92

	Tetrads	% Herts
Possible	3	1
Probable	1	0
Confirmed	1	0
Total	5	1

1967-73

	Tetrads	% Herts
Possible	3	1
Probable	0	0
Confirmed	0	0
Total	3	1

Shoveler

Anas clypeata

National population 1000-1500 pairs, Hertfordshire two pairs, slight increase.

In 'A History of the Birds of Hertfordshire', Sage (1959) remarked on the then recent appearance of Shovelers in the Lee valley, noting six at Rye Meads on 13 April 1957. Thirty years later the Lee valley is the main breeding area for Shovelers in the county and the wintering populations, particularly in the Lee valley but also in the Colne valley and at Tring Reservoirs, are of national significance.

Wintering Shovelers are now a feature of most of the larger waters in Hertfordshire. The increase in water-filled gravel pits has no doubt benefited the species. Nutrient rich waters provide the staple planktonic foods, principally tiny invertebrates suspended in the surface water. These are sieved out by the massive, spatulate bill. The 'took...took' calls of drakes and the dull rattle of Shovelers' wings as they rise to fly away should be familiar sounds to all birdwatchers in the county.

The Shoveler nests by shallow waters, pools and dykes, often with adjacent wet grassy habitats. The bulk of the breeding population nationally is in the east and south. The nest is on the ground, usually concealed amongst dense or tussocky grass.

Summering Shovelers are obvious, with drakes remaining on territory at least in the early stages of nesting. The distribution maps therefore show a good, even exaggerated, representation of the situation in the county. Records of broods are less than annual and the breeding population can only be between one and five pairs. Although numbers are minimal, the maps do suggest a slight increase between the two periods, almost entirely in the Lee valley.

The national population is thought to be increasing slowly. The availability of new gravel pits in both the Lee and Colne valleys is without doubt a major factor in any local increase. Unfortunately, most gravel pit sites lack the conditions favoured by Shovelers, which need shallow, well vegetated water in which to feed and breed. However, the specific management of individual sites in the Lee valley to provide such conditions has attracted birds to nest.

Tring Reservoirs appear to be of declining importance and there was no proof of breeding at the reservoirs during the new atlas. Tring has historically been a stronghold of breeding Shoveler, and indeed other duck, in the county. Its recent decline is a sad matter; increasing disturbance and insufficient, or inappropriate, management are likely to be key factors.

GJW

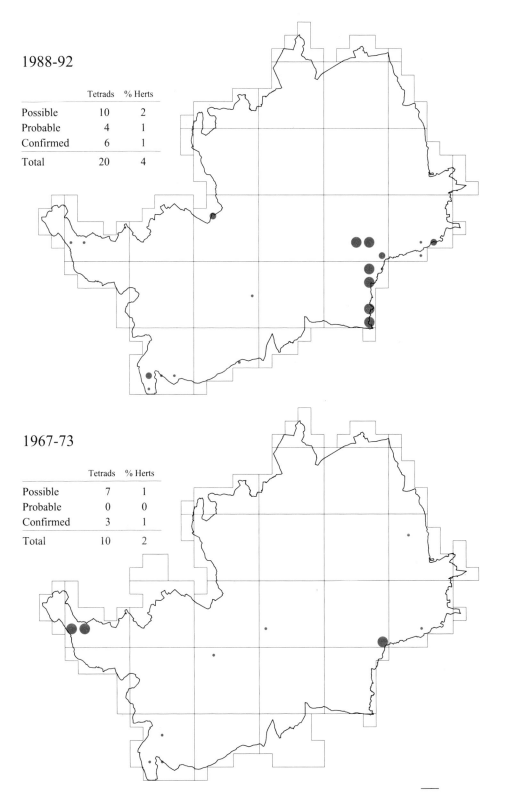

1988-92

	Tetrads	% Herts
Possible	10	2
Probable	4	1
Confirmed	6	1
Total	20	4

1967-73

	Tetrads	% Herts
Possible	7	1
Probable	0	0
Confirmed	3	1
Total	10	2

Pochard

Aythya ferina

*National population 400 pairs, Hertford-
shire nine pairs, no change.*

The Pochard is a widespread and familiar wintering duck on inland waters. Favoured sites are relatively shallow, usually less than three metres deep. Food is
obtained by diving and comprises mainly
vegetable matter, notably stoneworts and
pondweeds, but invertebrates are also
eaten to a lesser extent. Flocks often
seem to be largely inactive by day, with
many birds flighting to favoured feeding
areas at night. Ringing recoveries indicate that wintering birds originate from
eastern Europe and the Baltic countries.

The small British breeding population
is centred on south-east England (Fox 1991). The Pochard nests by lakes, pools and
especially coastal marsh 'fleets' or dykes. Gravel pits are used but to a lesser extent than
by the Tufted Duck. The nest is well hidden in dense vegetation, often on a platform of
reeds within emergent aquatic vegetation. The female lays 8 to 11 greenish-grey eggs
and incubates them for about 24-26 days. The first report of breeding in Hertfordshire
was around 1850 at Tring.

Pochard are easily recorded during the breeding season but the number of birds
present is a poor indicator of the size of the breeding population. Breeding is best
confirmed by recording broods later in the season. These are generally quite visible but
the seemingly high failure rate on many gravel pit sites often results in a total loss of
ducklings after only one or two days. Work by the Game Conservancy Trust (Giles
1992) has shown that high fish populations in many pits reduce the invertebrate food
available for ducklings which leads to low brood survival for the two species studied:
Mallard and Tufted Duck. It is probable that broods of Pochard are affected in the same
way.

The main sites in Hertfordshire are all well watched and the maps almost certainly
show a good representation of the breeding population. There was no change in the
number of tetrads with confirmed breeding between the two surveys but some differences in distribution are apparent. In both there is a clear correlation with open water
habitats; gravel pits, sewage water lagoons, reservoirs and other man-made stretches of
water. Whereas the old atlas shows a wide distribution, the new atlas appears to show a
consolidation into three main areas: Tring Reservoirs and the lower sections of the Lee
and Colne valleys. Given the slow increase of the national population, this pattern may
seem to be in conflict. However, it may be that the habitats in Hertfordshire are now
unsuitable for some reason. Certainly some gravel pit sites in the upper Colne valley are
now filled in or have developed a tall fringe of willow. One old site now has intensive
angling use.   GJW

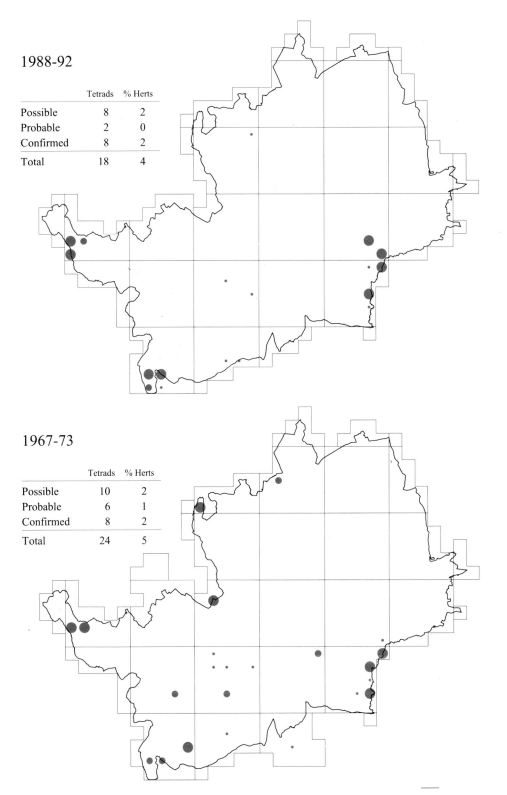

1988-92

	Tetrads	% Herts
Possible	8	2
Probable	2	0
Confirmed	8	2
Total	18	4

1967-73

	Tetrads	% Herts
Possible	10	2
Probable	6	1
Confirmed	8	2
Total	24	5

Tufted Duck

Aythya fuligula

National population 7000-8000 pairs, Hertfordshire 150-300 pairs, increasing.

Second in abundance only to the Mallard, the Tufted Duck shares much of the tolerance and adaptability of the former. This common diving duck is a familiar sight on most freshwaters, from urban parks to huge reservoirs. Although an omnivore, it feeds largely on a range of aquatic invertebrates but molluscs are particularly important.

The Tufted Duck has spread widely since the first British breeding record in 1849. It first bred in Hertfordshire in 1893 at Tring Reservoirs (Sage 1959). The initial increase, in Europe as well as in Britain, has been linked to climatic amelioration. Additional factors have been the continuing increase in the number of waters such as reservoirs and gravel pits and the Tufted Duck's ability to exploit them. The spread of the zebra mussel, an important food source, through these new habitats has also been claimed as a further reason for the growth.

The nest is located in rank or tussocky grassland, usually close to the water's edge. Gravel pits, lakes, park ponds and slow flowing rivers are all suitable habitats. Among the latest of the ducks to breed, broods are usually found into July. Even recently hatched ducklings are able to dive for food but also take many insects at the water's surface. Although gravel pits can provide excellent nesting habitat, success rates can be low, probably the result of low invertebrate food supply for the ducklings (Giles 1992).

Recording the summer presence of Tufted Duck is easy, especially on open lakes and gravel pits. Broods are also highly visible, usually spending considerable time on open water. However, breeding along secluded stretches of river may be more difficult to prove unless the broods are located.

The maps show a doubling in the number of occupied tetrads between the two surveys. This increase matches the continuing upward national trend. The new atlas map shows primarily an expansion along the river valleys, particularly where the tributaries join the River Lee around Hertford. Most gravel pits sites are well represented. Other than at Tring Reservoirs, the Tufted Duck is still, however, a rare breeder in north or west Hertfordshire.

The habitat association shows an increase in the range of habitats used over the last 20 years. In the old atlas Tufted Ducks were associated with open water, rivers, built-up areas and mineral workings. In the new atlas this had expanded to include streams and parkland.

The bulk of the breeding population is still centred on the lower Lee valley , as it was in the old atlas. Three sites, Amwell, Rye Meads and Cheshunt, together currently hold in excess of 100 pairs. The smaller waters and rivers will only hold one or two pairs though and the total breeding population is likely to be between 150 and 300 pairs.

GJW

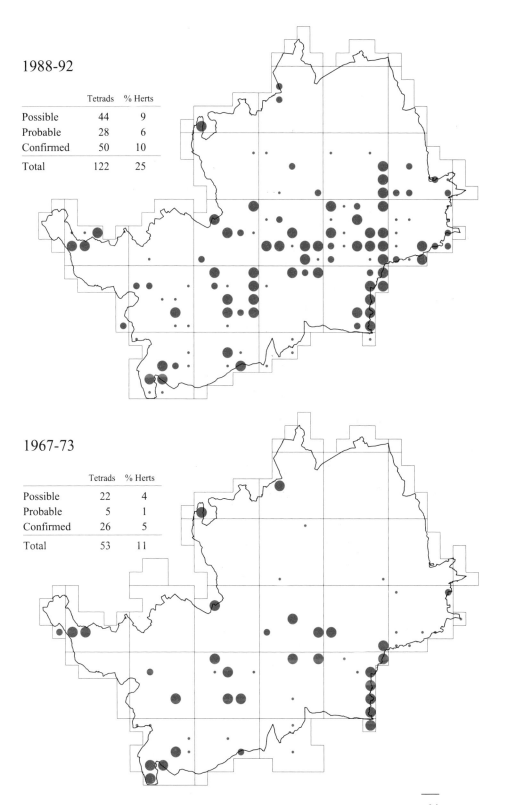

1988-92

	Tetrads	% Herts
Possible	44	9
Probable	28	6
Confirmed	50	10
Total	122	25

1967-73

	Tetrads	% Herts
Possible	22	4
Probable	5	1
Confirmed	26	5
Total	53	11

Ruddy Duck

Oxyura jamaicensis

National population approximately 570 pairs, Hertfordshire circa five pairs, increasing

In full breeding plumage the male Ruddy Duck is a striking bird, with a rich chestnut body, black-and-white head and brilliant blue bill. The female has a rather more subtle, mainly brown, plumage and sometimes goes undetected. Ruddy Ducks are small diving ducks with an increasing feral population in Britain. Pairs were imported during the late 1950s but unpinioned juvenile birds escaped from the Wildfowl and Wetlands Trust reserve at Slimbridge and first bred in Somerset (now Avon) in 1960. They soon

became established in the West Midlands and from here the species spread, first breeding in Hertfordshire at Tring in 1965. Ruddy Ducks are attracted, particularly in summer, to freshwater lakes and gravel pits with ample emergent vegetation.

Proof of breeding can be initially difficult to establish. The typical nest site is amongst thick vegetation and consists of a small floating platform of mainly dead material, anchored to fresh growth. A typical clutch, containing between six and ten eggs, is incubated by the female alone for 25-28 days. Ruddy Ducks can breed from the middle of April but ducklings often appear late in the season. There have been records in Hertfordshire of small ducklings well into October.

The maps show the progress of the Ruddy Duck's spread across the county. The single location on the old map represented the extreme south-east of the British range. During the ensuing twenty years the species has continued to breed in small numbers at Tring and has spread to both the Colne and Lee valleys. Other suitable habitat has held birds in the summer months, or the occasional one-off breeding pair.

The previous rapid expansion in breeding numbers, quoted at 25% per annum, has now slowed but continues where new areas are colonised. However, all the major sites in Hertfordshire have probably now been exploited by the species.

Judging from the records received there are probably around five pairs breeding in the county with a healthy non-breeding population also present during the summer months.

Hard weather and wandering birds have resulted in continental records from the Mediterranean to Scandinavia. In Spain, Ruddy Ducks have been reported amongst the local population of White-headed Duck *O. leucocephala* (Sharrock 1989) and fertile hybrids have been produced. To protect the endangered White-headed Duck, the Spanish authorities are now controlling Ruddy Ducks throughout Spain. The UK authorities have recognised their international responsibility and the Department of the Environment are sponsoring a project to test the feasibility of control measures here. The objective is to prevent dispersion of the Ruddy Duck throughout Europe to safeguard the Spanish and Turkish populations of White-headed Ducks. It remains to be seen whether Ruddy Ducks are still breeding in Hertfordshire in 20 years time.   RY

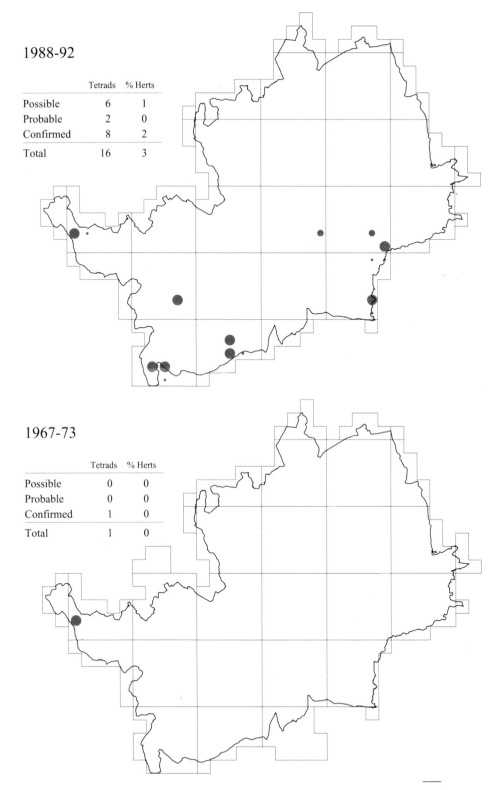

1988-92

	Tetrads	% Herts
Possible	6	1
Probable	2	0
Confirmed	8	2
Total	16	3

1967-73

	Tetrads	% Herts
Possible	0	0
Probable	0	0
Confirmed	1	0
Total	1	0

Sparrowhawk

Accipiter nisus

National population 32,000 pairs, Hertfordshire 300-500 pairs, increasing dramatically.

The Sparrowhawk is a raptor of woodlands and copses, which hunts mainly small and medium sized songbirds. It is most often seen soaring high or flying with long glides interspersed with occasional flaps. Very often the first indications that a Sparrowhawk is overhead are the alarm calls of small birds. The hunting technique is to surprise its prey by flying low and, at the last moment, to flash over a hedge or round an obstacle into the flock. In recent years Sparrowhawks have become frequent visitors to suburban gardens where there are often high numbers of potential prey attracted to bird feeders.

The nest is usually in a woodland tree, often larch or pine, but any species will do. Incubation of the eggs is carried out entirely by the female and during this period all food is provided by the male. After hatching the male initially provides all of the food but once the young are old enough to be left alone the female hunts as well.

The presence of birds in an area is relatively easy to detect but obtaining proof of breeding is more difficult and can be confused by non-breeding birds. In March pairs can sometimes be seen displaying over their breeding woods but from then on observers must normally rely on sightings of males carrying prey back to the nest. Once fledged, the young are very noisy, particularly when being fed, and many of the confirmed breeding records were obtained by observers hearing the commotion near the nest.

The remarkable increase in the number of occupied tetrads since the old atlas follows the recovery in numbers of Sparrowhawks after their almost total eradication from Hertfordshire during the period of organochlorine pesticide use in the 1950s and 1960s (Newton 1986). Sparrowhawks, being high in the food chain, are particularly vulnerable to the bio-accumulation of toxic residues. In the extreme this caused direct mortality of adults, but at lower levels resulted in breeding failures due to eggshell thinning (Newton and Bogan 1978). This combination of high adult mortality and low breeding success was devastating for the population which crashed throughout eastern and central Britain. The old atlas was completed when Sparrowhawks were just staging their recovery in Hertfordshire. Although now widespread there are areas, particularly in the north and east of the county, where the species is still rare.

The only significant positive habitat associations of Sparrowhawks are with areas of woodland. In the new atlas there are negative associations with various agricultural variables. The tetrads in the east which had no birds were also those with relatively low amounts of woodland and large areas of agricultural land. Over the next few decades it will be interesting to see whether Sparrowhawks can eventually colonise these areas as they have done elsewhere in Hertfordshire. KWS

64

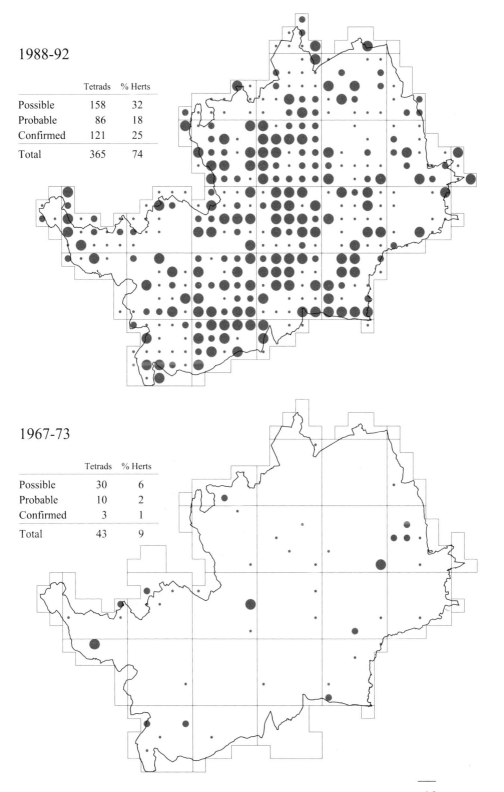

1988-92

	Tetrads	% Herts
Possible	158	32
Probable	86	18
Confirmed	121	25
Total	365	74

1967-73

	Tetrads	% Herts
Possible	30	6
Probable	10	2
Confirmed	3	1
Total	43	9

Kestrel

Falco tinnunculus

National population 50,000 pairs, Hertfordshire 300-400 pairs, increasing.

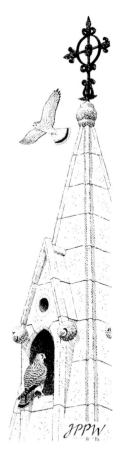

Probably Britain's commonest bird of prey, the Kestrel is a smallish falcon that is familiar to most travellers as the bird is often seen hovering beside motorways and railway lines. It feeds primarily on small mammals which it hunts either by hovering and pouncing or by watching and waiting at a high vantage point such as a telegraph pole.

Favoured nest sites in Hertfordshire are forks or cavities in isolated or parkland trees but ledges on buildings are also used. A clutch of usually four or five eggs is normally laid in April and incubation takes four weeks, the young hatching at approximately daily intervals. The young are normally brooded by the female for a further week, after which she takes part in catching food for them. At three weeks they will feed themselves on food brought to the nest by the parents and a week later they will fledge but will not become fully independent for at least another month.

The presence of breeding Kestrels in an area is not difficult to establish but locating the nest site and obtaining proof of breeding can be more difficult. Birds displaying near a potential nest site in early spring are often a good indication of where birds will eventually settle. However, because of the large territory size, birds seen carrying food may be breeding in an adjacent tetrad. Recently fledged young usually remain near their nest and so give a more precise breeding location.

Nationally, Kestrel numbers were reduced during the organochlorine pesticide era of the 1950s and 60s but not to the same degree as the Sparrowhawk. Numbers have apparently now recovered although the national population index is declining slightly. In Hertfordshire there has been a significant increase in distribution between the two atlases. In particular, birds are now far more common in the north and east of the county. In the first atlas there was a negative association with arable farming but this is no longer the case, suggesting that birds have expanded into some of the arable farming areas. It is probable that, at the time of the first atlas, Kestrel numbers had not fully recovered in these areas and over the last twenty years we have seen a continuation of this recovery.

Kestrel breeding density can vary a great deal from year to year and there is good evidence that it is determined by food supply (Village 1990). Village found that breeding numbers on arable farmland were determined by over-winter survival, which was itself related to food availability and the severity of the weather, but were not limited by nest sites. On his grassland study sites Kestrel numbers responded more directly to cycles in small mammal populations. With atlas fieldwork spanning at least five years in both surveys, it is unlikely that the changes in Kestrel distribution in Hertfordshire are related to short term cycles in small mammal numbers. TK

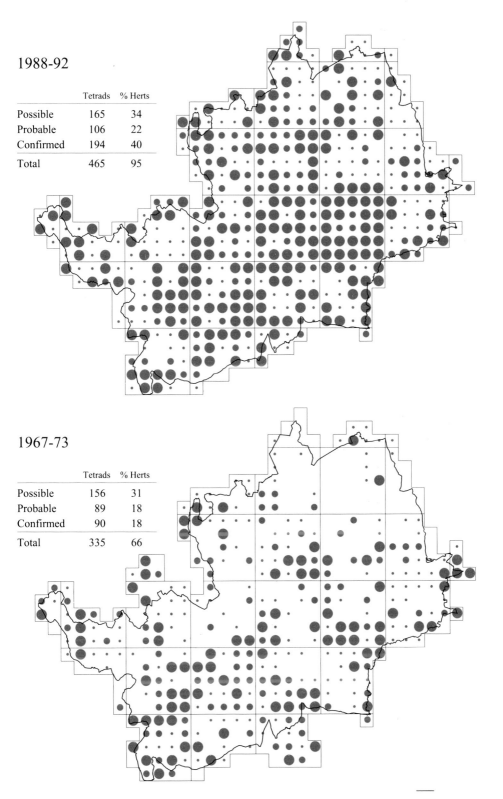

1988-92

	Tetrads	% Herts
Possible	165	34
Probable	106	22
Confirmed	194	40
Total	465	95

1967-73

	Tetrads	% Herts
Possible	156	31
Probable	89	18
Confirmed	90	18
Total	335	66

Hobby

Falco subbuteo

National population 500-900 pairs, Hertfordshire 20-30 pairs, increasing.

The Hobby is a small, elegant and highly skilled aerial predator which feeds on large insects, such as dragonflies, and various types of birds.

Breeding birds usually use the old nest of species such as Carrion Crow. The mixed farmland or woodland habitats favoured for nesting in Hertfordshire would seem to be a substitute for the dry, lowland heath which typifies the optimum habitat used in southern England and clearly the use of such habitat has enabled the Hobby to increase its range. The Hobby returns late from its tropical African wintering grounds, arriving mostly towards the end of May. The subsequent late breeding is timed to coincide with the abundance of young and aerially unskilled juvenile birds during late summer. Prior to hatching the three or four eggs the birds' diet is almost totally insectivorous. Subsequently, mainly birds are taken until a general return to insects around the time of the chicks' fledging 28-34 days later. Due to the species' diet, the available breeding season is relatively short and most birds have departed from the county by the end of September.

Breeding was confirmed in 22 tetrads with one instance of two nest sites within one kilometre. It is interesting to note that only one of the tetrads in which breeding was confirmed in the previous atlas held breeding birds during the new survey period. This apparent lack of site fidelity may be due to the relative weakness of the old nests utilised rather than any significant habitat degradation. With an increase of seven-fold in the number of tetrads with some presence and over three-fold for confirmed or probable breeding registrations, the Hobby has clearly increased considerably in Hertfordshire.

With such a low number of occupied squares any habitat associations need to be treated with caution. In the old atlas there were positive associations with broad-leaved and coniferous woodland and negative ones with wheat and potatoes. With more occupied tetrads in the new atlas positive associations with parkland, horticultural crops, grasslands and cattle have emerged in addition to broad-leaved woodland.

Prior to the 1960s, the last breeding record of Hobby in Hertfordshire was near Stevenage in 1884. In 1967 three or more pairs nested and by 1982 that number had increased to between nine and 13 pairs. When the original National Breeding Atlas was completed Hertfordshire represented the most north-easterly stronghold of the species but subsequently it has spread into East Anglian counties and north into the east Midlands. The current population in Hertfordshire is thought to be between 20 and 30 pairs with many other non-breeding birds also present. It is probable that this figure is an under-estimation due to the difficulties in locating nests although the disciplines imposed by atlas work are likely to have minimised this factor.   RY

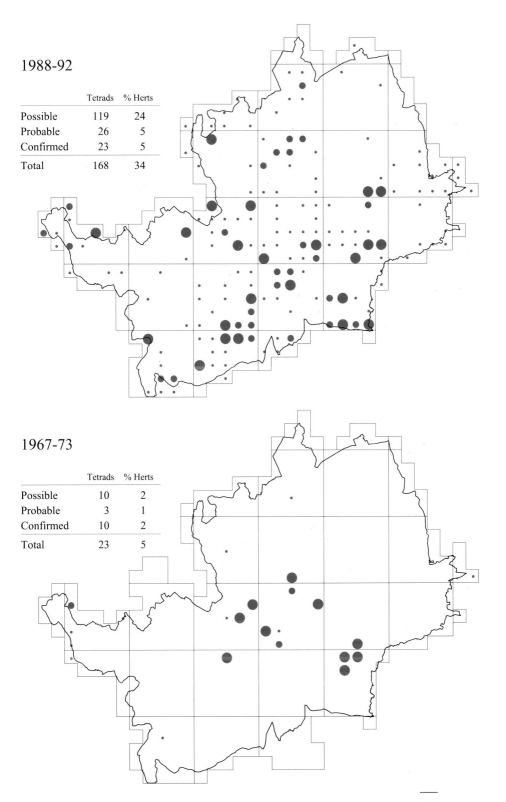

1988-92

	Tetrads	% Herts
Possible	119	24
Probable	26	5
Confirmed	23	5
Total	168	34

1967-73

	Tetrads	% Herts
Possible	10	2
Probable	3	1
Confirmed	10	2
Total	23	5

Red-legged Partridge

Alectoris rufa

National population >90,000 territories, Hertfordshire 2000-4000 pairs, increasing due to releases.

Originally introduced to this country in the 17th and 18th centuries, with further releases still continuing, the Red-legged Partridge is a familiar bird of large open arable fields, though it also occurs in a wide range of other agricultural habitats.

The nest is a simple scrape, usually in vegetation. A significant minority of birds lay two clutches, each parent taking responsibility for the incubation and rearing of one clutch. Territorial and solitary during the breeding season, it is gregarious for the rest of the year, often forming large and conspicuous coveys.

Already widely distributed at the time of the old atlas, though with a bias to the north and east, the Red-legged Partridge has not only maintained its position but has also been recorded in almost 50 additional tetrads. This results partly from the infilling of empty tetrads in otherwise widely occupied squares, but over half the increase is concentrated in just three squares, TL00, TL10 and TL11. The species is now more evenly spread across the county, but mostly absent from the more urban southern part.

The contrast between the fortunes of this species and those of the Grey Partridge is particularly marked. Although already noted as in long term decline, at the time of the old atlas the Grey Partridge was recorded in 11% more tetrads than the Red-legged Partridge: the latter now occurs in some 40% more tetrads than the former.

Unfortunately, because of the Red-legged Partridge's status as a game bird it is difficult to be certain whether this picture of success is apparent or real. Since about the mid-1970s there have been large scale releases, estimated at over 800,000 annually (Potts G R, in Lack 1986). These releases have included Chukars and Chukar x Red-legged Partridge. Although the hybrid is prolific in captivity (which accounts for much of its popularity), research by the Game Conservancy Trust (Potts 1989) has shown that in the wild, hybrid and mixed pairs breed much less successfully than pure bred birds. Although birds attempt to pair like with like, the scale of releases renders mixed pairs inevitable. The consequent reduction in productivity coupled with the increased shooting pressure that the releases are designed to support has, in fact, had a deleterious effect on the wild population, which can become locally extinct in the midst of plenty of released birds. Against this background it may be relevant to note that almost the entire increase in records is of probable rather than confirmed breeding.

In both atlases Red-legged Partridges were positively associated with arable crops – wheat, barley, oats and field beans. Only in the new atlas did an association with oilseed rape appear but this reflects the availability of this crop. In the old atlas there were associations with fallow and grass leys but the latter has disappeared. In both atlases there was a negative association with built-up areas. PJW

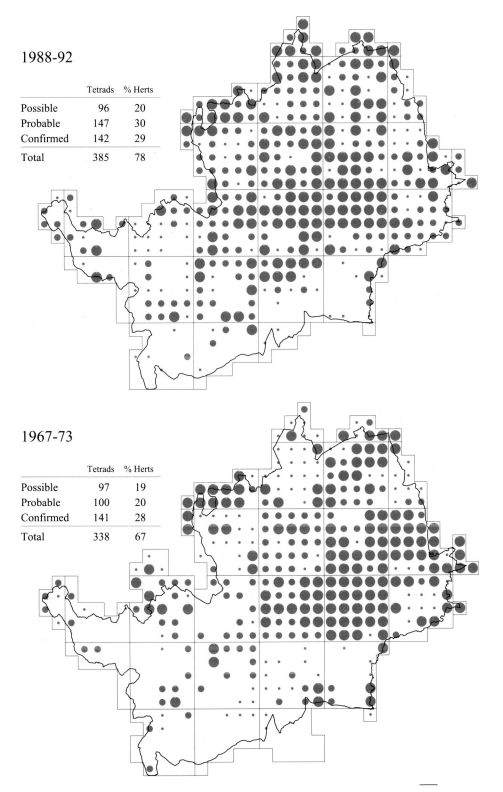

1988-92

	Tetrads	% Herts
Possible	96	20
Probable	147	30
Confirmed	142	29
Total	385	78

1967-73

	Tetrads	% Herts
Possible	97	19
Probable	100	20
Confirmed	141	28
Total	338	67

Grey Partridge

Perdix perdix

National population 150,000 pairs, Hertfordshire 1000-2000 pairs, decreasing.

A small but plump game bird, the Grey Partridge has very striking plumage when seen closely. Both male and female have barred flanks, reddish orange throat and grey breast with characteristic chestnut markings on the belly. However, from a distance, a group of Grey Partridges appears cryptic and well camouflaged, simply as blobs with no necks.

Found in open countryside and on both cultivated and uncultivated farmland throughout Britain, the Grey Partridge is often seen in pairs in spring or small family parties, known as coveys, in autumn and winter. When flushed they will initially run fast with heads up before taking flight with a noisy whirring sound from small rounded wings. The flight is low and fast and normally only for a short distance.

The nest is a scrape, lined with grasses and leaves, made by the female and usually hidden in a hedge bottom or long rough grass. It is normally located well away from habitation but can occasionally be found near farm buildings. Anything up to 20 or so eggs are laid and incubated by the female for 23-25 days. Chicks leave the nest very shortly after hatching and are able to fly in only two weeks.

Grey Partridges are fairly easy to see during the early part of the year before crops have grown too tall, but once nesting has started they become far more difficult to find. Empty egg shells scattered about are sometimes the only clue that breeding has been attempted. Later in the breeding season a pair with young may be seen crossing a farm track or headland, but care must be taken in recording these, as adults and young can wander long distances.

Nationally, the Grey Partridge has been in decline for most of this century and has been the subject of much detailed research, particularly by the Game Conservancy Trust (Potts 1989). The cause of the decline appears to be a combination of reduced nesting success resulting from poor habitat and lack of predator control, and poor chick survival because of modern intensive management of cereal crops. Schemes such as Conservation Headlands and Environmentally Sensitive Areas have been promoted to assist the Grey Partridge but as yet have not been adopted on a sufficiently wide scale to lead to a recovery of the national population.

Although still fairly widespread in Hertfordshire, the number of tetrads occupied by Grey Partridges has declined significantly over the last twenty years. It is also probable that the reduction in the number of pairs far exceeds the loss of occupied tetrads.

The habitat associations are positive for wheat, barley, potatoes and field beans. In the old atlas temporary grasslands and cattle were also selected but this was not the case in the new one.   DM

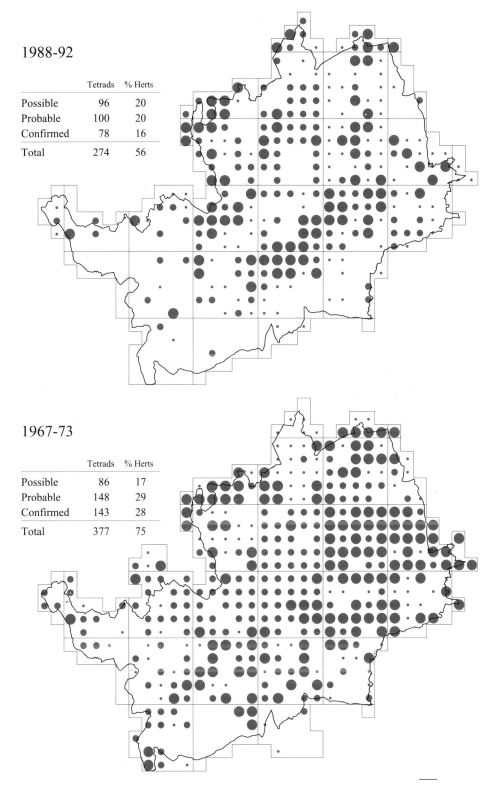

1988-92

	Tetrads	% Herts
Possible	96	20
Probable	100	20
Confirmed	78	16
Total	274	56

1967-73

	Tetrads	% Herts
Possible	86	17
Probable	148	29
Confirmed	143	28
Total	377	75

Quail

Coturnix coturnix

National population 100-300 pairs, Hertfordshire 0-22 pairs, erratic.

Andrew. P. Crick 93.

Our smallest and only migratory gamebird, the Quail resembles a tiny partridge. It is sandy brown with dark streaks above, paler below with some characteristic streaking on the flanks. The male has complex but variable dark streaking to the head and throat. In most years small numbers are recorded singing in southern England but occasionally there are major influxes, the last of which occurred in 1989 when 1655 calling birds were reported (Spencer *et al* 1993).

Quail spend the winter in sub-Saharan Africa and do not normally arrive in Britain until at least mid-May and sometimes even later. They are more usually heard than seen and have a very distinctive 'wet-my-lips' call. Although they call both during the day and night, it is on warm still summer evenings when one is most likely to hear these enigmatic birds.

Quail in Hertfordshire are usually heard calling from cereal fields and hay meadows, but it is only rarely that there is any evidence that the birds actually breed. The nest is a scrape on the ground, with a scant lining of grass or other vegetation, and the clutch of up to 12 eggs is incubated by the female for about three weeks whilst the male stays close by on guard. The chicks are able to leave the nest almost immediately after hatching but are unable to fly for another couple of weeks.

Although Quail are now relatively rare breeding birds in Britain there is evidence that historically they were far more numerous and were listed on banquet menus and poultry price lists. The reasons for the decline are not known but could have been related to changes in agriculture and pressure from spring hunting. Moreau (1951) thought that since 1940 there was a suggestion of an increase but this has certainly been slow in coming.

Although there was an overall decrease in the number of tetrads with records of Quail between the two atlases, the numbers are low and for a bird with such marked annual fluctuations it is difficult to interpret these figures. In the new atlas most of the records were from the north and west of the county but the association with the open chalk country noted in the old atlas is less clear. The major significant habitat association in the new atlas is with tetrads with large areas of barley.   DM

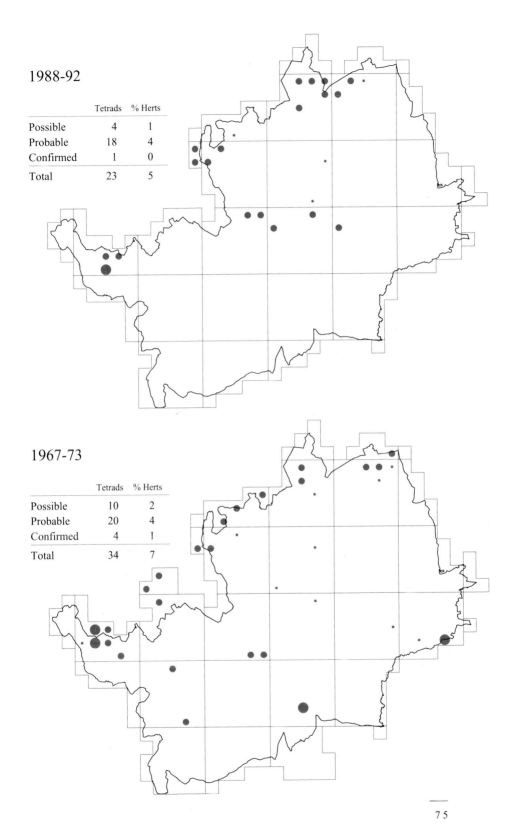

1988-92

	Tetrads	% Herts
Possible	4	1
Probable	18	4
Confirmed	1	0
Total	23	5

1967-73

	Tetrads	% Herts
Possible	10	2
Probable	20	4
Confirmed	4	1
Total	34	7

Pheasant

Phasianus colchicus

National population 1.6 million females, Hertfordshire up to 25,000 females, wild population possibly declining.

The Pheasant was the first introduction of the many alien bird species now resident in the wild in Britain. Initially introduced during the late 11th century, they became well established over the next 500 years. Pheasants have been managed throughout the centuries with numerous additions to the population at different times. Introduced birds have originated from various Asian locations and from several races of Pheasant. The result is that the British population now shows features associated with many of those different races. For example, birds with dark necks and rufous rumps of the nominate form (sometimes colloquially called 'Old English') were the original introduction from south-west Asia whilst those birds exhibiting a full white neck ring show a descent from the race *P. c. torquatus* originating from China.

The Pheasant is a popular bird in sporting circles and huge numbers are reared and released for this purpose. It is mainly a ground dwelling species although it does perch, and especially roost, in trees. The summer months may be spent some way from woodland, providing there is some cover for nesting, but the birds often retreat to more sheltered habitat in winter.

In the wild, Pheasants nest in loose concentrations on the ground and utilise the cover provided by thick vegetation. Eggs are laid between the end of March and June and the large clutch of 8-15 eggs is incubated for about a month. The young remain with the female for a further 70-80 days. Pheasants are very sedentary birds with studies showing that up to 61% of birds shot in a given area were within 400 metres of their release site.

With his bright plumage, strutting and noisy display, the presence of a male is not difficult to prove in the breeding season. Similarly females, with large broods in attendance, are also clear proof of breeding nearby, however, earlier in the season their cryptic plumage makes them very difficult to locate on the nest.

The maps show very little change in the distribution of the Pheasant in the county over the last 20 years, although with 92% of the tetrads occupied it would be difficult to detect anything other than a major decline. In both atlases Pheasants were positively associated with woodlands and all types of agricultural land and negatively with built-up areas.

It is impossible to say whether a viable wild population exists in the county. Studies by the Game Conservancy Trust have indicated that, where birds are no longer released, the wild population can decrease. The number of birds present in any given year clearly depends on gamekeeping activities and the percentage of birds which subsequently join the wild stock. The population could be as high as 25,000 females and 15,000 males although the dependency on releases makes it difficult to be more precise. RY

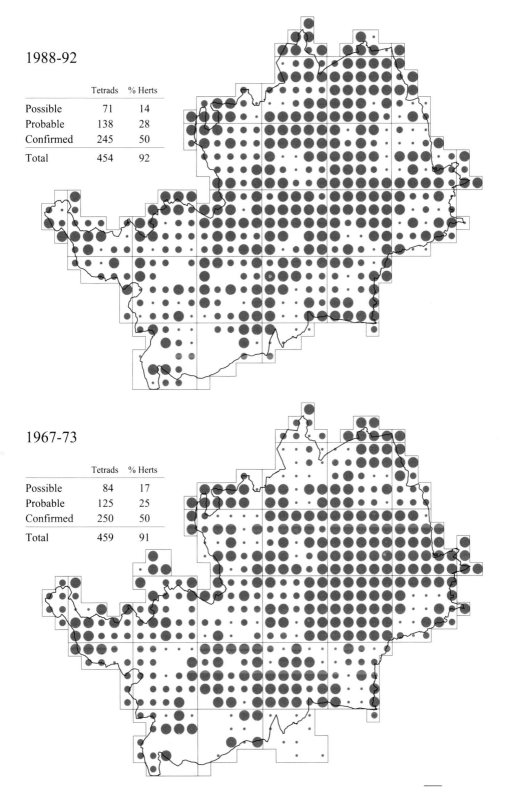

1988-92

	Tetrads	% Herts
Possible	71	14
Probable	138	28
Confirmed	245	50
Total	454	92

1967-73

	Tetrads	% Herts
Possible	84	17
Probable	125	25
Confirmed	250	50
Total	459	91

Water Rail

Rallus aquaticus

National population, 450-900 pairs, Hertfordshire, 0-10 pairs, declining.

In Hertfordshire the Water Rail is mainly a bird of passage and a winter visitor and, as such, is often only glimpsed as it dashes for cover. It is usually found anywhere with dense aquatic vegetation over shallow water such as reedbeds, watercress beds and the margins of ditches, lakes and ponds.

Smaller than a Moorhen, the long, red bill is absolutely distinctive. It walks with a deliberate rather high-stepping gait with head somewhat raised and tail often cocked. The bird's slender body enables it to move with ease through dense vegetation where its white striped flanks give it good camouflage.

The flight of the Water Rail is weak and fluttery, generally low down and lasting just a few seconds but, as many of our winter visitors are from central and eastern Europe, it is clearly capable of sustained long-distance flight.

During the breeding season Water Rails become very vocal, making pig-like squealing noises, particularly at night. They frequent reed beds and swamps with ample cover of coarse marsh vegetation, with or without trees and bushes, and swampy borders of rivers and ponds where they hunt for their varied diet of insects, spiders, molluscs, worms and small fish. The nest is amongst broken down dead reed and sedge, sometimes at some height above the water. Eggs are laid from early April onwards and are incubated by both parents. The young leave the nest soon after hatching and are fed by both parents up to fledging. A second brood is usually reared.

The Water Rail is an elusive bird and its presence in the breeding season may well go undetected unless its distinctive pig-like squeals are heard from likely habitat. However, confirmation of breeding often relies on the chance sighting of the female with young.

During the old atlas, the species was reported from 30 tetrads with breeding confirmed in five. The fieldwork for the current atlas produced records for only 11 tetrads with breeding not confirmed at all. The records of probable breeding in most cases represent birds calling from suitable locations at the right time of year and may, therefore, overestimate the true situation. It is unlikely that difficulties of locating and counting the birds would have resulted in such a large reduction in occupied tetrads. The reason for the decline is unclear but degradation and drying of the favoured aquatic habitats is the most likely explanation. It is surprising that the Water Rail has not been able to colonise the gravel pit habitats in the county to any great extent.

As expected, the habitat associations of Water Rail are positive for open water, marshland, rivers and built-up areas. Interestingly, the positive association for marshland was only found in the old atlas, suggesting a degradation in these habitats over the 20 years.

RD & KWS

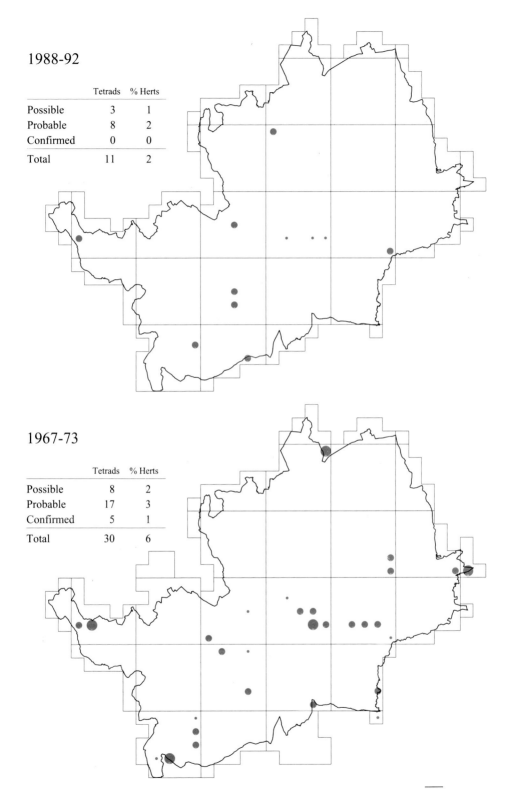

1988-92

	Tetrads	% Herts
Possible	3	1
Probable	8	2
Confirmed	0	0
Total	11	2

1967-73

	Tetrads	% Herts
Possible	8	2
Probable	17	3
Confirmed	5	1
Total	30	6

Moorhen

Gallinula chloropus

*National population 240,000 territories,
Hertfordshire 3200-5200 pairs, static.*

Familiar to everyone, the Moorhen is
widespread and common on almost every
area of water with sufficient vegetation
to provide cover for a nest. From village
ponds to large gravel pits, the tail jerking
action of the swimming bird can be seen
at all seasons with the loud and abrupt
call drawing attention to birds hidden in
bankside vegetation.

Adaptable in nesting habits, the Moorhen usually raises two broods of between two and eight young from successive nests built in a variety of situations
but always close to water. Care of the
eggs and young is undertaken by both sexes with the young remaining dependent on
parents for up to 70 days.

Small ponds hold a single pair but canals are markedly more successful for breeding
with densities at 2.9 pairs per kilometre found (Marchant & Hyde 1980). This species is
particularly vulnerable to adverse management techniques in such habitats as it is
almost totally dependent on bankside vegetation for nesting.

With its loud call, obvious habits and familiar habitats, records of breeding Moorhen
are easy to obtain and the map is an accurate picture of the distribution. Confirmed
breeding is relatively easy to establish, the young are obvious and the parents' alarm
calls similarly so.

As may be expected, the map shows the Moorhen to be a widely distributed bird in
Hertfordshire with occurrence in almost exactly the same number of tetrads as the old
atlas, with a remarkably similar distribution. It is still absent from the drier parts of
western and north Hertfordshire where there are neither ponds nor streams. The
Moorhen has no doubt benefited from the growth in gravel extraction in the last twenty
years and this has probably compensated for the decline in the number and quality of
farm and village ponds in the same period. However, with an average of over seven
ponds per tetrad (see Chapter two) at least a few have probably remained in a suitable
condition to support breeding Moorhens. This is borne out by the farmland CBC data
which shows a long-term decline over the last few decades whilst the Waterway Bird
Survey index has been stable in the same period.

Positively associated with open water, streams, rivers and ponds, it should be noted
that Moorhens will utilise even the smallest of water bodies for nesting purposes.

RNS

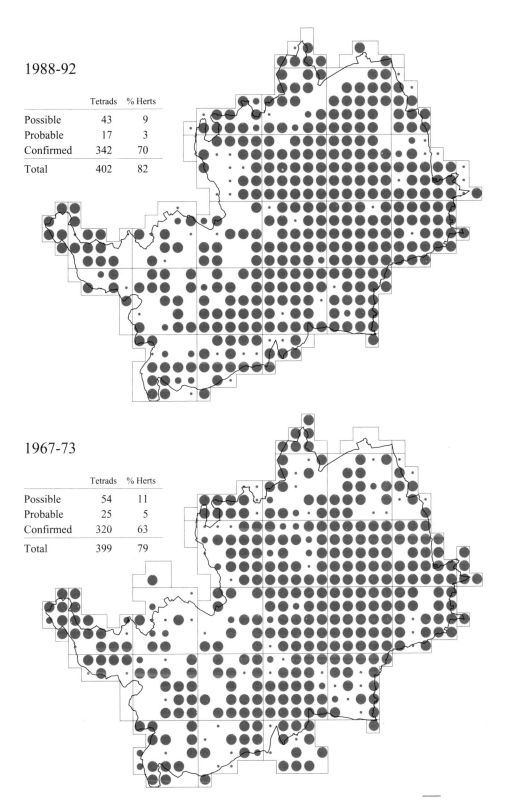

1988-92

	Tetrads	% Herts
Possible	43	9
Probable	17	3
Confirmed	342	70
Total	402	82

1967-73

	Tetrads	% Herts
Possible	54	11
Probable	25	5
Confirmed	320	63
Total	399	79

Coot

Fulica atra

National population 46,000 adults, Hertfordshire 390-1300 pairs, increasing.

The Coot is well known as a conspicuous resident of many areas of water in the county. Its strident call and often violent territorial disputes ensure that attention is drawn to its presence.

Coots are most likely to occur on lakes of more than half a hectare in area with sufficient shallow water to anchor a nest, although some also occupy slow moving rivers (Lack 1992). The bulky nest is generally partially concealed by vegetation but is sometimes in the open where water levels allow. Artificial nest sites such as rafts are readily used. Nests are built up in times of rising water levels and can be left high and dry by receding water, when they are often abandoned. With a clutch of between six and ten eggs and occasional second broods, many noisy young Coots may be seen in breeding areas in late summer.

Having fairly specialised habitat requirements and obvious behaviour, Coot records for the atlas represent a reasonably complete picture of the distribution. Both maps show very few 'possible' records (5% and 8% respectively) and this reflects the ease with which breeding may be confirmed when Coots are present.

The map shows a marked increase in the number of occupied tetrads in south-west Hertfordshire and seems to represent a gradual expansion out of the original areas to adjacent sites rather than a widespread expansion of range within the county. The distribution will always be restricted by suitable habitat and the new map reflects the general expansion of species in the south and centre of the county. The association with the main river systems of the county is clear from the distribution maps but the expansion onto other isolated water bodies is apparent in the new atlas.

A national trend of slow increase probably closely reflects the position in Hertfordshire. Analysis of winter populations at main sites in the county shows a substantial increase up to the early 1980s since when the population trend has flattened out. There is some evidence of aggression and food theft by Gadwall which, with their recent expansion, may be restricting the further growth of the winter Coot population in Hertfordshire. However, in winter numbers are augmented by many immigrants so the relationship between winter and breeding numbers is not clear. In addition, Coots are not able to tolerate sites which silt up and, as some of the earlier gravel pits become more and more overgrown, these factors may restrict their appeal.

Positive associations are evident for parkland, gravel pits, open water, marsh, built-up areas and rivers and streams, although it is notable that, unlike the Moorhen, the Coot is not associated with ponds.   RNS

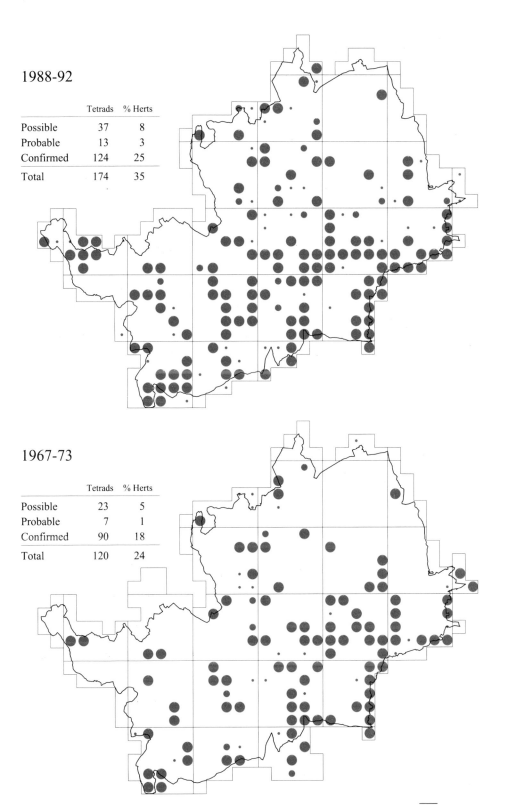

1988-92

	Tetrads	% Herts
Possible	37	8
Probable	13	3
Confirmed	124	25
Total	174	35

1967-73

	Tetrads	% Herts
Possible	23	5
Probable	7	1
Confirmed	90	18
Total	120	24

Little Ringed Plover

Charadrius dubius

National population 825-1070 pairs, Hertfordshire 15-25 pairs, increasing.

The Little Ringed Plover's colonisation of Britain did not start until 1938. Prior to this its status was one of an extremely rare vagrant. The first British breeding record was at Tring Reservoirs in 1938 followed by a further two pairs at Tring and one in Middlesex in 1944. Since that time the breeding population has increased steadily to its present level. Their arrival as a breeding bird coincided with a population increase in western Europe and, more importantly, the growth of the sand and gravel extraction industries as the demand for building materials increased. On the continent Little Ringed Plovers traditionally nest on the exposed shingle of river beds, a habitat not common in southern England. However, the exposed substrates of both redundant and quarried gravel pits, and to a lesser extent sewage farms, waste ground and reservoirs, have proved to be suitable alternatives.

Unlike the closely related Ringed Plover, the Little Ringed Plover is a summer visitor to Britain and Europe, wintering in sub-Saharan Africa. A smaller, slimmer bird than the former, it has a prominent yellow eye ring which at close range is diagnostic. Its feeding methods are typical of small plovers, with its main food source being insects and tiny molluscs. Breeding birds return to Britain during the early part of March, displaying both noisily and conspicuously prior to making a small bare scrape in the ground, where the clutch of four eggs is laid. Incubation of the eggs is carried out by both the male and female for a period of 24-25 days with the young fledging in approximately 26 days. One or two broods are raised.

Breeding birds are easy to find due to the restricted breeding habitat and their obvious behaviour. The open habitat also allows observation of the nesting location. Between the two atlases the number of pairs confirmed breeding has remained virtually static with a large increase in possible and probable breeding records. These records may come from transient sites where birds do not stay to breed. The reasons for failure to breed may include high levels of nest predation, disturbance of the nest site (although Little Ringed Plovers are known to be very tolerant of this) and competition with the larger Ringed Plover.

In the new atlas positive habitat associations are evident with mineral workings, open water, marsh, rivers and built-up areas and negative associations with agriculture.

GE

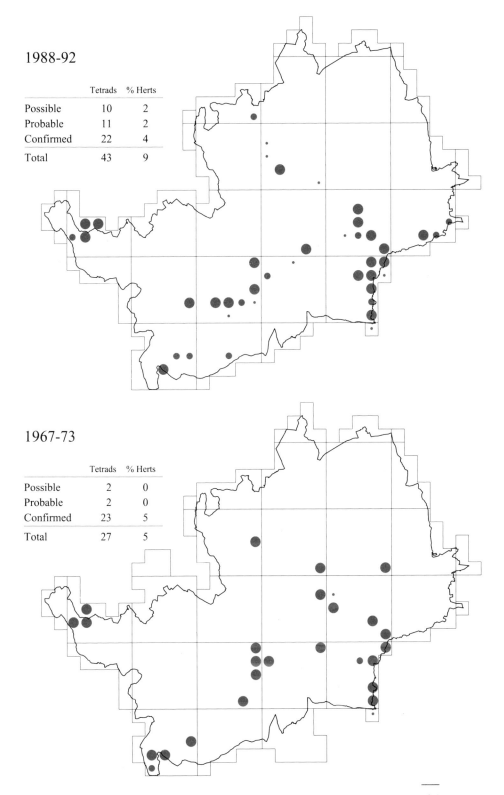

1988-92

	Tetrads	% Herts
Possible	10	2
Probable	11	2
Confirmed	22	4
Total	43	9

1967-73

	Tetrads	% Herts
Possible	2	0
Probable	2	0
Confirmed	23	5
Total	27	5

Ringed Plover

Charadrius hiaticula

National population 8480 pairs, Hertfordshire six to eight pairs, increasing.

The Ringed Plover is historically a bird of the shoreline, breeding and wintering around Britain's coasts. Inland it is often encountered on passage with arctic birds travelling to and from their northern breeding grounds. Ringed Plovers are small but stockily built plovers which in adult plumage have a striking black and white face pattern and a stubby, black-tipped orange bill. They are equally proficient at feeding on sand and stony beaches, on which they move around in typical stop-start manner, or mud flats where they will often be seen using their feet to disturb food items, forcing them to the surface.

Disturbance from development and leisure pursuits on the coast has led to more traditional nest sites being abandoned. Over the last 20 years there has been an increase in the number of inland nesting birds in southern and eastern England, including Hertfordshire. Inland breeding birds return to their territories in late February or early March and are usually well established on territory when the smaller Little Ringed Plover arrives. The male makes several shallow scrapes, one of which is chosen by the female to hold the clutch of three or four eggs. Both birds incubate the eggs which hatch after 24 days with the young fledging after another 24 days. Generally, most inland breeding birds have only one brood although coastal birds can have two, and in some cases three.

Due to birds generally nesting in well watched, accessible areas such as gravel pits and nature reserves, coupled with the fact that they will often give an indication of a nearby nest by distraction display, it is felt that comprehensive coverage has been achieved. The high percentage of confirmed breeding records gives an accurate account of the species' breeding distribution in Hertfordshire.

Ringed Plovers behave very aggressively towards Little Ringed Plovers often hounding them from their territories and there are many documented cases of the latter being forced to nest elsewhere and later in the season.

As can be seen from the old and new atlas maps, there has been significant increase in the number of occupied tetrads. This is thought to be a reflection of the move away from coastal habitats and the presence of more suitable inland nesting sites and is more pronounced in the south and east of the county where the majority of gravel workings can be found.

In the new atlas positive associations are evident with mineral workings, rivers and built-up areas and a negative association with all types of agriculture. GE

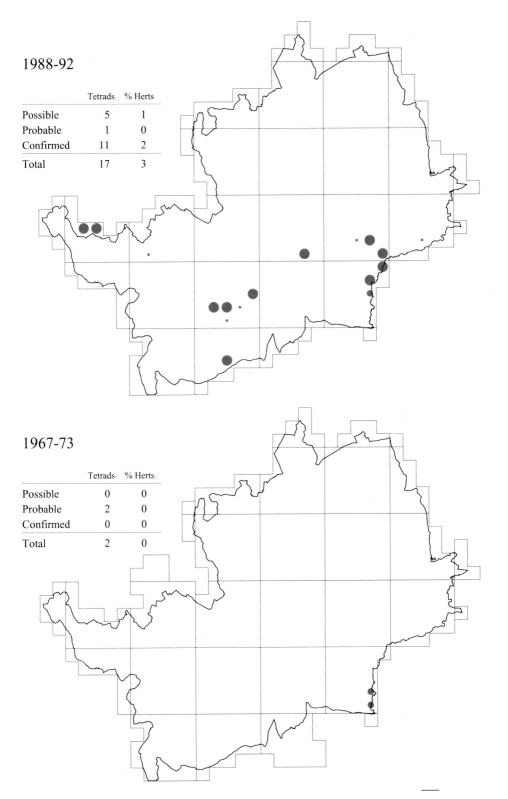

1988-92

	Tetrads	% Herts
Possible	5	1
Probable	1	0
Confirmed	11	2
Total	17	3

1967-73

	Tetrads	% Herts
Possible	0	0
Probable	2	0
Confirmed	0	0
Total	2	0

Lapwing

Vanellus vanellus

National population 185,000-238,000 pairs, Hertfordshire 120-360 pairs, declining.

The Lapwing is a conspicuous and common bird familiar to most birdwatchers in the breeding season. Its plaintive 'peewit' call, black and white plumage and energetic display flight make it relatively easy to detect. Its habit of mobbing any passing Carrion Crow means the presence of breeding pairs is easily revealed.

Nationally the Lapwing shows a clear preference for nesting on agricultural land, particularly spring tillage (Shrubb & Lack 1991). The nest is a shallow scrape on the bare ground with a clear all-round view for the incubating bird. Once the eggs hatch the young are led by their parents to good feeding areas where they feed themselves on invertebrates. These areas are either the margins of shallow pools or, in the more typical rural situations, grassland adjacent to the tilled nesting fields (Galbraith 1988). Invertebrates associated with cow pats are especially favoured by the young (Beintema *et al* 1991).

The numbers of breeding Lapwings have declined nationally in the last few decades largely as a result of changes in agricultural management. Nests and young are extremely vulnerable to destruction by farming operations. The shift from spring to autumn sowing of cereals and other crops has reduced the availability of nesting fields and the intensification of the management of grasslands has made them less suitable as incubating and chick rearing areas. Shrubb (1990), in an analysis of BTO nest record cards, has shown a progressive decrease in the average brood size over the last few decades. Beintema *et al* (1985) have shown that in the Netherlands the nesting season of Lapwings has been shifted earlier in the year as a result of the earlier growth of grasslands with modern fertiliser applications.

Currently Lapwing breeding populations are around 30% of those a few decades ago (Shrubb & Lack 1991, O'Brien & Smith 1992). Comparison of the two atlases shows a significant decline in the distribution of the Lapwing but not at the level expected from the national pattern. It is probable that most of the atlas records now represent only the odd pair managing to nest in a tetrad rather than the breeding groups that would have been present a few years ago.

In 1987 the Herts Bird Club organised a sample survey of breeding Lapwings in the county (Smith 1988). This resulted in an estimate of the breeding population of only 120-360 pairs. Most of the birds (77%) were nesting on agricultural land with the rest on gravel pits and sewage works.

In the atlas the main habitat associations were for cattle, permanent and temporary grasslands and, inexplicably, coniferous woodlands. It is interesting that in the old atlas the associations with cattle and grasslands were far stronger and in addition there were positive associations with barley and oats.   KWS & EWF

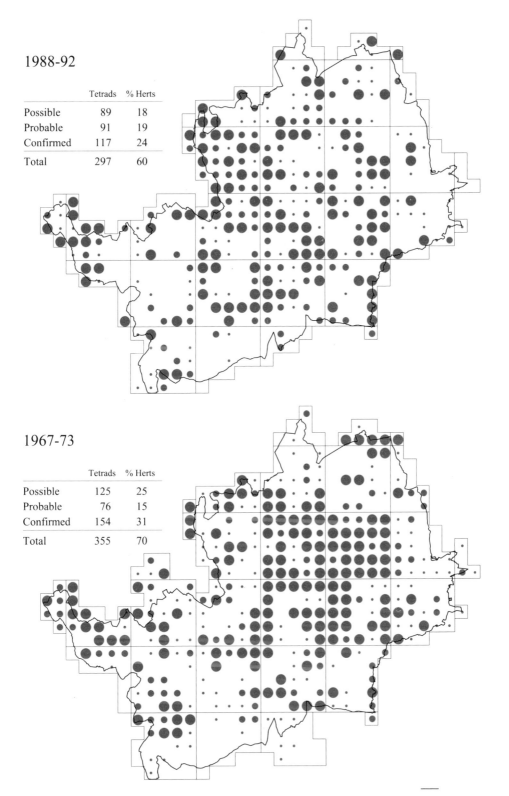

1988-92

	Tetrads	% Herts
Possible	89	18
Probable	91	19
Confirmed	117	24
Total	297	60

1967-73

	Tetrads	% Herts
Possible	125	25
Probable	76	15
Confirmed	154	31
Total	355	70

Snipe

Gallinago gallinago

National population 30,000 pairs, Hertfordshire 10-20 pairs, decreasing.

A bird of wet meadows, upland and lowland bogs during the breeding season, the Snipe is better known to present day Hertfordshire birdwatchers as a winter visitor to damp areas such as gravel pits and their associated marshland. With its camouflaged plumage and generally secretive nature the first indication of the presence of Snipe often comes with the distinctive rasping call and zig-zag flight when they are flushed.

A clutch of four eggs is laid in a simple nest concealed in short grass or other vegetation in wet areas. The length of the breeding season, and hence overall success, is critically affected by the conditions (Green 1988). Excess surface water delays breeding and any drying out of the habitat will bring breeding to a close. With high levels of nest loss from predation and trampling by stock, replacement clutches can be laid until September. Modern farming, with its preoccupation of draining all valuable land, is no doubt partly the cause of the decline in the numbers of Snipe both nationally and locally.

Breeding Snipe are obvious as a result of the well known aerial display flight during which a 'drumming' sound is produced from the tail feathers. Research (Green 1985) has shown that counts of drumming birds may, for various reasons, underestimate the numbers actually breeding. The length of the dawn and dusk drumming periods, and the variability between males on different days, make censusing the Snipe more difficult than previously thought.

Comparison of the two maps shows a significant reduction over the last 20 years in the range and quality of records in the Lee, Stort and Rib valleys where the population was formerly concentrated. Birds still breed in their former stronghold between Hertford and Ware; this area is almost the only remaining suitable habitat in the Lee valley. Records of probable and confirmed breeding have increased in the St Albans and Colne valley areas, probably as a result of the spread of gravel extraction and the different nature of the habitat created. Gravel extraction in the Lee valley generally results in very little wet grass; sites are normally sterile gravel which is rapidly colonised by scrub and generally rather dry. It is a characteristic of the sites around St Albans that low quality wet grassland is created either as the sites are quarried or when the pits are in-filled and left with insufficient drainage. Whilst initially attractive to Snipe these areas are susceptible to varying water levels and may represent suitable breeding habitat for only a few years.

Apart from mineral workings, positive habitat associations are evident for marsh, open water and rivers.   RNS

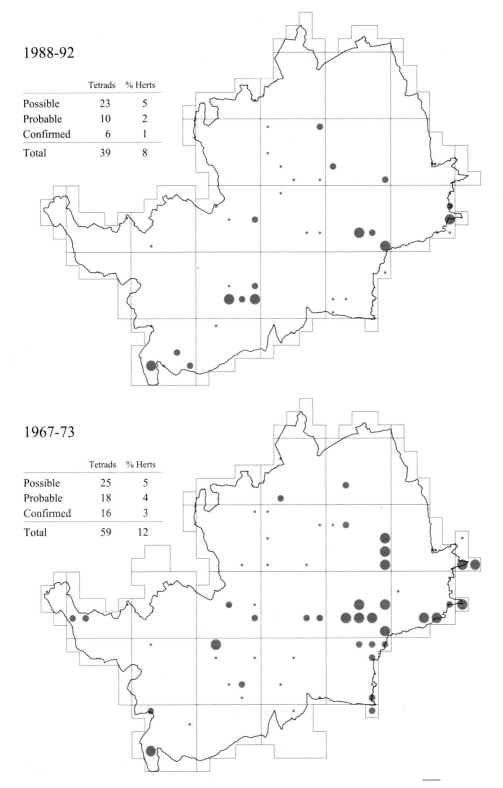

1988-92

	Tetrads	% Herts
Possible	23	5
Probable	10	2
Confirmed	6	1
Total	39	8

1967-73

	Tetrads	% Herts
Possible	25	5
Probable	18	4
Confirmed	16	3
Total	59	12

Woodcock

Scolopax rusticola

National population 8500-21,500 pairs, Hertfordshire 50-100 males, declining.

This unusual wader is highly adapted to our larger woodlands. Its superb camouflage blends in with leaf-litter and its long beak is used for probing in damper areas. It is also largely crepuscular hiding motionless during the day and flying to feed at dusk. Males are most often seen 'roding' over woodlands, giving a piercing 'kwik', and a strange frog-like croaking call.

Flying males locate receptive females when they detect a 'fluttering' response from the ground. The male stays briefly with the female during the egg laying period and the female selects a dry area of leaf litter – often associated with bracken or bramble – to make her simple nest. Males are polygamous and leave to search for another mate. Three to five cream and buff blotched eggs are laid any time between mid-March and mid-July – with two, sometimes three broods per year. The female is amazingly well camouflaged and sits very tightly, only being disturbed if very closely approached and thus confirmed breeding is extremely difficult to establish. After 20-23 days the eggs hatch and the young are led away from the nest. Many reports have suggested that the female can carry her young between her legs in flight, and this has now been confirmed. The young are fully fledged after five to six weeks.

The breeding biology of Woodcock makes it a difficult species to census, most records being of 'roding' males which rove widely in any habitat, making them difficult to count accurately. Also, unless by sheer chance a nest or young are found, the breeding females cannot be detected. Radio-telemetry (Hirons 1980, 1982) has provided most of our more recent information on breeding biology and has shown that males may 'rode' an area of over 100 hectares and may even display over a number of separate woodlands. Density estimates are therefore very difficult to produce and there is no reliable figure for the British breeding population. It is known that numbers have shown a continued decline, especially since 1980, and this seems to have been reflected in our county population, with a marked reduction in possible or confirmed breeding throughout the county, but especially in the west. Woodcock are seriously affected by hard winters when frozen ground makes probing impossible, but recent winters have mainly been very mild. It is possible that shooting of the largely immigrant winter population is gradually eroding some of our resident breeding birds. It seems that the decline is real and that Woodcock may soon become a very rare breeding bird in the county. There may well be a case for restricting winter shooting.

In both atlases there were positive associations with woodlands of all types and streams with built-up areas being avoided. JNT

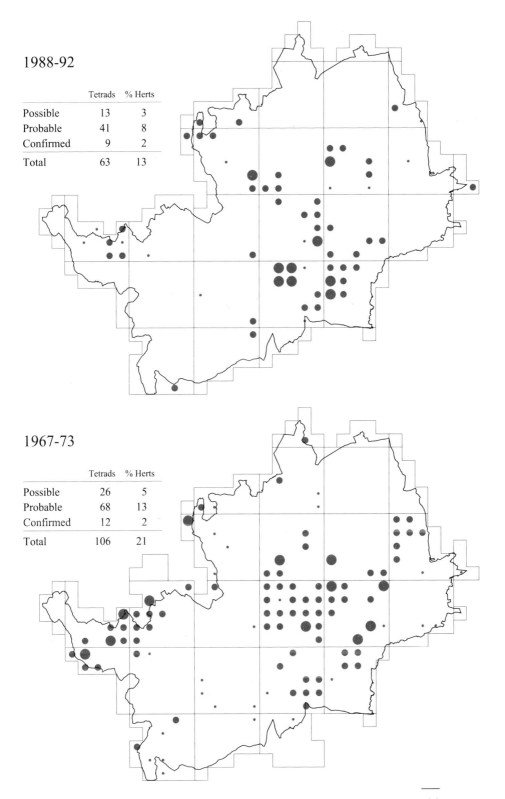

1988-92

	Tetrads	% Herts
Possible	13	3
Probable	41	8
Confirmed	9	2
Total	63	13

1967-73

	Tetrads	% Herts
Possible	26	5
Probable	68	13
Confirmed	12	2
Total	106	21

Redshank

Tringa totanus

National population 30,600-33,600
pairs, Hertfordshire 5-12 pairs, static.

Familiar mainly as a bird of coastal habitats, this noisy wader has always bred on wet meadows inland. The combination of a strong wing bar and loud alarm call make Redshanks very obvious in all breeding habitats and a typical scene of 50 years ago would have been a Redshank displaying from the top of a fence post in the middle of an area of wet grazing land. Regrettably this habitat is much under threat and considerably diminished in the county in recent years.

The simple nest is usually situated in or adjacent to a tussock of grass. In traditional nest sites grazed by livestock, losses occur from trampling and predation.

Good coverage of the normal nesting areas of Redshank in the county is obtained for the annual Hertfordshire Bird Report and the records fit well with the distribution shown on the new map. It can be seen that a major change has taken place. In the earlier period, breeding was confined almost entirely to the Lee valley with its wet grasslands and similar sites. Since then much of this habitat has been quarried for sand and gravel and some of the historic sites have been abandoned as a result of drainage and improvement. At the same time a complex of gravel pits has been dug around St Albans resulting in the group of records in TL00. Breeding was also confirmed in the Tring area.

Positive habitat associations are evident in the new atlas for mineral workings, open water and built-up areas and negative associations with altitude and arable land.

Wet meadows are under major pressures and cannot easily be replaced. Gravel pits offer suitable habitat for breeding Redshanks for only a few years following development: it is at these times that conversion back to agricultural or leisure use undoubtedly has an adverse effect on the Redshank population.

The good coverage obtained for the bird report enables an accurate assessment of the number of pairs successfully breeding in the county in the atlas period:

1988	1989	1990	1991	1992
1	4	7	1	2

These figures compare with the nine pairs found in 1982 (Smith 1983). The recent trend is not encouraging and the toe-hold which the Redshank retains as a Hertfordshire breeding bird is tenuous. As the gravel pit sites mature and are not replaced, the species will become more dependent on the active manipulation for breeding waders of sites such as Amwell and Rye Meads.

RNS

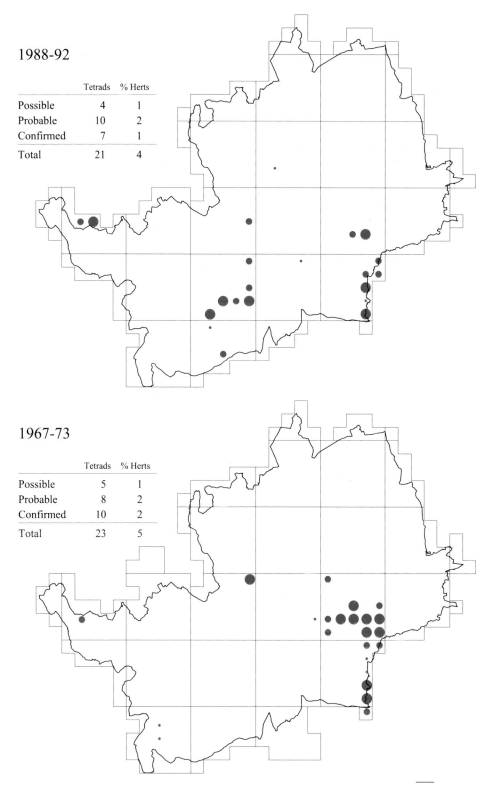

1988-92

	Tetrads	% Herts
Possible	4	1
Probable	10	2
Confirmed	7	1
Total	21	4

1967-73

	Tetrads	% Herts
Possible	5	1
Probable	8	2
Confirmed	10	2
Total	23	5

Common Sandpiper

Actitis hypoleucos

National Population 15,800 pairs, Hertfordshire nil pairs, erratic.

Known to most bird watchers in southern England as a regular spring and autumn passage migrant, the Common Sandpiper is a bird whose breeding is associated with upland areas characterised by fast-flowing streams and lakes with rocky shores. On passage it frequents the edges of gravel pits, reservoirs and rivers and is often seen flying away from the observer with a low fluttering flight showing the white wing bar and giving a 'Twee-wee-wee' call. The relative lack of the preferred breeding habitat within lowland Britain means that nesting in these areas can at best be described as erratic.

With the numbers passing through the county on spring passage it is to be expected that pairs will occasionally summer and more rarely breed. In Hertfordshire there were seven instances of nesting prior to 1958 (Sage 1959) and birds bred at King's Meads in 1961 and at Rickmansworth in 1967 (Mead & Smith 1982). Pairs were present through the summer, but without definite evidence of breeding at King's Meads in 1958 and 1969 and Rickmansworth in 1968 (Gladwin & Sage 1986). Such occurrences will normally come to the attention of birdwatchers but breeding territories can be as small as a 0.2 kilometre stretch of river in Scotland and there is no reason to suppose that pairs may not occupy similarly small territories on less well watched rivers in Hertfordshire. However, with the level of coverage obtained for the atlas, the map probably represents a comprehensive picture of the species' status as a very rare breeding bird of Hertfordshire.

The new map plots nine possible breeding records, which are likely to refer to late passage migrants, and one record of probable breeding. The latter came from Amwell gravel pit where breeding was suspected in 1988 and where one or two summered and displayed but did not breed in 1989. This is one of the few sites in the county that has a small area of habitat suitable for breeding Common Sandpipers. Few other rivers have the characteristic rocky banks and fast flowing water.

In conclusion we may expect the Common Sandpiper to be only a rare and occasional breeding species in Hertfordshire. RNS

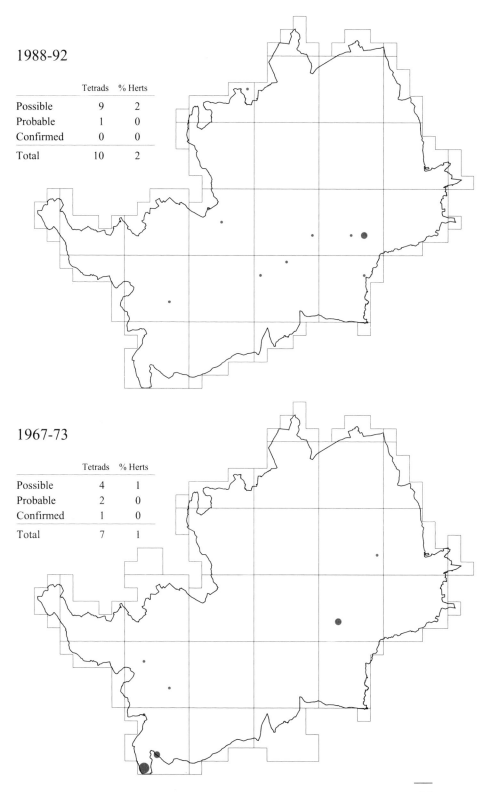

1988-92

	Tetrads	% Herts
Possible	9	2
Probable	1	0
Confirmed	0	0
Total	10	2

1967-73

	Tetrads	% Herts
Possible	4	1
Probable	2	0
Confirmed	1	0
Total	7	1

Common Tern

Sterna hirundo

National population 12,900 pairs (500 inland), Hertfordshire 54 pairs, increasing.

The Common Tern is the most widespread of the three medium-sized terns that breed in Britain and the only one that regularly nests inland outside Scotland and Ireland.

It is a summer visitor, arriving from its west African wintering grounds in April. During the summer months, birds are regularly seen fishing in rivers, lakes, gravel pits and reservoirs, often at long distances from their breeding sites and also at places where a crossing of farmland has to be made.

It is a relatively recent colonist in Hertfordshire, primarily being attracted to summer on the gravel workings and their islands in the Lee valley in the early 1960s. The first confirmation of breeding was on a gravel island at Cheshunt gravel pits where a single pair bred in 1963. Regular breeding began in the same area in 1966 and the number of pairs increased gradually to the end of the decade without reaching double figures. In 1972 an experimental floating raft, covered in shingle, was constructed at Rye Meads to encourage breeding terns. It was immediately adopted and the number of birds using this and further rafts at the same site grew and stabilised at around 40 pairs by the early 1980s (Harris 1987). Productivity has been high with an average of two young per nesting attempt and ringing has shown that these young return to the Lee valley and other inland sites to breed.

Over the past ten years rafts have been installed at other sites in the Lee valley (Amwell gravel pit, Cheshunt gravel pits), at Stockers Lake in the Colne valley and more recently at Tring Reservoirs. Although nesting does occasionally occur on natural islands, the success of these rafts in consolidating the population is clearly shown on the new distribution map.

Whilst the county stronghold remains at Rye Meads, the size of this colony remains stable and is not limited by the availability of nesting space. Indeed the entire Lee valley population is growing more slowly than in the 1970s so there must be other restraining factors.

Common Terns are conspicuous during the breeding season and use wetland sites which are often intensively watched. It is likely that the new map is an accurate representation of the species' current status. The existence of possible breeding records away from the traditional sites indicates the potential for new locations to become established whilst those in the Lee, Stort and Colne valleys demonstrate the distances breeding birds may be travelling to find food.   MH & EWF

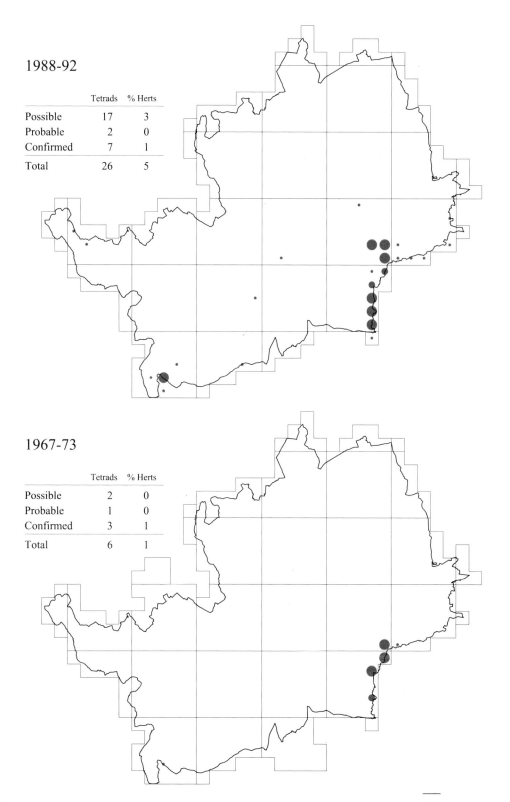

1988-92

	Tetrads	% Herts
Possible	17	3
Probable	2	0
Confirmed	7	1
Total	26	5

1967-73

	Tetrads	% Herts
Possible	2	0
Probable	1	0
Confirmed	3	1
Total	6	1

Feral Pigeon

Columba livia

National population perhaps 80-100,000 pairs, Hertfordshire probably 3,200 pairs, trend unknown.

The Feral Pigeon is familiar to the general public as an integral part of the urban scene. Wild birds have interbred with semi-domesticated and racing stock over the centuries to produce the vast array of plumages present in every town in the county. Although familiar, there has been very little study of the Feral Pigeon. They are treated by many birdwatchers with the contempt usually reserved for the farmyard chicken or the Aylesbury duck. Goodwin (1984) even suggested that many of the plumages illustrated in recent field guides are, at best, unlikely, indicating a lack of detailed study of the bird. Hastings (1988) highlighted the inconsistent approach to the species in literature with many publications making no reference to it whatsoever.

The natural preference of the wild population for a nesting site is a sea cave or cliff ledge and Feral Pigeons are able to find ample passable substitutes within the modern urban Hertfordshire environment. They nest colonially, a typical scenario being several pairs nesting on a building or under a bridge crossing a busy street. Due to the associated problems with soiling, many buildings are given protective netting to prevent colonies becoming established. Unfortunately this netting can lead to birds becoming trapped and these individuals inevitably perish. The clutch size is relatively small, usually of two eggs. The young are fed in the nest and take approximately 35 days to fledge. Feral Pigeons are renowned for their extended breeding season with up to five broods per year; breeding activity has been recorded in all months of the year.

The Feral Pigeon was omitted from the original atlas project and consequently comparisons are impossible. The new map illustrates a distribution closely linked to the spread of urban development in the county.

This is probably one of the easiest species for which confirmation of breeding can be obtained within an urban tetrad. Despite this a full census of the species may be difficult because many Feral Pigeons no doubt nest on private or industrial sites with limited access.

With the ability to breed throughout the year and its catholic taste in food there would seem few restraining factors on the population and spread of this adaptable species. However, the precise requirements for breeding remain unknown. Birds can be almost tribal in their associations within a flock, with adjacent flocks remaining discrete entities and there may be important factors governing the size of such flocks.

Breeding was confirmed in a quarter of the tetrads and at least possible in three quarters. The population is therefore likely to be several thousand birds with possibly as many as 3,200 pairs breeding.   RY

1988-92

	Tetrads	% Herts
Possible	198	40
Probable	67	14
Confirmed	123	25
Total	388	79

Stock Dove

Columba oenas

National population 240,000 territories, Hertfordshire 2100 territories, increasing.

Although the preferred habitat of Stock Doves is parkland, woodland and farmland with old trees – essentially the typical nesting sites – the bird is most catholic in its choice and it has been recorded inhabiting old buildings, cliffs and quarries. Although Hertfordshire is not rich in cliff sites, the Stock Dove has taken advantage of all its other habitats and consequently is widespread throughout the county, being the third most common dove, not far behind Woodpigeon and Collared Dove. They have a real liking for weed seeds, even when commercial grain is available. Charlock and chickweed are spring favourites with fat-hen and knotgrass assuming greater importance later in the year. Outside the breeding season they readily form flocks, often with Woodpigeons, and groups of up to 100 birds are encountered annually.

Stock Doves are hole (or crevice) nesters which prefer large mature or dead trees although any nook will be prospected. Churches and rabbit burrows have been used and there is even one record of a nest in a water tower at Hunsdon. They either make a feeble attempt at a nest, placing a few twigs or roots at the base of the hole, or do not bother. Incubation, about 17 days in duration, is by both sexes as is the feeding when the young force the parents to regurgitate a milky secretion from their crops. The young fly after around four weeks at which time a second, or sometimes a third, brood will be raised.

Stock Doves have a distinctive flight display where two or more birds circle and loop each other often gliding with raised wings and sometimes accompanied with wing clapping. This indicates probable breeding and the majority of records fall into this category. Proof of breeding is a little harder to achieve, depending on knowledge of an actual nest site or observing fledged young.

A healthy increase in the number of occupied tetrads has occurred in the last twenty years and this follows the national trend on both woodland and farmland habitats. The longer term history of distribution did show a 90% drop in the national population in the 1950s as the Stock Dove was one of the hardest hit species to suffer from organochlorine poisoning from treated seed dressings. Numbers did not return to the levels of the 1940s until after 1980, since when there have been only minor fluctuations in numbers. The growth between the atlas periods in Hertfordshire is probably representative of the latter part of the overall recovery which began with the restriction in the use of the offending chemicals in the early 1960s.

Positive associations with woodland and barley in the old atlas remain in the new and negative associations with ponds and streams are both carried over. In addition, the new atlas provides positive associations with altitude, oats, leys, permanent grass and cattle.

EWF

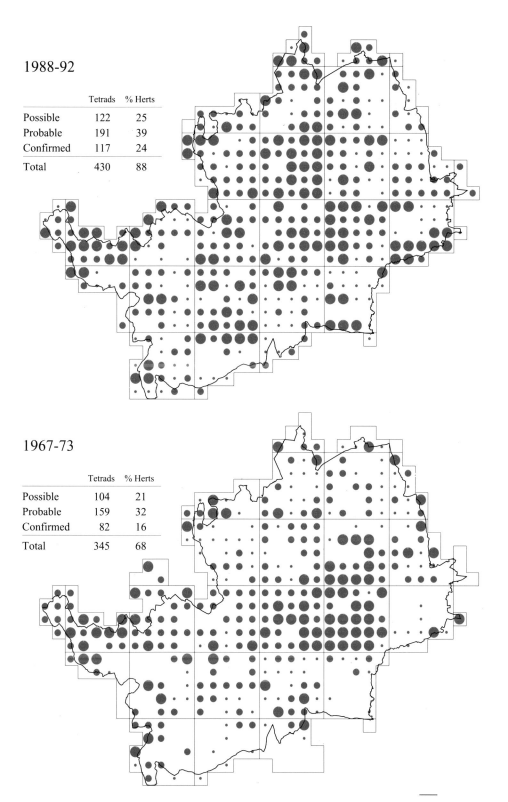

1988-92

	Tetrads	% Herts
Possible	122	25
Probable	191	39
Confirmed	117	24
Total	430	88

1967-73

	Tetrads	% Herts
Possible	104	21
Probable	159	32
Confirmed	82	16
Total	345	68

Woodpigeon

Columba palumbus

National population 2.55 million pairs, Hertfordshire 20,000 territories, increasing.

This bird, not surprisingly, has been recorded in every tetrad in the county. It is abundant in all types of habitat from farmland, where it is officially classified as a pest and can be destroyed by landowners without formality, to the centre of the large towns where it becomes fairly tame. Originally the species, the largest of the Britain's pigeons and doves, was an inhabitant of deciduous woodland but has spread during the 19th and 20th centuries to rural, agricultural, suburban, urban and even industrial areas.

Highest concentrations are found close to farmland where it does immense damage to crops. Its ravages are unremitting: early in the year it feeds on clover and green crops; in spring it turns to newly sown grain and peas; in summer it feeds on the ripening grain and later it stays in the fields, feeding on stubble. It has recently been suggested that oilseed rape, an increasingly common crop in Hertfordshire, aids the bird's winter survival. Large flocks are formed in winter, recent examples being two of 5000 birds at Shenley and London Colney in 1989.

The female builds a thin, but well constructed, flat platform of fine twigs. It can be in a bush, tree, hedge, on a ledge or rarely on the ground. Eggs have been found in Woodpigeon's nests in every month of the year although most are laid in the traditional breeding season. There was a marked tendency for birds nesting in rural localities to lay in August and September such that the young were hatched just as the year's crops were ripening but the more recent switch to autumn sowing, and thus earlier ripening of cereals, has offset this pattern to a growing extent. Incubation is by both sexes and lasts 17 days after which the young are fed by both parents with pigeon's 'milk' from their crops (but later some solid foods) and fledge at around 30 days.

Proof of breeding was very easy to obtain as the nests are most conspicuous and not difficult to locate. Only eight other species exceeded the Woodpigeon's statistic of confirmed breeding in 392 tetrads. It is probable that a still higher incidence actually occurred.

The distribution between the atlas periods was essentially static (the previous atlas indicated just one tetrad where no birds were found); however, the percentage of confirmed and probable breeding records grew from 90% to 97%. Being so numerous and widespread, tetrad atlases are unlikely to identify any changes in the population. National CBC results suggest an increase over the last 20 years.

Habitat changes for such an ubiquitous bird bear little analysis and no real conclusion is drawn other than the fairly obvious comment that Woodpigeons are very adaptable and are able to compensate for most threats to their welfare, be they human or environmental.

EWF

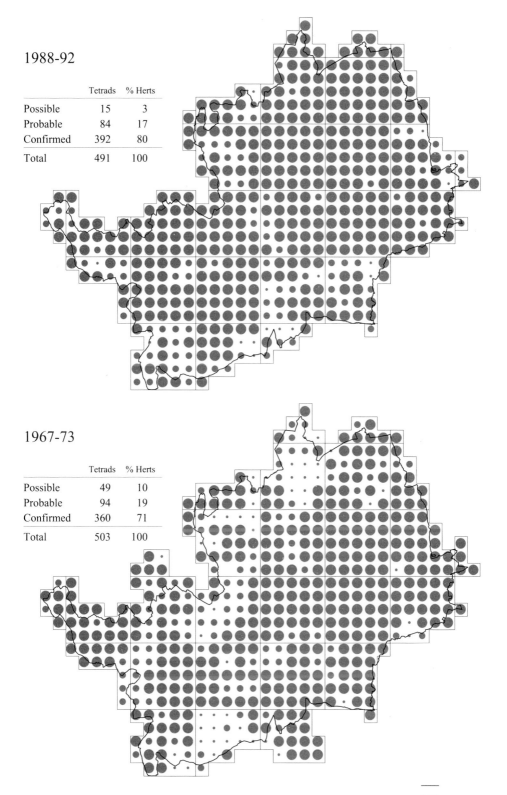

1988-92

	Tetrads	% Herts
Possible	15	3
Probable	84	17
Confirmed	392	80
Total	491	100

1967-73

	Tetrads	% Herts
Possible	49	10
Probable	94	19
Confirmed	360	71
Total	503	100

Collared Dove

Streptopelia decaocto

National population 200,000 territories, Hertfordshire 1400-1800 pairs, increasing.

The Collared Dove is the bird known to most people as the prime example of opportunistic niche exploitation. This familiar dove is at home alongside human habitation, although it still tends to avoid large city centres. Its favoured habitat is built-up areas where grain and seeds are plentiful, such as maltings, mills and farmyards (a flock of 800 on one Sussex farm was estimated to consume 50 kilogrammes of grain each day, equal to roughly 18.25 tonnes per year) but most areas of suburbia and villages have now been colonised. The presence of trees, overhead wires with supporting poles or pylons or other handy perches for resting, roosting or nesting is also important. In some areas their noisy behaviour, coupled with their voracious appetite, have led them to be classed as pests.

The nest is a platform of twigs and roots, on average seven metres from the ground, occasionally so flimsy that its capacity for supporting the clutch of eggs plus the incubating bird seems to be in doubt. Trees and tall hedges are favoured but nests have been located in bushes, on pylons and in guttering. The nest is invariably built by the female, with the male bringing the materials to the site for her to arrange. Up to three broods are not uncommon, occasionally four or five if not interrupted, with both birds sharing the incubation.

Prospective breeding is easy to detect during the courtship stage due to the male's cooing and alighting calls. Whereas some nests, particularly those in conifers, are more difficult to find, recently fledged juveniles are fairly obvious and proof of breeding is not difficult to obtain. Even so, it is probable that some tetrads with records of possible or probable breeding did, in fact, hold breeding pairs.

In Hertfordshire, Collared Doves first bred close to Ware (TL311) in 1958. In the old atlas birds were present in 242 tetrads which has doubled to 484 in the last 20 years, leaving only seven tetrads unoccupied. The bird now occupies all major habitats, although its density in the town centres and the more open areas of farmland is certainly low. This dramatic increase echoes similar patterns throughout most of the UK as the bird continues to exploit its niche and expand into the less favourable habitats. The CBC indicates a stabilisation in the increase around 1982 when maximum densities were reached, with a minor decrease since then, maybe as farmers have begun to protect their grain more.

There is a positive association with built-up areas in both atlas periods and with rivers during the old atlas. With the spread of the species a previous negative association with wheat has become positive. The negative associations with temporary and permanent grassland remain.

EWF

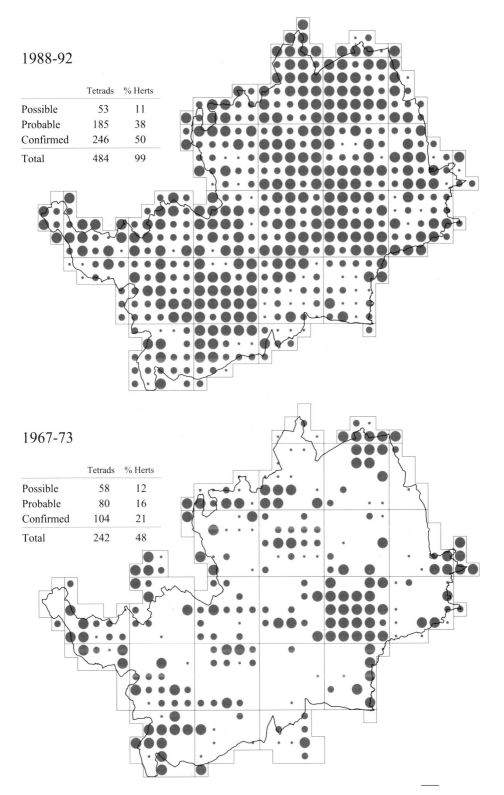

1988-92

	Tetrads	% Herts
Possible	53	11
Probable	185	38
Confirmed	246	50
Total	484	99

1967-73

	Tetrads	% Herts
Possible	58	12
Probable	80	16
Confirmed	104	21
Total	242	48

Turtle Dove

Streptopelia turtur

National population 75,000 territories,
Hertfordshire 670 territories, decreasing.

The readily recognised, soporific purring sound of the Turtle Dove, the smallest of our breeding doves, is, to many, the true confirmation that summer has finally arrived. This bird is the only fully migratory European dove, spending winter in sub-Saharan Africa and returning to north-west Europe in late April or early May. Unlike the closely related Collared Dove, it does not favour built-up areas preferring open, rural localities and arable farmland with nearby shrubs or trees for nesting.

The nest is placed in a tree, shrub or hedge, hawthorns being particularly favoured. It is a typical dove's nest – a flimsy platform of twigs but with some finer lining – and is built by the female with the male gathering the large majority of the materials. The young are fed by both parents, at first on crop milk but later on seeds and other plant material. Multiple clutches through the nesting season are usual.

Turtle Doves display openly and locating singing males in the breeding season is relatively straightforward, but obtaining confirmation of breeding is less easy. Compared with other doves, Turtle Doves are less obvious during incubation, which resulted in the low percentage of confirmed breeding records in the atlas. Overall, the records are, however, considered to give a good picture of the distribution of this species in Hertfordshire.

There was a significant reduction in the distribution of Turtle Doves between the two atlases, particularly in the south and west of the county. This is also reflected in the national population index which has fallen by around a factor of two over the same period. The reasons for the decrease are not yet fully clear. Several factors could be involved including the droughts in the main African wintering areas, large-scale hunting in the Mediterranean during spring migration and changes in agricultural management reducing the availability of weed seeds on which the birds feed.

Nationally, it has been noted that the breeding distribution of the Turtle Dove matches well the distribution of the arable weed, common fumitory. Indeed, seeds of the plant form an important constituent of the diet of the birds. The likely explanation is that the birds need weedy areas in which to feed and fumitory is a good indicator species for weedy arable land.

The habitat associations have changed little between the two atlases. Those tetrads occupied by Turtle Doves had higher areas under arable cultivation and lower areas built-up than those unoccupied. Interestingly, tetrads with high areas of fallow land were selected, in spite of fallow being a rare habitat in modern Hertfordshire.   EWF

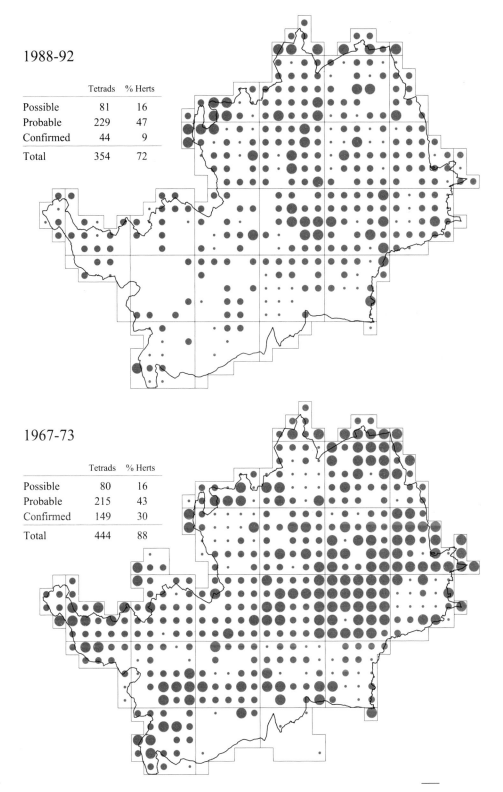

1988-92

	Tetrads	% Herts
Possible	81	16
Probable	229	47
Confirmed	44	9
Total	354	72

1967-73

	Tetrads	% Herts
Possible	80	16
Probable	215	43
Confirmed	149	30
Total	444	88

Cuckoo

Cuculus canorus

National population 13,000-26,000 pairs, Hertfordshire 680-1700 females, slowly increasing.

The Cuckoo is familiar to both birdwatchers and the general public. The first bird of the year is a notable occurrence and prompts letters to 'The Times'. Unique as Britain's only parasitic species, the life history of the Cuckoo is only inadequately understood and there is much research to be done on the population dynamics. The Cuckoo is both parasitic and promiscuous. Both sexes defend a territory and both will mate with intruders which may well be young birds returned late to their natal areas. This leads to difficulty in estimating breeding populations and examining trends.

Sage (1959) listed 20 species known to have acted as Cuckoo hosts in Hertfordshire and of these Dunnock is the most widely used. Where Reed Warblers occur, they are particularly favoured and this leads to concentrations of Cuckoos in suitable areas. The short incubation period and forcible ejection of the competing eggs or young by the young Cuckoo are well known. Females specialise in one host species but if that species is in short supply other hosts will be used, particularly early in the season.

The new map shows a range expansion for the Cuckoo. Of particular note is the number of records from the north-east of the county. Mead & Smith (1983) commented upon the absence here but this is no longer the case. The main host in Hertfordshire, Dunnock, occurs throughout the county but information on changes in breeding density are not available, although it is unlikely that the increase of Cuckoo distribution can be attributed to an increase in density or range of the host species.

Apart from continued absence in built-up areas, the other feature of the map is the in-filling that has taken place. The increase in records of probable or confirmed breeding is also notable. Young Cuckoos are dependent upon the host for two or three weeks after fledging and can be noisy and obvious during this period. Ringing programmes at Reed Warbler colonies also yield records of confirmed breeding.

The main habitat associations are now broad-leaved woodland, wheat, field beans, oilseed rape, fallow and grassland. In the old atlas there were also associations with wetlands but this is no longer the case, possibly a reflection of the wider distribution of the species. There were also negative associations with wheat and field beans which have now been reversed.

As previously mentioned, the breeding behaviour of Cuckoos is unusual and as a result the term 'pair' is difficult to apply. Counts usually refer to calling males and population estimates to laying females. Even with these definitions, clear national trends are uncertain.

RNS

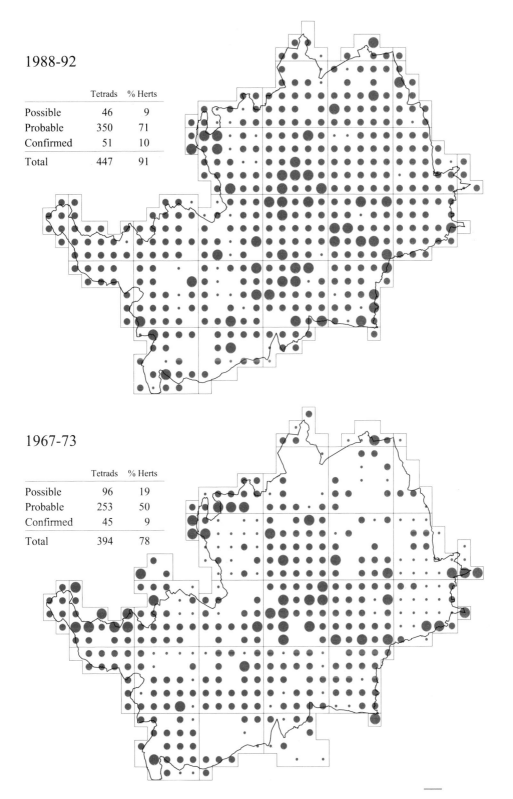

1988-92

	Tetrads	% Herts
Possible	46	9
Probable	350	71
Confirmed	51	10
Total	447	91

1967-73

	Tetrads	% Herts
Possible	96	19
Probable	253	50
Confirmed	45	9
Total	394	78

Barn Owl

Tyto alba

National population 4400 pairs, Hertfordshire 10-14 pairs, declining.

The Barn Owl is a specialist feeder on small mammals, usually frequenting open grassland and woodland edge. Nest and roost sites are mainly cavities in ancient trees or in undisturbed farm buildings. Although Barn Owls will defend the site and remain paired outside the breeding season, they are not strongly territorial, occupying a home range of about two or three square kilometres.

The average clutch size is five, with incubation beginning soon after the first egg is laid, usually in late April or early May. Normally three young fledge when about eight weeks of age, becoming independent in October to November. This is the time of peak juvenile mortality, but a second peak, affecting more adult birds, occurs in the harsher months of January and February.

The Barn Owl, though highly elusive, solicits considerable interest and it is unlikely that the reduced distribution shown in the new atlas map is a result of less survey effort than for other species. The map highlights a marked decrease from the previous atlas when optimism had been voiced that numbers were recovering following the pesticide era of the 1950s and 1960s. However, this optimism has proved to be unfounded.

The present atlas shows confirmed breeding in only nine tetrads. The distribution seems to be strongly aligned to river valleys, where flood meadows and grazing land still tend to predominate.

Although the organochlorine insecticides which probably contributed to the Barn Owl's decline are no longer used, 'second-generation' rodenticides can be a potential hazard (Newton *et al* 1991). Loss of nest sites, through barn conversion, demolition and increased human presence at those which remain, has been implicated in the Barn Owl's decline. Dutch elm disease has caused the loss of many suitable hedgerow trees since the last survey and busy roads now account for around 50% of reported Barn Owl mortality nationwide (Shawyer 1987). In Hertfordshire, although loss and fragmentation of rough grassland is significant, the few remaining birds are probably now unable to produce enough offspring to match the excess mortality due to human induced pressures.

Over the atlas period there were confirmed or probable breeding records from 23 tetrads. However, the home breeding range may cross tetrad boundaries and birds may breed in adjacent tetrads in different years, so the true population is estimated to be 10-14 pairs. Reintroductions are unlikely to have influenced the last atlas but captive-bred and released Barn Owls in Hertfordshire numbered at least 195 during the 1988-92 survey and produced a minimum of 69 known offspring (Dockerty *in prep*). Nevertheless, with the low population shown by this atlas, it is doubtful that the species can be retained in the county in the long term.   CRS & TD

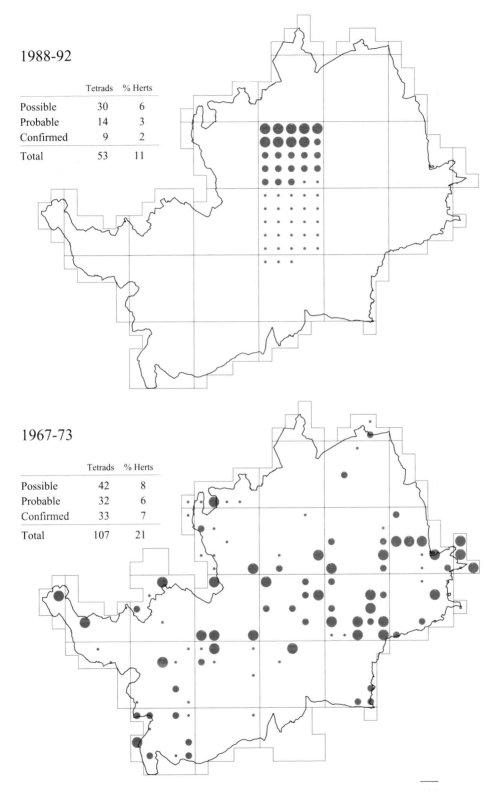

1988-92

	Tetrads	% Herts
Possible	30	6
Probable	14	3
Confirmed	9	2
Total	53	11

1967-73

	Tetrads	% Herts
Possible	42	8
Probable	32	6
Confirmed	33	7
Total	107	21

Little Owl

Athene noctua

National population 6000-12,000 pairs, Hertfordshire 240 pairs, stable.

The Little Owl was first recorded in Hertfordshire in 1877, following several organised releases of continental birds in the UK over the previous 20 years. It remained a rare vagrant until breeding was first proved at Easneye in 1897. Between 1897 and 1930 the spread to its current breeding levels was dramatic, both in the British Isles and in Hertfordshire.

Although the smallest of our owls, the Little Owl is the most frequently and easily observed, often appearing well before dusk. The breeding habitat is very varied, ranging from mixed agricultural farmland, fenland, sand-dunes, quarries and industrial wasteland. Most habitats, except for treeless farmland and densely populated city centres, seem to suffice, as long as accessible old barns or buildings, mature hedgerows or old or pollarded trees are available for nest sites. In the old national atlas the Little Owl was even found in the fens where it had colonised pollarded willows, perhaps taking advantage of the lack of Tawny Owls which are known to prey on this smaller species.

The Little Owl's diet includes most small mammals, anything in size up to half grown rabbits, and birds. Although mammalian prey makes up a reasonable proportion, invertebrates such as earthworms, leather-jackets and snails are also taken.

Nesting takes place in holes in trees, buildings and occasionally in rabbit burrows. Three to five white eggs are laid and subsequently incubated by the female for four weeks. The young are fed by both parents for a further four weeks.

Minor fluctuations in the national population have occurred since the initial population explosion in the 1930s. The national CBC index has been available since 1964 and it, too, has fluctuated widely without any clear trend. The Little Owl is particularly vulnerable to severe winter weather and some of the population troughs were probably the result of this, although cycles in the availability of its prey are also likely to be involved.

In Hertfordshire there has been a small decrease in the number of occupied tetrads since the old atlas. Given the extended survey periods of both atlases, this is unlikely to be the result of cyclical fluctuations. The losses are mainly from the south and west of the county with the birds appearing to be doing well in the north and east.

There were positive habitat associations with mixed woodlands, arable crops and the numbers of cattle, and negative associations with built-up areas. The aversion for built-up areas is supported by a number of well documented cases of the loss of breeding pairs from areas subject to the expansion of housing, particularly in 10 kilometre squares TL10, TL20 and TL22.

JD

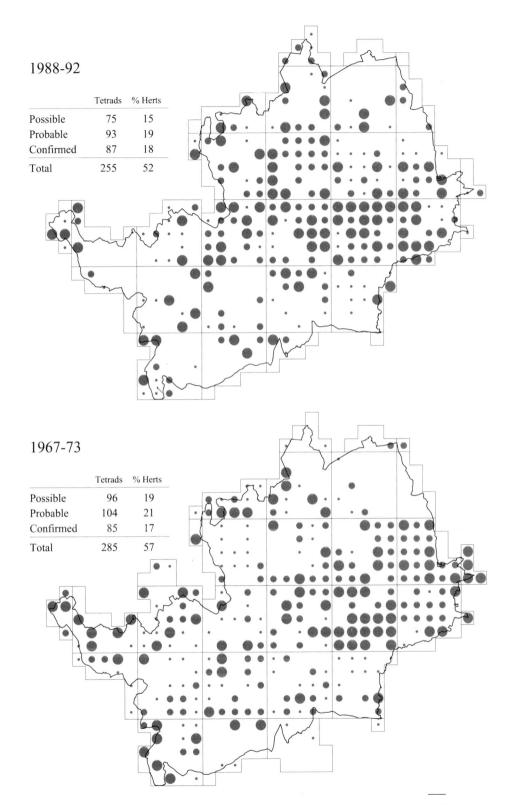

1988-92

	Tetrads	% Herts
Possible	75	15
Probable	93	19
Confirmed	87	18
Total	255	52

1967-73

	Tetrads	% Herts
Possible	96	19
Probable	104	21
Confirmed	85	17
Total	285	57

Tawny Owl

Strix aluco

National population >20,000 pairs, Hertfordshire 1000 pairs, stable.

The Tawny Owl is the most numerous and widely distributed owl in the county, particularly in well wooded areas. It is predominantly nocturnal but can occasionally be seen before dusk on a prominent perch or flitting across a road, between hedgerows. Daytime activity sometimes occurs in harsh winters, especially when food supply is restricted, or in summer when the young are being fed in the nest and the nights are short. Birds roost in cover during the daytime but their presence is often betrayed by the loud mobbing calls of small woodland birds. This mobbing is often so intense that the owl is forced to fly to another site to avoid further harassment.

During the breeding season the Tawny Owl is usually recorded by its variety of calls. From January to March the male's repeated whistled hoots, and the female's distinct 'kewick' calls, often give away the establishment of breeding territories. Later in the summer, during June and July, the young birds' persistent contact calls, a hissing 'sheeep', generally confirm that breeding has occurred in the vicinity.

In Hertfordshire, the Tawny Owl mainly breeds in mixed woodland, copses, parks, churchyards and large gardens. Holes in trees, often opening upwards, are used for the nest site as are chimneys and nest boxes. Disused nests of other species, squirrel dreys and even rabbit burrows have been recorded, but the use of the latter is rare in the county. The breeding season is early, beginning in March and sometimes in January or February. Anything from two to seven white eggs are laid at intervals and incubated by the female for 30 days. The female initially broods the chicks until both parents are forced to hunt. The young leave the nest after 32-37 days.

The breeding of Tawny Owls depends greatly on the density of their small mammal prey which tends to be cyclic. In years of high small mammal numbers, owls lay large clutches and raise large broods but in years of low density they may not breed at all.

The national population index has been relatively stable with small fluctuations over the last twenty years. In Hertfordshire the number of occupied tetrads was virtually identical in the two atlases although, interestingly, there were rather more records from the predominantly arable north of the county in the new atlas.

In both atlases the Tawny Owl's distribution was positively associated with all types of woodland but in the new atlas there was an additional positive association with built-up areas, perhaps reflecting an increased tendency to nest in suburban areas.   JD

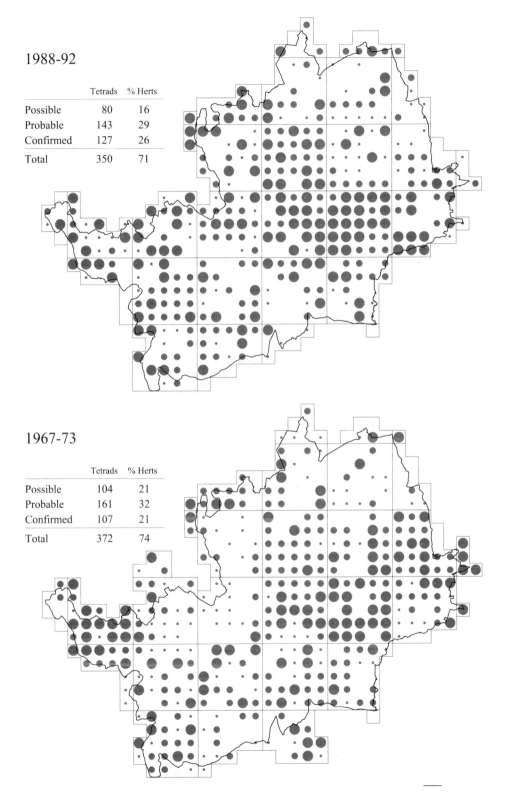

1988-92

	Tetrads	% Herts
Possible	80	16
Probable	143	29
Confirmed	127	26
Total	350	71

1967-73

	Tetrads	% Herts
Possible	104	21
Probable	161	32
Confirmed	107	21
Total	372	74

Long-eared Owl

Asio otus

National population 1100-3600 pairs, Hertfordshire 0-10 pairs, declining.

The Long-eared Owl is the most nocturnal of British owls, being more wary than the Tawny Owl with which it may compete for feeding and nesting territory. It can be distinguished from the Tawny Owl because it is less brown, smaller and slimmer. Close up the long ear tufts and bright orange eyes are distinctive. The local breeding population is largely sedentary. However, most county records in recent years are from the winter when in some years the number of Long-eared Owls can increase dramatically due to influxes from continental Europe. At this time individuals or small groups may roost in shelter belts, tall bushes, sometimes even in gardens.

The eggs are usually laid in an old nest of a Magpie or Carrion Crow often in a tree or bush in an area of immature woodland scrub. Small conifer plantations, copses and open areas of woodland are favoured, possibly because they provide fewer nest sites for Tawny Owls than mature deciduous woods and consequently less competition. Incubation is by the female alone. After hatching the female remains on or close to the nest, feeding the young with food brought by the male and only hunting towards the end of the nesting period. The young become independent after a further eight or nine weeks.

The chief prey is small mammals, especially voles, with a few birds and larger mammals. Long-eared Owls hunt mostly at night along forest rides and over rank grassland where small mammals are abundant.

The drawn out, almost haunting, triple call of the male can be heard in autumn and again from early spring onwards. Consequently possible and probable breeding records are relatively easy to obtain. However, as most atlas work was done in the daytime, it is possible that some pairs were overlooked. Confirmed breeding relies on hearing the grating call of the young in the nest or on sightings of family groups prior to darkness in the long days of summer.

The few atlas records are all from tetrads that contain at least some woodland. Ironically two of the records of confirmed breeding are both just outside the county boundary. In Britain generally the Long-eared Owl has declined as a breeding species this century whilst the Tawny Owl has increased. Comparison with the previous atlas suggests that this decline is continuing in Hertfordshire, possibly accelerated as newly planted woodlands, with their abundant vole populations, have matured during the last 20 years and rough grassland has been lost to development and over grazing.

Although it may be slightly under-recorded, the Long-eared Owl is now a rare breeding bird in the county with only a handful of pairs documented during the atlas period.

MK & CRS

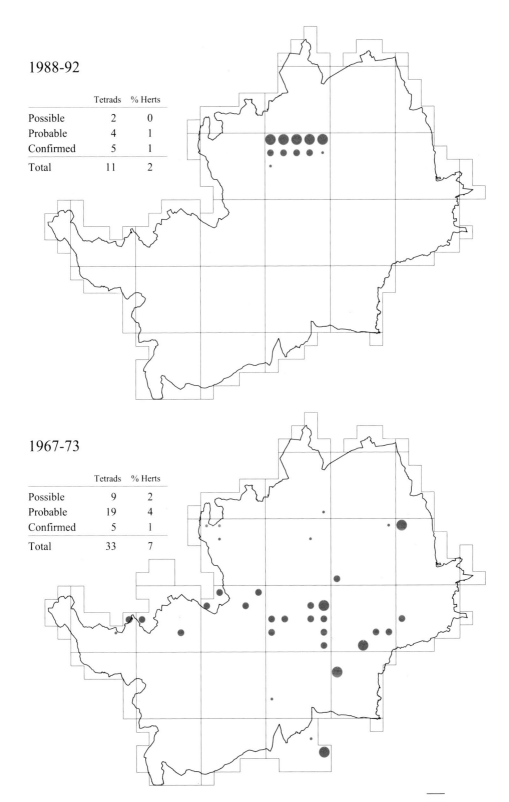

1988-92

	Tetrads	% Herts
Possible	2	0
Probable	4	1
Confirmed	5	1
Total	11	2

1967-73

	Tetrads	% Herts
Possible	9	2
Probable	19	4
Confirmed	5	1
Total	33	7

Nightjar

Caprimulgus europaeus

National population 2000 males, Hertfordshire 0-1 pairs, declining.

How many birdwatchers have seen a Nightjar in daylight? Yet all know of its amazingly cryptic plumage and behaviour. The Nightjar is sometimes glimpsed as a ghostly apparition in car headlights or as a falcon-like silhouette after sunset, but this almost exclusively nocturnal bird is most familiar through its churring song. It has always been associated with lowland heaths of birch scrub, bracken and heather but, as this habitat has decreased or fallen into mis-management, it has taken to cleared woodland and young conifer plantations.

Nightjars winter south of the Sahara, arriving in Britain in April or May, although until June churring males may still be passing migrants. The nest is simply a scrape on the ground with no nesting material and is usually situated in open areas with some trees. The two or three eggs are incubated, and the young brooded, mostly by the female although the male may take over if a second brood is started before the first has fledged. The first young are independent by early August and most Nightjars have left Britain by the end of September.

The Nightjar feeds almost exclusively on insects, mainly moths and beetles, caught on the wing. It is an accomplished flier generally keeping low in the air and spotting its prey against the night sky. It feeds mainly at dusk and dawn.

The presence of birds in an area is relatively easy to establish because the churring song can be readily identified. It is a much more difficult task to prove breeding especially as the species is sensitive to disturbance. It is unlikely that many, if any, Nightjars have been overlooked in the county. In recent years records have been few and only from well known sites, the annual bird report always stressing the need for birdwatchers to avoid disturbing the few remaining birds. The distribution map from the previous atlas was, by the time of publication, already an over-estimate of Nightjar numbers and the present situation shows considerable further loss. However, the number of birds shows little change from 1981 (Smith 1983). The long term decline of the Nightjar is thought to be due to habitat loss, pesticide use and disturbance. In Hertfordshire it is the first of these that has had the greatest impact. Nightjars switched from traditional but dwindling heaths to conifer plantations which have now become unsuitable as they have matured, although as woods are cleared and re-planted there will be new opportunities to exploit. Coniferous woods up to ten years after planting can provide suitable habitat, especially where they are on light, sandy soil.

The Nightjar is now a very rare breeding bird with only a few pairs each year. This toe-hold existence in the county is the best that can be hoped for in the near future, while the complete loss of the species as a breeding bird is a distinct possibility.   MK

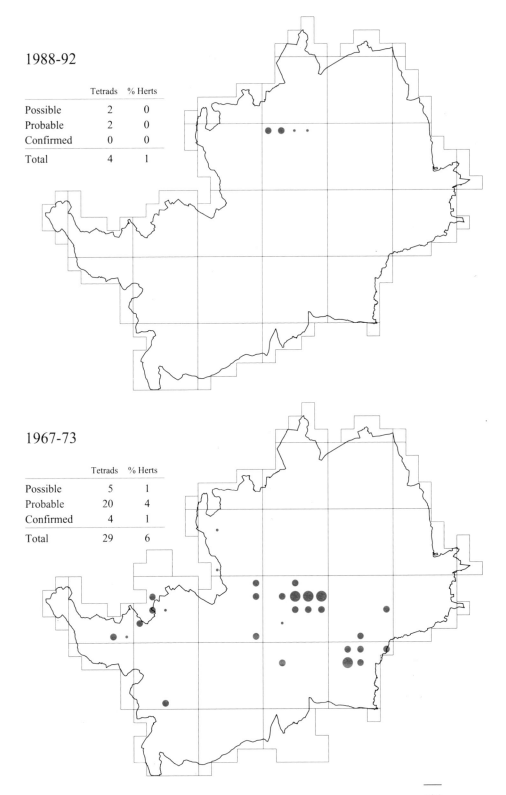

1988-92

	Tetrads	% Herts
Possible	2	0
Probable	2	0
Confirmed	0	0
Total	4	1

1967-73

	Tetrads	% Herts
Possible	5	1
Probable	20	4
Confirmed	4	1
Total	29	6

Swift

Apus apus

National population 80,000 pairs, Hertfordshire 1100-2200 pairs, stable.

The presence of the 'Devil' bird throughout the summer is obvious from the persistent high pitched screaming of groups of birds flying above our towns and villages. This aerial activity continues well into August, when the birds vanish as quickly as they appeared. In Hertfordshire it is a bird of villages, 'old towns', isolated mansions and churches. Increasingly though, new housing developments provide adequate breeding chambers, particularly if accessible tiling and soffit vents are available.

As the Swift spends most of its life on the wing, including mating, sleeping and feeding, it is very easily observed. Problems of identification should rarely occur although the Swallow could be confused from a distance. The larger Swift is almost completely black, with a whitish chin. Its short forked tail and long scimitar wings should distinguish it from other species.

In Europe the Swift often breeds in cliffs, rocky outcrops and woodpecker holes. In Hertfordshire it is confined mainly to buildings. The nest is a collection of stems, leaves and feathers, gathered in flight. These are glued together with saliva to form a shallow cup and placed on a beam or ledge. Normally a single entrance hole is used for several breeding pairs. Usually three white eggs are laid at two to three day intervals and are then incubated for a further 19 to 27 days. The fledging period varies from five to eight weeks, depending almost entirely on summer weather conditions: cold, wet summers cause severe fatalities at all stages from hatching to fledging, mainly due to the lack of insects in these conditions.

The national status of the Swift is not clearly known. It is a notoriously difficult species to census, due mainly to many birds using one nest hole and also to the presence of non-breeders within a colony.

The first national atlas and the BTO trends guide both state that there has been little change in numbers this century, despite lack of suitable breeding sites, atmospheric pollution and the occasional cold, wet summer. Micro-climate variations probably average out good and bad breeding seasons. Swifts do, however, appear to be affected by extreme weather conditions on migration or in their wintering grounds.

In Hertfordshire the numbers of probable and confirmed records appear not to have altered significantly over a twenty-year period. The only noticeable changes are decreases in the Gade valley in the west of the county, Hertford, Ware and Bishop's Stortford. These appear to be matched by increases elsewhere, for instance around Letchworth and Baldock. The very high incidence of 'possible' records is indicative of complete coverage and individual interpretation of the fieldwork criteria. These records are probably feeding birds from an adjacent breeding site. JD

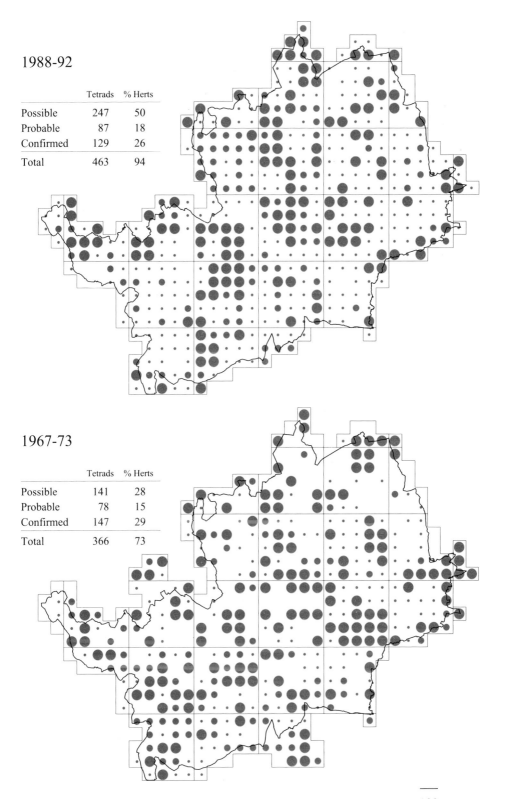

1988-92

	Tetrads	% Herts
Possible	247	50
Probable	87	18
Confirmed	129	26
Total	463	94

1967-73

	Tetrads	% Herts
Possible	141	28
Probable	78	15
Confirmed	147	29
Total	366	73

Kingfisher

Alcedo atthis

National population 3300-5500 pairs, Hertfordshire 100 pairs, static.

The Kingfisher is a small bird well known for its bright blue plumage, dashing flight and general aura; exciting for both birdwatchers and non-birdwatchers alike. It lives entirely on small fish which it catches by means of spectacular dives.

The nest is a chamber made at the end of a tunnel normally excavated in a steep earth bank above a stream or river. In areas where such sites are in short supply it is not uncommon for the tunnel to be made in the earth around the roots of a fallen tree although birds often abandon such holes when they are impeded by tree roots. The first clutch of up to seven eggs is laid in April and hatches about three weeks later. About a week after this the male will prepare a further nesting chamber in preparation for a second clutch. A third clutch may be raised in the original chamber. This pattern can be upset by the polygamous behaviour of a few birds but whatever strategy is employed there is a potential to produce a large number of young per adult in a season. Kingfishers are very vulnerable to freezing conditions and were almost totally wiped out in Hertfordshire after the 1962/63 winter. However with their prodigious breeding output they are capable of rapidly increasing their numbers after such set-backs.

The presence of birds on a stretch of river is not difficult to detect, particularly as they quite often make their high pitched call in flight. Apart from seeing an adult feeding one of its offspring the best proof of breeding is to hear young calling in the nest hole or find a used nest with the white remains of droppings splattered around the entrance. The presence of young is not always conclusive as they can disperse considerable distances soon after leaving the nest.

In both atlases breeding was probable or confirmed mainly in tetrads with rivers or other wet areas with avoidance of higher ground and there were positive habitat associations with all types of wetland. In tetrads common to both surveys the number of confirmed records is almost the same although the distribution is slightly changed. There is a significant increase in the number of possible records over the previous survey but whether this represents surplus population spread into sub-optimal habitat after a series of mild winters or improved observer skills and coverage is difficult to assess. However, the new centres of population in the north of the county are likely to be real. It may also be significant that birds appear to have been lost from the upper reaches of some rivers – most notably the rivers Rib and Stort. Whether this is the temporary result of water shortages over the atlas period remains to be seen.   TK

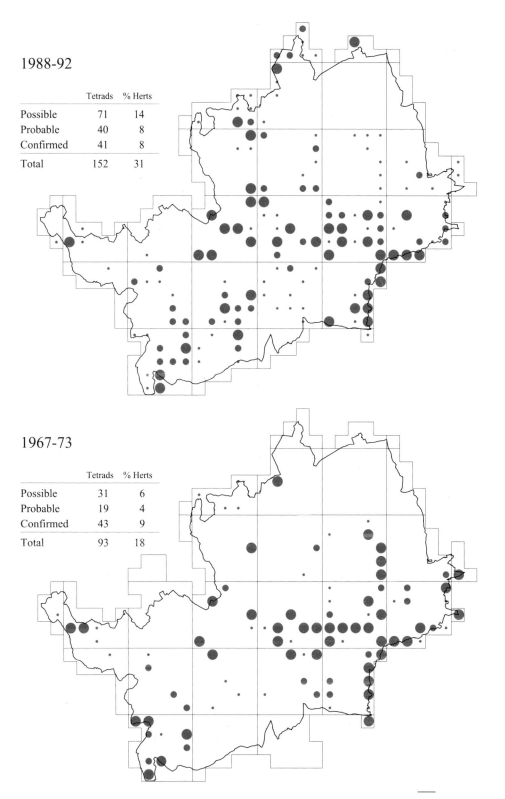

1988-92

	Tetrads	% Herts
Possible	71	14
Probable	40	8
Confirmed	41	8
Total	152	31

1967-73

	Tetrads	% Herts
Possible	31	6
Probable	19	4
Confirmed	43	9
Total	93	18

Green Woodpecker

Picus viridis

*British population 15,000 pairs, Hert-
fordshire 590 territories, increasing.*

With their loud, laughing 'yaffle' call,
Green Woodpeckers are heard far more
often than they are seen. They are larger
and more colourful than our two other
woodpecker species, with bright green
plumage and red crown markings. Their
brilliant yellow rump is most striking as
they fly away with their characteristic
flight – short bursts of flapping interspersed with long swooping glides.

Resident in central and western Europe, Green Woodpeckers in Britain are
at their densest in Wales and England
south of a line from the Dee to the Wash
and are currently expanding their range in Scotland (Thom 1986). Frequenting wooded
areas with open ground, parkland and farmland with plenty of mature trees, they feed
mainly on the ground on ants and their pupae. Early in the morning they may be seen
feeding on garden lawns, but disappear at the slightest hint of human disturbance.

Adults hold large individual territories in winter and pair in spring. The nest hole, up
to 15 metres above the ground in a mature tree in an isolated or open woodland edge
setting, is excavated by both adults. The single clutch of five to seven eggs is laid in
May; both birds incubate the eggs and feed the young by regurgitating large numbers of
ants and pupae from their gullar pouch. On fledging the brood is normally divided
between the parents. Finding noisy young in the nest or fledged youngsters being fed
offers the best chance of confirmed breeding for the atlas.

Numbers are known to be badly affected by severe winters, especially when there is
prolonged snow cover. Nationally the first atlas was during a period of recovery from
the effects of the 1962/63 winter. The national CBC index shows an increasing
population until 1973 and then stability until a slight decline from the mid 1980s
onwards.

In Hertfordshire the population was also low at the time of the first atlas with probable
and confirmed breeding in only 136 tetrads (27%). The distribution was also restricted
to the southern half of the county and was correlated strongly with areas of woodland.
Gladwin (1983) reported a large decrease in central Hertfordshire between 1956 and
1980 but thought that numbers had been stable since 1970. However the evidence from
the new atlas refutes this, the number of occupied tetrads increased substantially in
central Hertfordshire and elsewhere. Overall evidence of breeding was found in 225
tetrads (46%), a dramatic increase over the 20 years.

The Green Woodpecker distribution is positively associated with woodlands, parkland, grasslands, open water and built-up areas. Between the two atlases there has been
a reduction in the strength of the association with grasslands. LMS

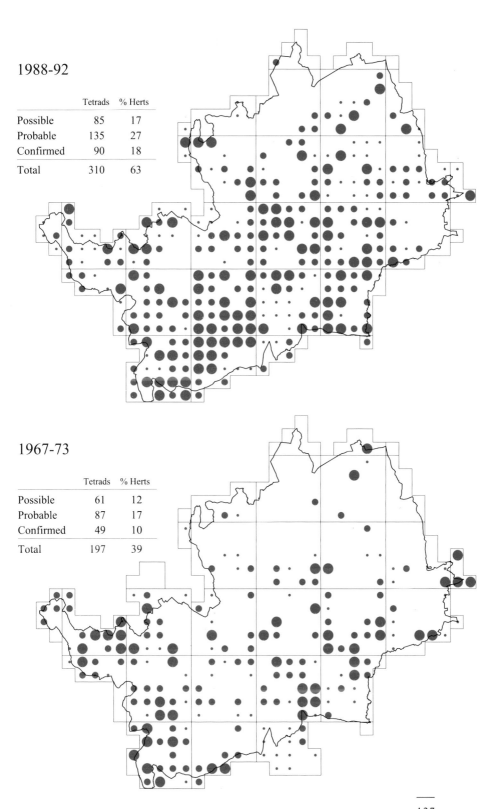

1988-92

	Tetrads	% Herts
Possible	85	17
Probable	135	27
Confirmed	90	18
Total	310	63

1967-73

	Tetrads	% Herts
Possible	61	12
Probable	87	17
Confirmed	49	10
Total	197	39

Great Spotted Woodpecker

Dendrocopos major

National population 25,000-30,000 pairs, Hertfordshire 1100 pairs, increasing.

A distinctive black, white and red bird about the size of a Blackbird, the Great Spotted is the most numerous and wide-spread woodpecker in Hertfordshire. It is likely to be encoun-tered anywhere there are trees but in the breeding season prefers mature broad-leaved woodland. Often the first indica-tion of the presence of a Great Spotted Woodpecker is a loud 'tchik' call delivered from a high perch, or noisy tapping as the bird pecks at a dead branch in search of invertebrate prey. Although the main foods are invertebrates and their larvae excavated from dead wood and from beneath the bark of dying timber, they are increasingly exploiting bird feeders in subur-ban gardens.

In the breeding season the highest densities are found in broad-leaved woodland but any woods will be occupied pro-vided there are suitable nest sites. The Great Spotted Wood-pecker excavates a nesting cavity in a dead tree stump or substantial limb. Although many of the nesting trees are dead, particularly birch, this is not always so and nests are frequently in mature oak or ash trees.

Territorial birds are fairly easy to locate by their drumming, noisy mating displays and frequent chases through the tree tops. Proof of breeding is more difficult to obtain but is usually the result of locating a nest containing noisy young which can often be heard from up to 100 metres away. This is particularly so in years when caterpillars, the main food brought to the young, are in short supply (Smith 1987).

Andrew. P. Chick 93.

The Great Spotted Woodpecker has undergone a remarkable increase in its distribu-tion between the two atlases. This parallels the national trend where the CBC indices have increased two to threefold between 1970 and 1990. The reasons for this are still obscure. It has been suggested that Dutch elm disease, which led to many dead and dying trees in the countryside, was the cause (Osborne 1983) and indeed the initial rise in woodpecker numbers occurred at the right time. But dead elms have long since disappeared from the Hertfordshire landscape and are therefore unlikely to be sustain-ing the current high populations. Climatic changes have also been suggested and cannot be ruled out. Another more likely explanation is that many woodlands in Hertfordshire and elsewhere are no longer managed intensively and are therefore increasing in maturity and holding increasing amounts of dead wood, thus providing abundant feeding sites for Great Spotted Woodpeckers. The major storms in 1987 and 1990 also created much dead wood but it is unlikely that there has yet been any impact on woodpecker populations.

In both atlases Great Spotted Woodpeckers were associated with broad-leaved and mixed woodlands. In neither were they associated with coniferous woodland.   KWS

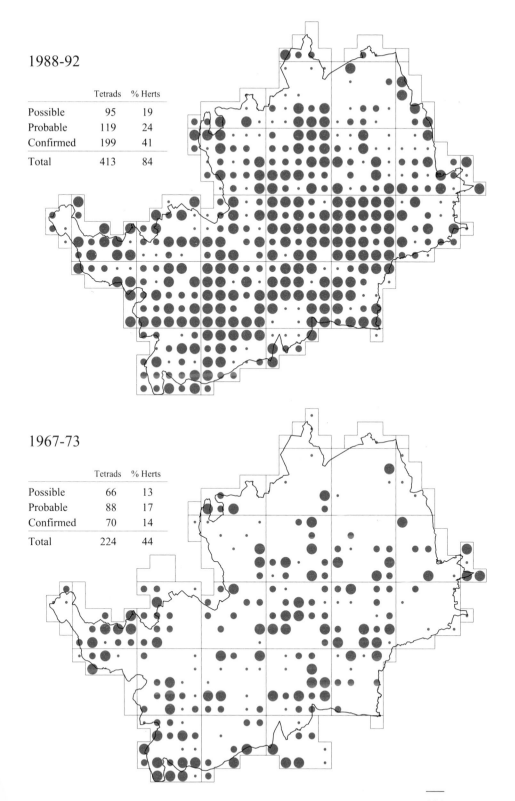

1988-92

	Tetrads	% Herts
Possible	95	19
Probable	119	24
Confirmed	199	41
Total	413	84

1967-73

	Tetrads	% Herts
Possible	66	13
Probable	88	17
Confirmed	70	14
Total	224	44

Lesser Spotted Woodpecker

Dendrocopos minor

National population 3000-6000 pairs, Hertfordshire 170 pairs, declining.

The Lesser Spotted Woodpecker is our smallest and most elusive woodpecker, being only the size of a House Sparrow and spending much of its time feeding high in the crowns of trees. It is usually found in deciduous woodlands, parks, gardens and orchards, although outside the breeding season it often wanders with other birds in hedgerows and shrubs. It is at the extreme edge of its European breeding range in Britain and is restricted to England and Wales with the distribution becoming less dense in the north.

Andrew. P. chick 93.

In the breeding areas in early spring birds can be detected by their 'pee...pee...pee' calls and butterfly like display flights. Their drumming is much softer and of longer duration than that of the Great Spotted Woodpecker and is delivered less frequently.

Confirmation of breeding is not easy to obtain. The nesting cavity is often as high as 25 metres above the ground, usually on the underside of a dead limb. There is a single nesting attempt each year with a clutch of four to six eggs laid in late April. The entrance hole is only about three centimetres in diameter and is therefore extremely inconspicuous and difficult to find. Successful nests can sometimes be located by listening for the noisy young but this is not reliable and is only effective for a few days before the young leave the nest.

In Hertfordshire the distribution has increased significantly since the last atlas and this increase has also been apparent in the national population indices over the same period. These simple statements, however, mask an interesting history over the last 20 years. The Lesser Spotted appears to be the woodpecker species which benefited most from the spread of Dutch elm disease (Osborne 1983). Dead and dying elms harboured high populations of bark beetles and their larvae which were preyed upon by the woodpeckers. In the period when the elms were dying woodpecker populations increased spectacularly (Flegg & Bennett 1974) but since the elms have disappeared Lesser Spotted Woodpecker numbers have collapsed again. Consequently, in Hertfordshire, we are now in the position that the population has probably increased in the last 20 years but is currently in decline. It will be interesting to see just how far numbers do fall before stabilizing.

In both atlases there are positive associations for broad-leaved and mixed woodlands and wetlands. The latter reflects the well known association with river valley woodlands, especially stands of alder. In the new atlas there is an association with built-up areas, perhaps reflecting the species' recent move into suburban areas.   KWS

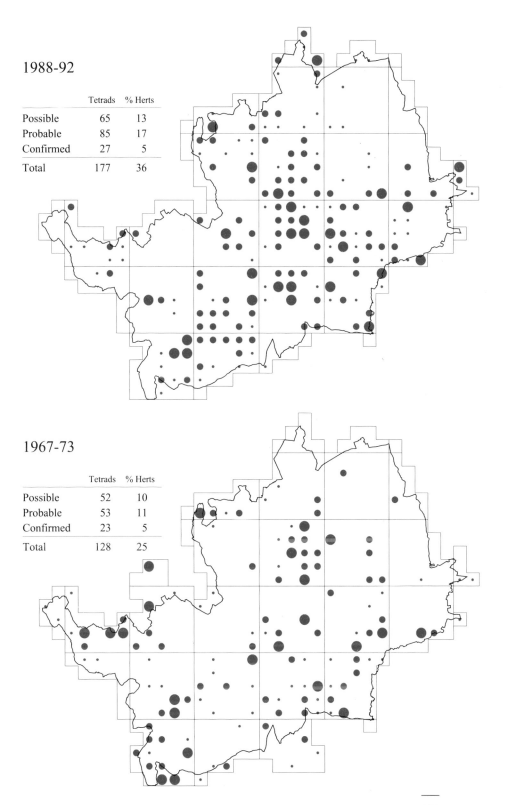

1988-92

	Tetrads	% Herts
Possible	65	13
Probable	85	17
Confirmed	27	5
Total	177	36

1967-73

	Tetrads	% Herts
Possible	52	10
Probable	53	11
Confirmed	23	5
Total	128	25

Skylark

Alauda arvensis

National population 2 million territories, Hertfordshire 8400-23,000 territories, stable.

The Skylark evokes images of wide open spaces and broad summer skies: once clear of the ground, the male starts to sing a seemingly endless song, as he climbs ever higher before eventually dropping silently back to earth. In this large-scale environment, often with strong light, the bird appears small and pale. When seen close up however, its proportions give it a stocky look and, although not colourful, the striated plumage is not dull. It is a bird of short vegetation, avoiding trees and tall hedges. It is therefore ideally suited to the chalk hills in the north of the county but is equally familiar on all types of mixed farmland, water meadows and the areas of sparse vegetation surrounding gravel workings. Skylarks feed almost exclusively on the ground on a varied diet of invertebrates, seeds and other vegetation, the balance changing with the seasons.

Typically the female lays three or four eggs in a shallow depression, which she has lined with grass, in thick vegetation. The young can fly about three weeks after hatching and are independent a few days later. On average about half the eggs laid reach this fully fledged stage and with two, three or even four clutches possible, the potential productivity from one pair in a season is high.

The distribution of the bird shows little change from the previous atlas. The song of the Skylark is very familiar and so can be readily used to establish probable breeding. The bird's use of a variety of open habitats means that it is absent only from tetrads with extensive urbanisation or, exceptionally, those that are predominantly woodland. For example, two tetrads in TL30 are probably blank for this reason. It is likely that most reports of probable breeding represent territorial pairs, but confirmed breeding is harder to establish. The numbers of tetrads with probable and confirmed breeding have increased slightly between the two atlases but the change is not significant.

Skylarks are now found to be positively associated with all types of agricultural land although in the old atlas they were only associated with higher ground and with wheat, barley, oats, field beans, fallow and sheep. In the new atlas there was a strong negative association with built-up areas.

Nationally the CBC index has fallen since 1981 so that the breeding population in 1990 was about 60% of that estimated by Sharrock (1976). The birds are vulnerable to hard winters, but the major factor is probably increased specialisation in agriculture. The introduction of set-aside in recent years may help to reverse the trend.   MK

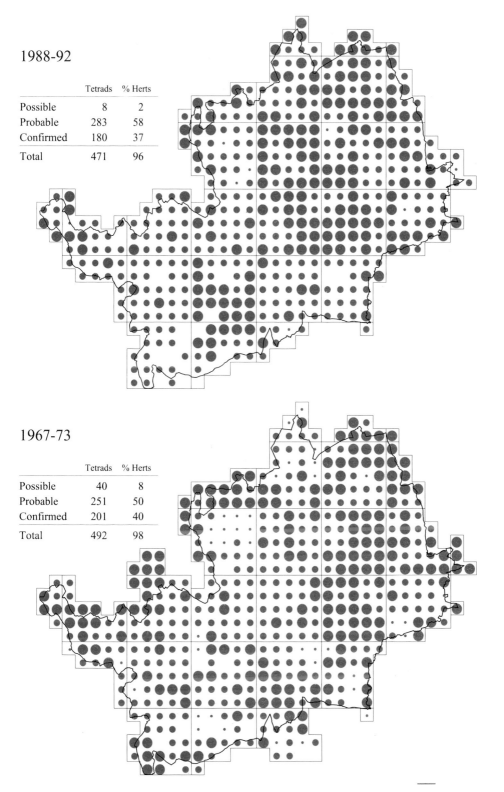

1988-92

	Tetrads	% Herts
Possible	8	2
Probable	283	58
Confirmed	180	37
Total	471	96

1967-73

	Tetrads	% Herts
Possible	40	8
Probable	251	50
Confirmed	201	40
Total	492	98

Sand Martin

Riparia riparia

National population 77,500-250,000 nests, Hertfordshire 970 nests, stable.

The Sand Martin is Britain's smallest hirundine and is usually the first harbinger of spring, appearing in mid-March. Gregarious in most of it habits, it is a colonial breeder, usually seen in flocks when feeding and migrating.

The birds excavate their nest chamber. Traditionally riverside banks were favoured although in modern times the species has taken to nesting in the freshly excavated faces of sand and gravel workings. Nesting holes are usually quite close together, at times no more than ten centimetres apart, but not all may be in use simultaneously. The first birds arrive in March but egg laying does not begin in earnest until May. The normal clutch contains four to six eggs and with two broods the last young fledge at the end of August. The nest may be used for roosting for about a week after fledging but most young will use an unoccupied tunnel elsewhere in the colony.

The Sand Martin is not a difficult species in which to confirm breeding as young birds can easily be seen at the entrance of the breeding tunnel when being fed before fledging. Records of possible breeding are probably the result of sightings of prospecting birds or solitary males.

Although the overall pattern of the distribution of the Sand Martin has stayed remarkably similar between the two surveys there has been a significant reduction in number of occupied tetrads. This is perhaps not surprising since in Hertfordshire it is dependent upon the gravel extraction industry for the supply of suitable habitat for breeding and the distribution of this habitat is relatively unchanged. In terms of number of birds there has, however, been a considerable decline. Confirmed and probable breeding has fallen from 60 to 22 tetrads.

Although the closure and deterioration of some gravel workings may account for the loss of a few breeding sites the main cause of the reduction in numbers lies outside Hertfordshire. The Sand Martin is one of the species that has suffered most from the changing conditions in its wintering area in the Sahel zone of Africa. During the last atlas period in 1969, numbers of Sand Martins returning to breed crashed and numbers then remained low until a further crash in 1984. Mead (1984) estimated that numbers were then only around 10% of the pre-crash figures. Subsequently numbers have recovered somewhat. It is now accepted that low rainfall in the Sahel region was the cause of the crash (Winstanley *et al* 1974). The decline has followed the pattern of other species whose mortality is correlated with the rainfall in that area (Baillie & Peach 1992).

In the new atlas Sand Martins are positively associated with mineral workings, open water, rivers, and horticultural crops, whilst in the old atlas the positive associations included parkland, streams and built-up areas. TK

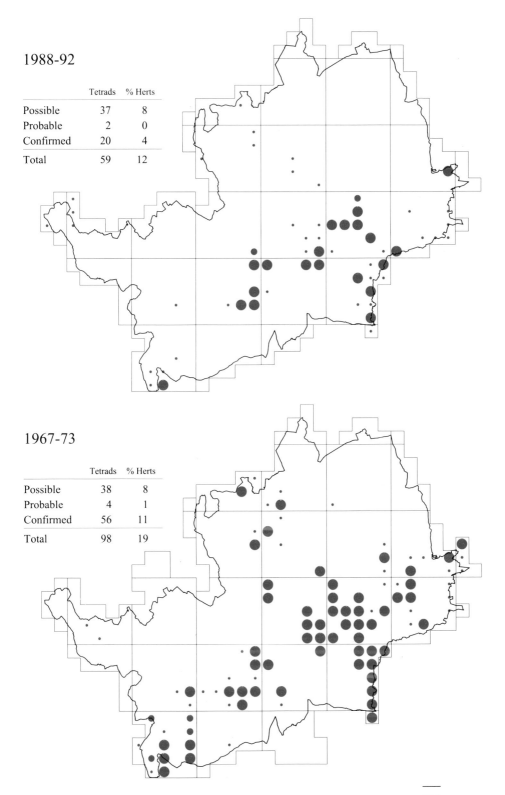

1988-92

	Tetrads	% Herts
Possible	37	8
Probable	2	0
Confirmed	20	4
Total	59	12

1967-73

	Tetrads	% Herts
Possible	38	8
Probable	4	1
Confirmed	56	11
Total	98	19

Swallow

Hirundo rustica

National population 570,000 territories, Hertfordshire 4400 territories, declining.

The Swallow is a small migrant aerial feeding bird which is perhaps the best known indication of the incipient arrival of summer. It feeds in open areas such as farmland or parkland and around farm buildings where it usually nests. In Hertfordshire, farm buildings are favoured nest sites but nests on eaves and porches of houses are also quite common.

Whilst the majority of Swallows nest as solitary pairs they can occasionally be found breeding in loose colonies of a few to several dozen pairs. Recent research has revealed that colonial nesting Swallows show a significant level of promiscuity, egg dumping and even infanticide (Turner 1991). The clutch usually comprises four or five eggs which hatch a couple of weeks after the last is laid. The nestlings leave the nest some three weeks later and are split between the parents for post fledging care. Two broods are quite common while three may be achieved by experienced parents in a good year.

Swallows are amongst the easiest of species to find and prove to be breeding. Food is gathered on the wing and the bird can easily be watched back to the nest site where it appears to be relatively unafraid of human observers. Many Swallows return to traditional nest sites year after year.

The Swallow is widespread throughout Hertfordshire but comparison of the two atlases results shows a significant decline over the last 20 years. Most of the decline appears to have occurred in the south of the county and the increase in records in the north is probably a result of improved coverage there. A similar decline has been noted nationally but it is as yet unclear whether this is caused by local conditions or drought in Africa affecting the birds on migration. Our birds spend the winter in southern Africa and so could experience problems there or anywhere en route to and from western Europe.

The Swallow's distribution is so widespread that few habitat associations have emerged. The only ones in the new atlas were for wheat, barley, potatoes, field beans and oilseed rape. The associations for grasslands and cattle found in the first atlas are no longer present.

TK

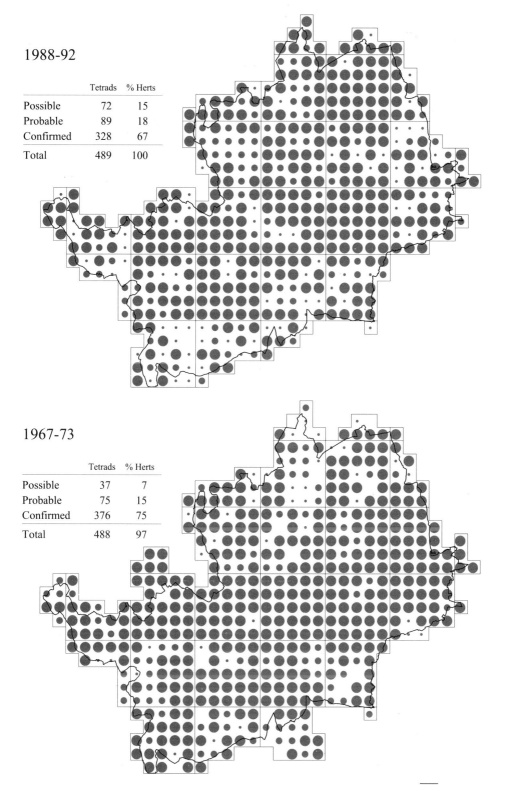

1988-92

	Tetrads	% Herts
Possible	72	15
Probable	89	18
Confirmed	328	67
Total	489	100

1967-73

	Tetrads	% Herts
Possible	37	7
Probable	75	15
Confirmed	376	75
Total	488	97

House Martin

Delichon urbica

National population 250,000-500,000 pairs, Hertfordshire 5000 pairs, stable.

The House Martin is a common species which has a patchy distribution throughout Hertfordshire. Breeding on buildings and other man-made structures in both urban and rural areas, it is the most abundant of the three hirundines to be seen in the county. It is best distinguished from the Swallow by its lack of any tail streamers and from the Sand Martin by its wide white rump. House Martins are a common sight of summer, flying in loose groups over villages with erratic twittering flight as they chase airborne insects, and swooping into their nest sites under the eaves of houses.

They nest gregariously in loose social colonies usually of two or three nests per site, but occasionally in much larger numbers. The size of these colonies can often vary from year to year, for instance during the years 1973-83 the number of nests on Ashridge House varied from almost forty in some years to less then ten in others (*pers obs*). The nest cup itself is constructed from mud pellets collected by the birds from any available patch of muddy ground and is lined with down, feathers or other soft materials. It is usually situated under a convenient overhang between two to 50 metres above the ground. House Martins take readily to artificial nests provided at existing colonies, new nests often being attached to the man-made ones forming House Martin 'tenements'.

The House Martin is the last of the hirundines to arrive at its traditional nesting sites in spring, often not appearing until the first half of May. Early birds may, however, be seen over open waters, gravel pits and sewage works in early April; the earliest record for Hertfordshire being on 25 March 1989 at Tring Reservoirs. They can be late departing in the autumn with records of young still being fed in early October. Most pairs are double brooded, sometimes changing nest sites to rear their second family.

Comparing the previous atlas map with the present it can be seen that there has been very little apparent change in the distribution of the House Martin within Hertfordshire. The fact that the nests are on the outside of man-made structures makes is relatively simple to locate the birds and obtain confirmation of breeding. There is also no evidence of an overall change in national populations over the last twenty years.

The House Martin has benefited from the improvement in air quality in urban areas over the last thirty years and is now found nesting closer to the centres of cities than in the past. In Hertfordshire, the expansion of the new towns has provided more nesting opportunities, perhaps at the expense of the more rural populations. Certainly an impression of a decline in recent years in the west of the county might readily be explained by a more widespread dispersal of nesting birds throughout the expanding towns. The only major habitat association was for built-up areas.   JET

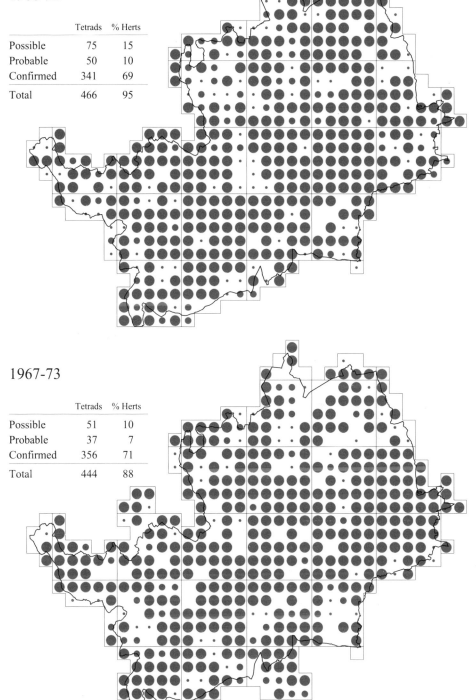

1988-92

	Tetrads	% Herts
Possible	75	15
Probable	50	10
Confirmed	341	69
Total	466	95

1967-73

	Tetrads	% Herts
Possible	51	10
Probable	37	7
Confirmed	356	71
Total	444	88

Tree Pipit

Anthus trivialis

National population 120,000 territories, Hertfordshire 100 territories, declining.

The Tree Pipit is a local summer visitor to the county, where typically it is found on the edges of open woodland or in young conifer plantations with adjacent tall trees from which males carry out their distinctive 'parachute' song flights. Males arrive from mid-April and carry on singing until July, thus making it fairly easy to locate occupied territories. Tree Pipits are generally slightly bulkier birds than Meadow Pipits, with finer streaking on the flanks.

Breeding begins in mid-May when the pair construct a large grass cup, lined with finer roots and hair, under cover of a grass tussock, usually next to an area of more open ground. Four to six eggs are laid, which are very variable in ground-colour and covered in blotches and streaks. The female incubates for 14-16 days after which both parents feed the young, often perching conspicuously with beaks full of food and giving alarm calls, so making it easy for atlas workers to confirm breeding. The young fledge after about 12 days.

Although the national CBC index shows a slight but consistent decline over the last 20 years, the Tree Pipit has decreased markedly in eastern England and Hertfordshire is no exception. The old atlas showed probable and confirmed breeding in 127 tetrads which has now fallen to only 52. There can be no doubt that a decline that was first recorded in the early 1970s has continued to date. It is interesting to note that the northern spread into Scandinavia has continued, so that climatic changes can be ruled out as the cause of the reduction. The Hertfordshire decline is almost certainly due to changes of habitat.

The Tree Pipit distribution appears to be entirely related to the presence of woodland. Although the areas of woodland have changed very little over the 20 years there has been a marked change in the character of the woodland. Most of our Tree Pipits are found in young conifer plantations or clearings, but represent only temporary populations. As soon as the canopy closes the birds move on. During the 1960s Hertfordshire had a number of large tracts of recently-planted conifer forest (for example Bramfield, Broxbourne and Symondshyde) created under the Forestry Commission's Dedicated Woodlands scheme. In addition, coppice management has virtually ceased. Traditional coppiced woodlands were ideal for Tree Pipits but since that time they have matured and the planting of conifers has ceased to be fashionable. The decline seems therefore to represent a lack of habitat, with the remaining occupied territories related to areas of major woodland with suitable clearings.

JNT

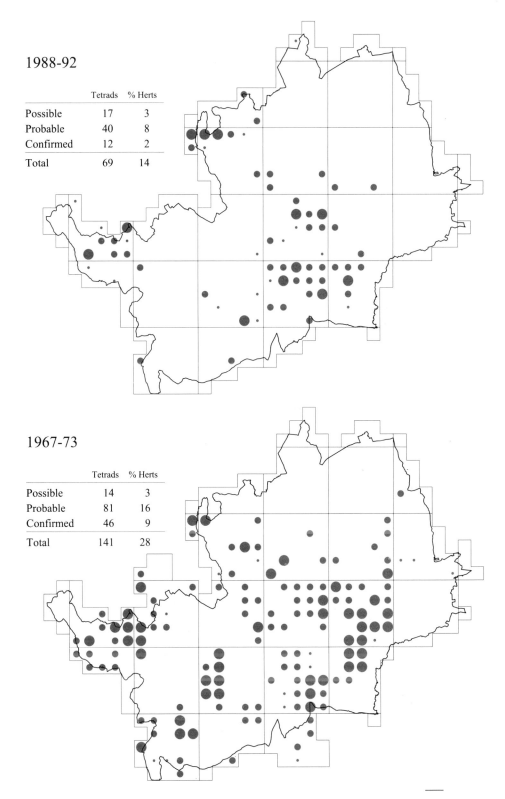

1988-92

	Tetrads	% Herts
Possible	17	3
Probable	40	8
Confirmed	12	2
Total	69	14

1967-73

	Tetrads	% Herts
Possible	14	3
Probable	81	16
Confirmed	46	9
Total	141	28

Meadow Pipit

Anthus pratensis

National population 1.9 million territories, Hertfordshire 260 territories, declining.

Meadow Pipits are small, rather fine birds with a heavily streaked and usually brownish plumage. The 'tseap' call and the flashes of white down the sides of the tail, noticed when in flight, are distinctive and characteristic. In upland Britain this busy little bird seems everywhere. In Hertfordshire it is mostly confined to the northern edge of the county on the chalk grassland of the northern escarpment and also on land in the Colne and Lee valleys. Elsewhere breeding is scattered and sporadic and only occurs in open areas with few, if any, trees. During the autumn and winter much of the local population migrates, being replaced by birds from the north of Britain and the continent. Meadow Pipits feed on invertebrates with seeds becoming important in the colder months.

The nest is on the ground, hidden within vegetation and is built by the female from grass and lined with finer material such as hair. Typically four or five eggs are laid, hatching about two weeks later with the young fledging a further two weeks after that. Two broods are normal and on average half the eggs laid will result in fledged birds, so that one pair will produce four or five young in a season. Within Britain it is one of the main host species for the Cuckoo with up to one in five nests being lost in this way.

The Meadow Pipit's song is distinctive and it calls readily so is hard to overlook. When returning with food for its young it behaves nervously and this makes it relatively easy to establish confirmed breeding. The distribution map is therefore probably an accurate record of its present range and shows little change from the previous atlas. However the proportion of confirmed breeding records has decreased, perhaps indicating a decline in overall numbers and the birds around Royston appear to have declined. The high number of possible breeding records in the new atlas is, perhaps, the result of late passage birds being recorded as potential breeders. Nationally the CBC index has declined steeply since 1981 with some recovery during 1987 bringing the population to about 60% of its level of the 1970s This decline is thought to be the result of a series of cold winters during the 1980s.

The Meadow Pipit distribution has shown no positive habitat associations in either atlas. The most surprising result, given the species' links with grasslands, is a negative association in both atlases with both grassland and cattle.   MK

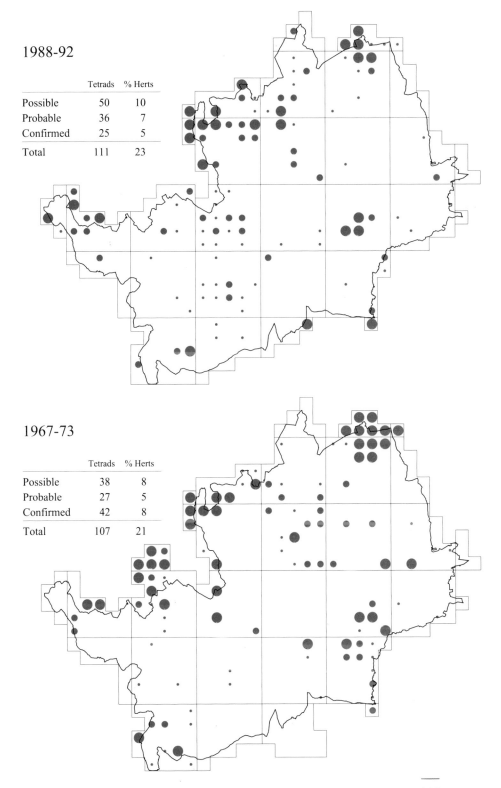

1988-92

	Tetrads	% Herts
Possible	50	10
Probable	36	7
Confirmed	25	5
Total	111	23

1967-73

	Tetrads	% Herts
Possible	38	8
Probable	27	5
Confirmed	42	8
Total	107	21

Yellow Wagtail

Motacilla flava

National population 50,000 territories,
Hertfordshire 80 territories, increasing.

The Yellow Wagtail is probably our most striking wagtail and, in spring, groups of bright yellow males are a welcome sight in damp meadows, running amongst the feet of grazing cattle. Its usual call, a musical 'tsweep', frequently the first sign of its presence, is given incessantly either as it feeds or flies by.

The majority of breeding records in the county refer to the British race, *M. f. flavissima*. The European Blue-headed Wagtail *M. f. flava* is an occasional visitor in spring and autumn but does not normally stay to breed, although a female paired with a male Yellow Wagtail bred at Rye Meads in 1988.

In Hertfordshire, the Yellow Wagtail is confined to low ground, all proven records being below 100 metres above sea level. Although not actually a riparian species, it is often found in waterside meadows and the margins of flooded mineral workings and older sewage works. A preference is also shown for pasture land on the gault clay northwest of Tring and to the north of the county on the Cambridgeshire and Bedfordshire borders. More recently the bird has taken to nesting in oilseed rape and bean fields, exhibiting a particular flair for colour co-ordination!

The nest is built in a hollow amongst thick herbage with the eggs laid in May or early June. The male accompanies the female while she builds the nest of dried grass stems and roots, thickly lined with horse or cow hair. Incubation, lasting for up to 14 days, is by both sexes. Although the young leave the vicinity of the nest after 12 days, they continue to be fed by the parents for a further two to three weeks. This, combined with the long breeding season, makes proof of breeding relatively easy to obtain although some atlas records are probably only spring passage birds which did not subsequently stay to breed.

Between the two atlases, the national CBC index for Yellow Wagtail has shown large fluctuations with big peaks in 1968 and during the mid 1970s. Since 1980 there has been a decrease so that overall there has been little change between 1970 and 1990. In Hertfordshire there appears to have been a genuine increase in distribution with almost twice as many tetrads occupied in the new atlas. A comparison of the two maps shows an increase in the Colne valley south-east of St Albans and the continued presence in the Lee valley. In the two gault clay areas there has been a decrease in the Vale of Aylesbury, but a notable increase in proven breeding records around the head-waters of the rivers Ivel, Hiz and Cam.

As to be expected, the main positive habitat associations in both atlases were for open water and rivers. It is interesting that in the first atlas there were also positive associations with permanent grassland and cattle which are no longer significant, perhaps reflecting the move of some birds into arable crops. JET

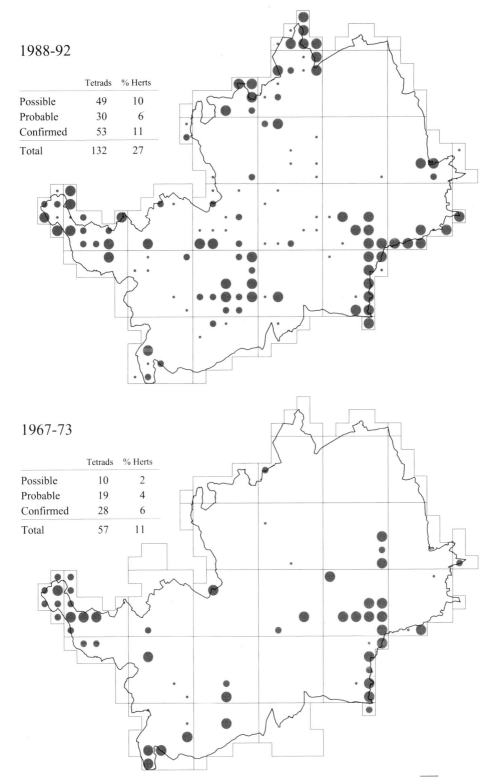

1988-92

	Tetrads	% Herts
Possible	49	10
Probable	30	6
Confirmed	53	11
Total	132	27

1967-73

	Tetrads	% Herts
Possible	10	2
Probable	19	4
Confirmed	28	6
Total	57	11

Grey Wagtail

Motacilla cinerea

National population 34,000 pairs, Hertfordshire 80-160 pairs, increasing.

The Grey Wagtail is possibly the most elegant of our wagtails, most often associated with fast flowing water where it is commonly seen flitting along the edges and perching on boulders or overhanging trees. It generally occurs singly or in pairs and its behaviour is like that of other wagtails, running to catch insects and manoeuvring in flight with its long tail, which makes it very conspicuous.

Primarily a bird of fast flowing upland streams, in the lowlands the Grey Wagtail is often found nesting near mills and weirs on streams with shallow gravel and riffles. The nest is usually built on a masonry ledge, in a culvert or drainage hole beneath a bridge, in tree roots or ivy on overhanging banks. It is built by both sexes and constructed of moss, twigs, leaves and roots. The eggs, normally four to six, are laid as early as March or early April, with second and third broods or replacements still being in the nest until August. Incubation is by both sexes for 13-14 days. The young are fed by both parents and fly when about 12 days old.

The presence of birds in the breeding season is relatively easy to detect and the frequent use of man-made sites makes nests easy to find. The adults are noisy and conspicuous when flying to the site with nesting material or food for the young, making it easy to prove breeding, even when the nest is not found.

The Grey Wagtail has shown a significant increase in distribution in Hertfordshire in the period between the fieldwork for the two atlases. Examination of the distribution maps shows that the species is still scarce in the drier north-eastern area of the county but indicates particular increases in the range in the extreme west and in a central band from Hemel Hempstead to Ware. The increase in numbers is in accordance with the national trend where numbers appear to be influenced by winter temperatures with high numbers during the relatively mild 1970s which then decreased during the 1980s and have subsequently increased again during the recent warm winters. As with the Pied Wagtail, the milder winters in the late 1980s may have allowed the species to continue its spread in Hertfordshire.

In the first atlas the distribution of the Grey Wagtail was positively associated with rivers and open water. By the second atlas the increased numbers resulted in a wider choice of habitats with positive associations with parkland, mineral workings, open water, marsh, rivers and built-up areas. In both atlases there were negative associations with altitude and farmland.

RD & JM

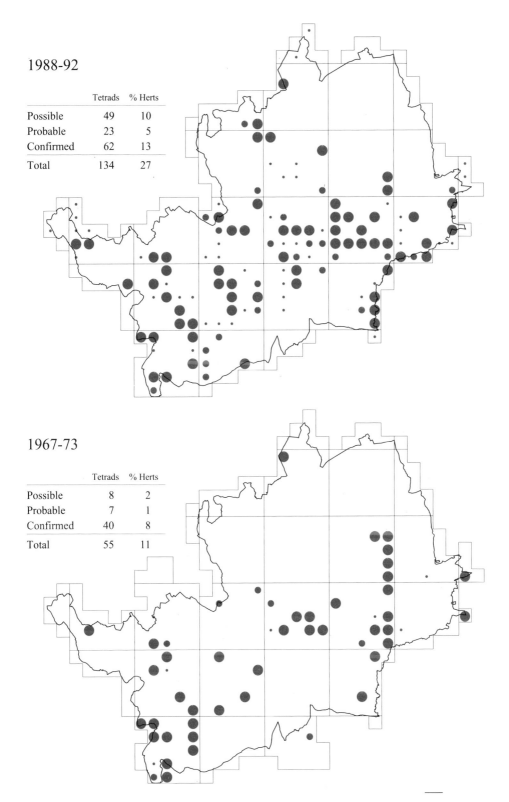

1988-92

	Tetrads	% Herts
Possible	49	10
Probable	23	5
Confirmed	62	13
Total	134	27

1967-73

	Tetrads	% Herts
Possible	8	2
Probable	7	1
Confirmed	40	8
Total	55	11

Pied Wagtail

Motacilla alba

National population 300,000 territories, Hertfordshire 1400 territories, increasing.

The Pied Wagtail is a small, long-tailed black and white bird, often associated with water but also seen on grasslands, buildings and sewage works. It is regularly seen feeding on insects at ground level and is found away from woodlands in all parts of the county. The Pied Wagtail has a diagnostic flight with its bounding progress being the most pronounced of all small passerines.

The open nest is built by the female in walls, sheds, banks or ivy and consists of moss, dead leaves and twigs lined with hair and feathers. The first clutch of five or six eggs is generally laid in April but two or three clutches are laid in an extended breeding season. Incubation is by the female for about 14 days. Both parents feed the young which fly when about 15 days old.

The distinctive call note and bounding flight of the Pied Wagtail make it fairly easy to find in the breeding season but the nests can be difficult to locate. The adults can be wary as they approach the nest, but observers seeing adults with food in their bills can be sure that nestlings or fledglings are nearby.

Outside the breeding season, the Pied Wagtail forms large communal roosts in autumn in reedbeds or shrubberies but in winter it shows a preference for buildings. There is a marked spring and autumn passage with birds from northern Britain arriving to spend winter with us and others migrating to and from their wintering areas in France, Spain and Portugal.

Pied Wagtails are widely distributed in Hertfordshire, particularly in the western and central parts of the county but they are still rather thinly distributed in the north-east. The distribution of the species increased significantly between the two surveys: the increase occurring throughout the county but most markedly in the north and north-eastern areas, where the species was found in previously unoccupied tetrads.

The run of relatively mild winters during the period of fieldwork for the new atlas may have resulted in a higher than average winter survival rate and a consequent expansion of breeding range. Williamson & Batten (1977) found birds expanded into agricultural habitats when populations were high.

In both atlases Pied Wagtails were associated with open water, rivers and built-up areas. An association with parkland in the old atlas has now disappeared.   RD & JM

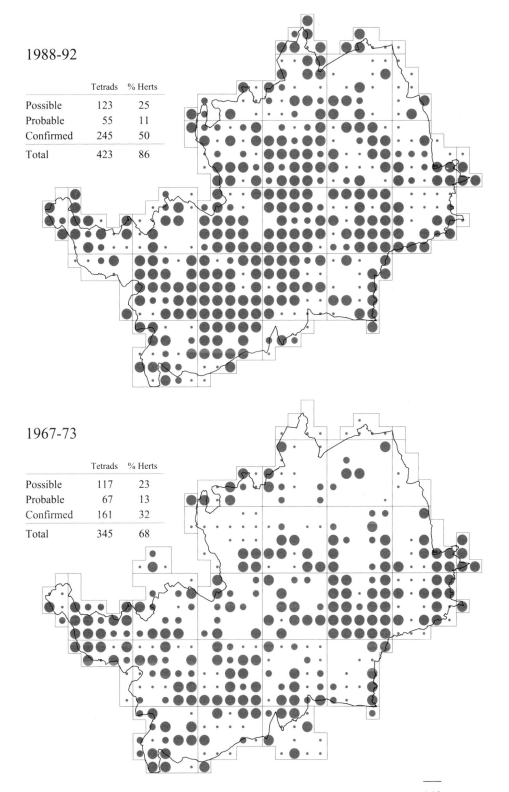

1988-92

	Tetrads	% Herts
Possible	123	25
Probable	55	11
Confirmed	245	50
Total	423	86

1967-73

	Tetrads	% Herts
Possible	117	23
Probable	67	13
Confirmed	161	32
Total	345	68

Wren

Troglodytes troglodytes

National population 7.1 million territories, Hertfordshire 37,000-67,000 territories, stable.

The Wren is one of the commonest and most widespread birds in Britain. Its small size and almost mouse-like behaviour make it also one of the most endearing. However, it is not always easy to see, having a speckled brown plumage and a tendency to remain within the cover of vegetation. Its preferred habitat is woodland with plenty of ground cover, such as bramble, but it is also common in gardens and hedgerows and may be found almost anywhere except in totally urban areas or open farmland. Wrens feed primarily on invertebrates but will also take other items: berries, tadpoles and even small fish have been reported.

The nest is a ball of moss and grass usually sited near to the ground in thick bramble, in a hole in a wall or in any hollow or nook. The male builds between five and eight such nests and the female selects one in which she usually lays five or six eggs, incubating them alone. Both parents feed the young which fledge around 17 days after hatching, becoming independent two or three weeks later. Second or third broods are common and the male may be polygamous, occasionally with two females laying in the same nest, leading to potentially high productivity.

The male Wren has a powerful and distinctive song so records of possible and probable breeding are easy to obtain. Evidence of confirmed breeding is usually provided by seeing recently fledged young or adults carrying food to the nest. A small group of barely-flying young Wrens flushed from cover is a common sight in mid-summer.

In both atlases the Wren was recorded in almost every tetrad and there is no evidence of a change in distribution over the period although many of the apparent gaps in the old atlas have now been filled in.

This is not to say, however, that they have not changed in abundance. Being such a small bird, the Wren has a large surface area to volume ratio, so it has a high rate of heat loss compared with its capacity to generate and store heat. It is therefore very vulnerable to severe cold weather and the population of Wrens can fall dramatically after a hard winter. Wren numbers were, for instance, extremely low after the winter of 1962/63 but had increased tenfold by 1974. Since the 1970s numbers have been relatively stable with small variations probably related to winter weather conditions from year to year.

Being extremely widespread, it is not surprising that no strong habitat preferences are found.   MK

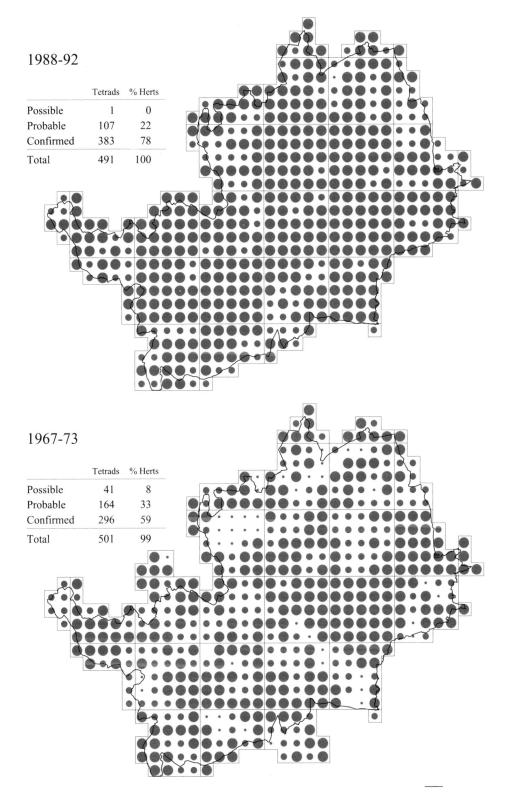

1988-92

	Tetrads	% Herts
Possible	1	0
Probable	107	22
Confirmed	383	78
Total	491	100

1967-73

	Tetrads	% Herts
Possible	41	8
Probable	164	33
Confirmed	296	59
Total	501	99

Dunnock

Prunella modularis

National population 2 million territories, Hertfordshire 15,000-27,000 territories, stable.

The Dunnock is one of ten species recorded in every tetrad during the fieldwork for the new atlas. It is at home in all types of scrubby vegetation throughout the county, being seen in gardens, parks, woodland and hedgerows – in fact in any area containing bushes, shrubs or low growth. Even the extensive open farmland to the north, with its relative paucity of hedges, possesses its complement of Dunnocks, albeit at low density. Despite being very common, the birds are unobtrusive by nature, preferring to forage within or close to cover. They become more vocal during the breeding season when their reedy songs draw attention to their wing-flicking display, often given by several birds in close company.

The nest is a substantial, yet very well camouflaged, open cup. It is built by both birds and consists of tiny twigs, plant stems and small leaves with some moss and is lined with feathers, hair and wool if available. Up to six, but more commonly four or five, bright blue eggs are laid and are incubated by the female. Two, and sometimes three, broods are raised each year.

Although, in appearance, one of our dullest breeding birds, the Dunnock's mating habits are anything but dull. Both sexes have been regularly recorded as being polygamous and there are even instances of polygynandry where several males share several females (Davies 1987). Such behaviour is most likely to occur in areas with high densities of Dunnocks.

Nests are located low down in thick cover and are not easy to find. The most effective way of confirming breeding was for observers to watch for adults visiting the nest with food or departing with faecal sacs. Breeding was confirmed in almost 80% of tetrads in the new atlas but was less likely to be confirmed in the open country in the north-east of the county although even here, in practice, most pairs undoubtedly bred.

As Dunnocks were present in virtually all tetrads in both atlases there was little opportunity to show any changes in distribution. The atlas did not census population density but it is interesting to note that the national CBC indices show Dunnocks increasing in numbers up to the middle of the 1970s, followed by a steady decline for the following ten years with an upturn beginning again in 1988. Numbers are now returning to the levels of 20 years ago and this is probably the current position in Hertfordshire.

Habitat does not have a major influence on the birds' distribution – they are content so long as there is sufficient scrubby undergrowth of which there is plenty across all of the county. However, the larger open fields in the north have resulted in fewer woods and hedges with the accompanying difficulty in initially locating the birds and subsequently proving breeding.

EWF

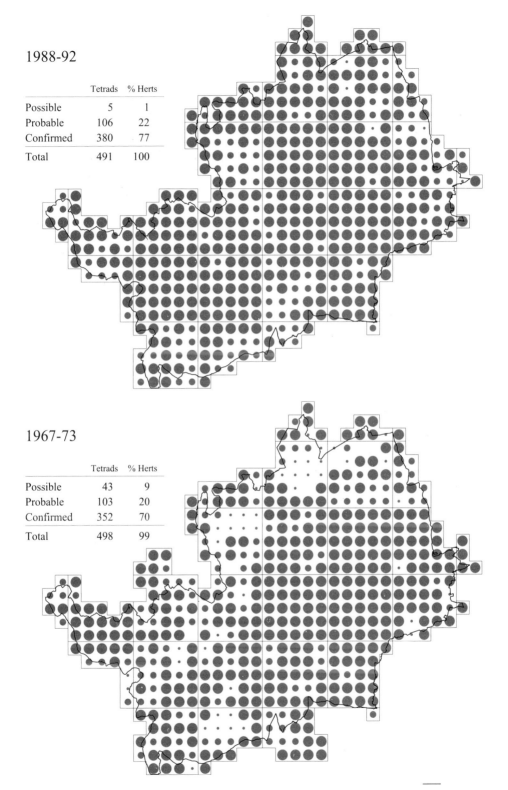

1988-92

	Tetrads	% Herts
Possible	5	1
Probable	106	22
Confirmed	380	77
Total	491	100

1967-73

	Tetrads	% Herts
Possible	43	9
Probable	103	20
Confirmed	352	70
Total	498	99

Robin

Erithacus rubecula

National population 4.2 million territories, Hertfordshire 28,000-46,000 territories, static.

The Robin is a species that scarcely needs description being a familiar garden bird and the star of many Christmas cards. However, it is essentially a bird of broad-leaved woodland from which it has adapted to live in man-made habitats. Those that have taken up residence in suburban areas have become particularly confiding. In Hertfordshire the species is predominantly sedentary and any factors affecting its status will have been applied locally.

Robins nest in a variety of situations. The woodland birds generally make a well disguised nest resembling a pile of dead leaves close to or on the ground. Suburban birds may make similar nests which at times will be sited inconspicuously behind a row of cans on a shelf in a shed or other out-building. The main breeding season is from March to early July although there are records of occupied nests in all months of the year.

While establishing and maintaining territory the song of the Robin makes it an easy bird to locate. But this is not so during the incubation and nesting periods when the species can be so secretive that is not until their spotted young appear that any evidence of nesting is obtained. Evidence of breeding therefore is most easily obtained once the young have fledged and the feeding adults are forced more into the open. The character-istic begging calls of young being fed are also helpful in confirming breeding.

With confirmed breeding in 91% of Hertfordshire tetrads and probable breeding in all but one of the remainder, the Robin can truly be described as a ubiquitous bird. There has been an increase in the fraction of records of probable or confirmed breeding between the two atlases. However, the areas with the extra records are in the north of the county where coverage in the first atlas was lowest. It is therefore not possible to say whether these are genuine increases or simply a result of better coverage but probably the latter.

The national CBC results for Robin show that, apart from losses during hard winters such as 1962/63 and the few subsequent recovery years, the index has rarely deviated far from 100.

Since the species is so widespread it is difficult to associate Robins with any particular habitat, however in the first atlas there were negative associations with some arable crops and positive associations with woodland, parkland and built-up areas, but these are not significant in the new atlas. As discussed above, it is not clear if this is the result of improved coverage or genuine spread into a wider range of habitats.   TK

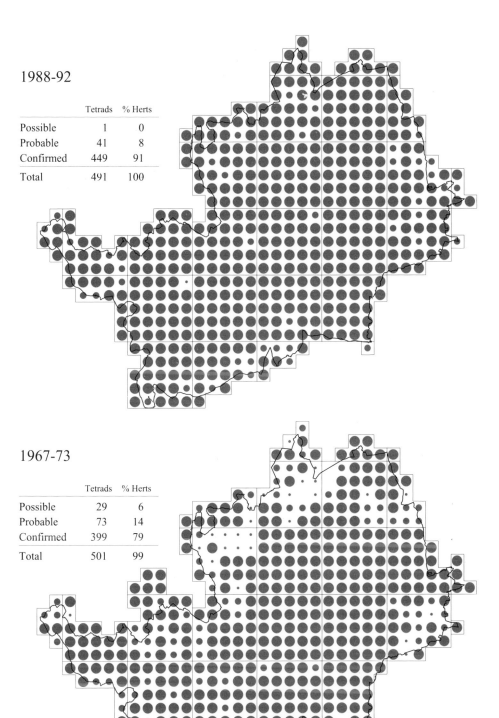

1988-92

	Tetrads	% Herts
Possible	1	0
Probable	41	8
Confirmed	449	91
Total	491	100

1967-73

	Tetrads	% Herts
Possible	29	6
Probable	73	14
Confirmed	399	79
Total	501	99

Nightingale

Luscinia megarhynchos

National population 5000-6000 pairs, Hertfordshire 3-12 pairs, declining.

The Nightingale, arguably our best songster, is a bird of deep, dense cover, where its skulking habits makes it very difficult to observe. In Hertfordshire its preferred habitat is old blackthorn thicket, much of which has been cleared in recent years (e.g. Cuffley and Watery Grove, Stevenage). Records have invariably been of singing males; very rarely are nests found or feeding of young observed. Indeed the recent records include only one confirmed nesting!

Nesting begins in mid-May when the female builds a loose nest of dead leaves (usually oak) and grasses, lined with roots and hair, amongst dense tree growth. The nest is usually on the ground amongst leaf litter and twigs, in Hertfordshire often associated with nettle patches. A clutch of four to five eggs are laid which hatch after 14 days. Both parents then feed the young, mainly on insects and especially caterpillars, for 11 to 12 days in the nest, and continue after fledging. A number of studies have shown that Nightingales are found at highest densities in coppice of five to eight years of age since cutting (Fuller & Moreton 1987, Stuttard & Williamson 1971, Fuller & Henderson 1992). Once the canopy is fully closed numbers decline. In Hertfordshire much hornbeam coppice has now been uncut for many years and is therefore unsuitable.

Nightingales are extremely common birds in the south of Europe and southern Britain represents the northern limit of their range. As such, numbers can be expected to fluctuate from year to year but there has also been a long-term contraction of range from the western and central counties of England towards the south-east. This reduction has also been reflected in Hertfordshire, where in the old atlas probable or confirmed breeding was recorded in 83 tetrads whereas the current survey reveals a total of only 24 such records – a sad decline and one that makes the Nightingale a very uncommon breeding bird in the county. In any one year only a few tetrads are occupied, whereas, as recently as 1980 a full survey of singing Nightingales in Hertfordshire (Sawford 1981) found 21 males, many of which were in woodland sites.

Population estimates for this species are also subject to some difficulties. Evidence of breeding is based upon locating singing males. Does each bird find a mate? It is known that some singing males cannot be relocated later in the breeding season and may have moved on. It is therefore possible that counting singing males does not give a good estimate of population. Notwithstanding this qualification, the estimate of 3 to 12 territorial singing birds in any one year is considered to be reasonable.   JNT

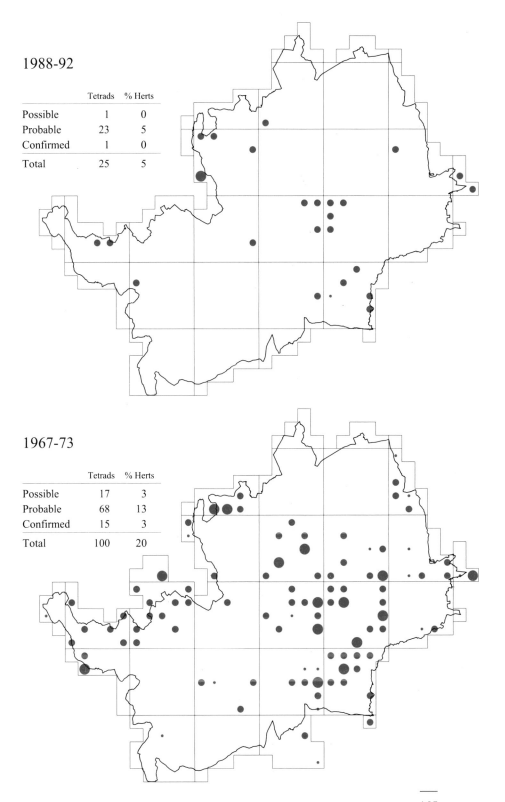

1988-92

	Tetrads	% Herts
Possible	1	0
Probable	23	5
Confirmed	1	0
Total	25	5

1967-73

	Tetrads	% Herts
Possible	17	3
Probable	68	13
Confirmed	15	3
Total	100	20

Black Redstart

Phoenicurus ochruros

National population 82-119 pairs, Hertfordshire 0-1 pairs, static.

The Black Redstart is an attractive chat
which, in Britain at least, is associated
with urban environments such as industrial sites and power stations. It is usually a much darker bird than the common
Redstart. Older males have a grey back
and sooty black bib and breast but young
birds are less striking. Like the Redstart
it has a rusty red tail which it constantly
'shivers'. In continental Europe it is common and widespread and is found not
only in urban environments but also in
rocky, mountainous areas, particularly
on boulder strewn slopes and scree.

Nationally it is a rare breeding bird which, apart from a few isolated records, only
colonised Britain in the 1920s. By the 1940s the population had become established,
particularly on bombed sites in London. Its appearance in Britain is part of a larger range
expansion in north-western Europe. Primarily a summer visitor, it is also a seen in
winter, although only as a scarce visitor. Some birds may be resident, although not
necessarily sedentary.

The nest is a loose cup of grass, leaves, stems and other plant material, lined with
wool, hair and feathers. It is typically one to four metres (but can be up to 45 metres)
above the ground, placed on a ledge or in a hole in rocks, buildings or walls. Normally
four to six eggs are laid and these are incubated by the female alone. The young are
attended by both parents and fledge 12-19 days after hatching. Two broods are common.

Although the Black Redstart is an urban bird, it is easy to overlook, particularly in
areas where singing birds cannot be heard over traffic or industrial activity. The song is
a particularly thin metallic warble. These areas are not likely to be frequented by
ornithologists, even assuming that access is available. It is therefore possible that the
species has been under-recorded but not greatly so.

The new atlas map shows only one tetrad with confirmed breeding against five in the
old atlas. This probably represents normal population fluctuations. The national situation is also unclear. The population has varied between 82 and 119 pairs in the period
1986-90 (Spencer *et al* 1993) and a BTO survey in 1977 recorded 100 breeding pairs
(Morgan & Glue 1981), suggesting little real change in the last ten years. In both cases
the bulk of the records were in the east and south-east of England.

It is likely that the three records of possible breeding related to passage migrants and
not birds staying to breed.   J & CD

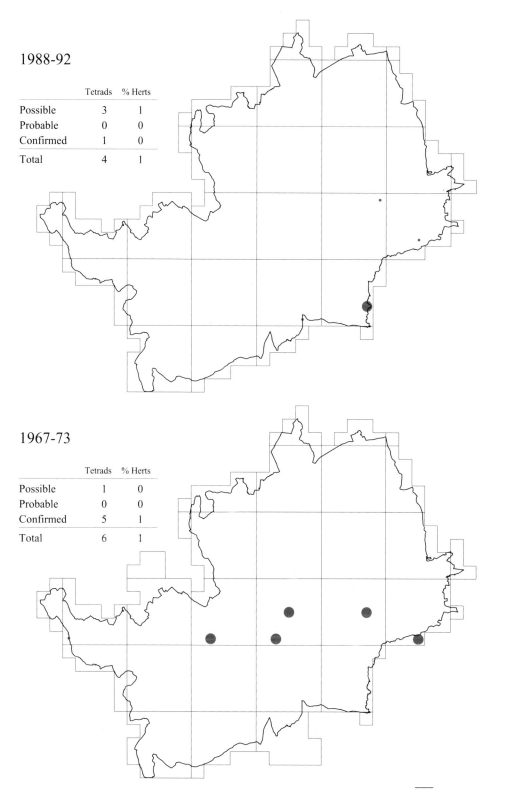

1988-92

	Tetrads	% Herts
Possible	3	1
Probable	0	0
Confirmed	1	0
Total	4	1

1967-73

	Tetrads	% Herts
Possible	1	0
Probable	0	0
Confirmed	5	1
Total	6	1

Redstart

Phoenicurus phoenicurus

National population 90,000 pairs, Hertfordshire 0-6 pairs, declining.

The Redstart takes its name from the old English 'red steort', meaning red tail, and this is the most striking feature of this beautiful bird. The male has a black face and throat, white forehead and red rump and tail. The female is more dull, grey-brown above and orange buff beneath but still with the characteristic red tail.

Males are easy to find because of their liking for prominent song posts at the edges of woodland glades and their habit of making gliding song flights across these areas. The song is sweet and rather melancholic in tone, weak in volume with a repetition of the main phrases similar to that of a Robin, with a characteristic jangle at the end.

The Redstart has always been thinly distributed in eastern England and is most numerous in western and northern counties, where it often shares the oakwood habitat with the Wood Warbler and Pied Flycatcher. The national population index took a serious dip from 1969 through to 1973 but has subsequently recovered to its former level. Nationally, it seems likely that the biggest influence on population levels over the last four decades has been conditions in the African winter quarters, rather than in Britain.

Sage (1959), considered the Redstart a local summer visitor to Hertfordshire being fairly numerous in a few favoured localities. Since then, numbers have declined drastically so that in the new atlas there were just four confirmed breeding records and one of these was at Telegraph Hill just across the county border in Bedfordshire. A pair were seen feeding young in the nest at Hitch Wood, St Paul's Walden in 1988; recently fledged young were seen at Heath End on the Hertfordshire/Buckinghamshire border and in 1991 adults were seen feeding young at a nest at a regular site on the Ashridge estate.

The national recovery of the last twenty years has certainly not occurred in Hertfordshire. For instance, the woods at Ashridge have always been considered very suitable habitat for Redstarts with extensive tracts of mixed deciduous trees containing many open glades and much dead timber to provide nesting holes. Yet, even here, numbers have continued to decline. In 1982 there were still four singing males in the Hertfordshire part of the estate but only one could be found during the atlas fieldwork. In Broxbourne Woods and Northaw Great Wood the number of pairs has tumbled from 40-50 in the early 1960s to just two in 1982 and none during the atlas period.

The reasons why Redstarts have failed to recover their numbers in Hertfordshire are not clear, but may be related to woodland management. In their strongholds in western oakwoods and the New Forest they require the open structure of grazed woodlands (Stowe 1987, Smith *et al* 1992). It is interesting that much of the Ashridge woodlands are old wood pastures and Hitch Wood has the open structure of a grazed woodland suggesting that grazing may be an important factor.   JET

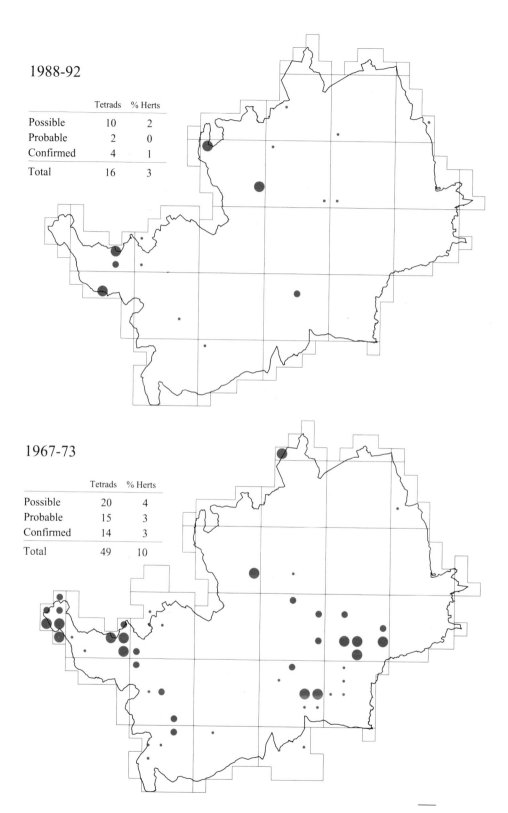

1988-92

	Tetrads	% Herts
Possible	10	2
Probable	2	0
Confirmed	4	1
Total	16	3

1967-73

	Tetrads	% Herts
Possible	20	4
Probable	15	3
Confirmed	14	3
Total	49	10

Whinchat

Saxicola rubetra

*National population 14,000-28,000 pairs, Hertfordshire 0-2
pairs, virtually extinct.*

Although the Whinchat is a trans-Saharan migrant, it is similar
in many ways to its close relative, the Stonechat. It is shorter
tailed and longer winged, but, if not a male in breeding plumage, can be confused. Nationally it is more of an upland bird
than the Stonechat, but any habitat that provides a combination
of tussocky grass and song posts of about a metre in height may
be suitable. It is apparently not as dependent on woody shrubs
as its relative but equally will sing from tree tops. It can breed
in small tracts of habitat and may appear and disappear from a
suitable site from year to year. It arrives at the breeding site in
April or early May.

The nest is a cup of grass stems, leaves and moss, lined with
finer material and hair. It is usually on the ground in tall grass
or low vegetation. The clutch, typically five or six eggs, is
incubated by the female and the young are fed by both parents.
In Britain Whinchats are frequently double brooded.

Whinchats frequently perch prominently and have a loud,
distinctive and pleasant song, so are easily detected both early
in the season and later when feeding fledged young. It is
therefore unlikely that any breeding pairs were missed.

The atlas maps show the extent of the decline. At the time of
the first atlas there were 13 tetrads with confirmed breeding
and in the new atlas there are no confirmed nesting and just two probable records. The
previous breeding records were concentrated in and around the water meadows of the
Lee valley and on the Chiltern scarp. Both habitats still exist, although the growth of
scrub at the latter may now make it unsuitable. Both maps have a scattering of records
of possible breeding which almost certainly relate to individuals on migration. If these
individuals find suitable habitat and a mate, breeding could occur.

In the old atlas the Whinchat was associated with rivers but there are now insufficient
records to analyse.

The national atlas shows the population to be concentrated in the west and north
where it has probably always been more common than in the lowlands of the east and
south. The reasons for the decline in the county are not entirely clear, but the trend is
mirrored throughout the south and east. Habitat loss undoubtedly plays a part, as
Hertfordshire has become more urbanised and some marginal land, which would have
provided nesting habitat, has been developed.

Being a trans-Saharan migrant the Whinchat could be expected to suffer the effects of
drought conditions in the Sahel region of Africa but this appears not to have been the
case. J & CD

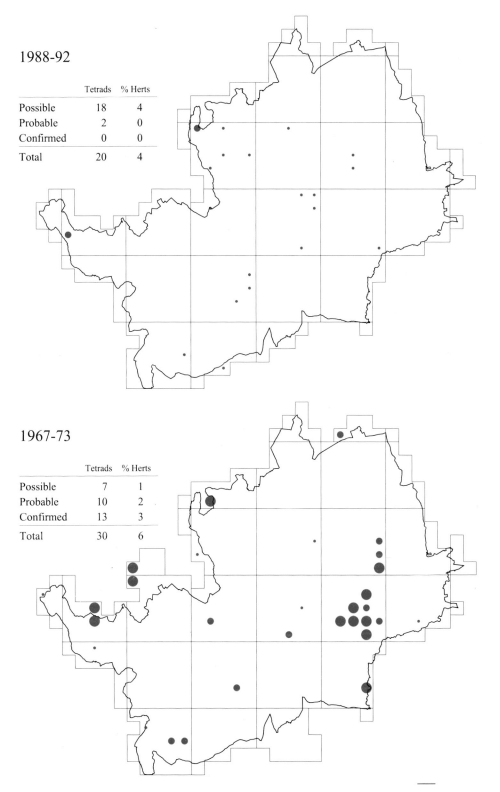

1988-92

	Tetrads	% Herts
Possible	18	4
Probable	2	0
Confirmed	0	0
Total	20	4

1967-73

	Tetrads	% Herts
Possible	7	1
Probable	10	2
Confirmed	13	3
Total	30	6

Stonechat

Saxicola torquata

*National population 8500-21,500 pairs,
Hertfordshire 0-1 pairs, declining.*

The Stonechat is a typical resident of coastal and lowland heath, particularly where there is gorse. The optimum habitat features a scattering of bushes, posts and walls or other perches, with areas of short grass. Stonechats also use young conifer plantations where there is suitable ground cover such as heather. Areas of continuous long grass are generally avoided. Although resident, some birds from inland sites appear to move to the coast for the winter.

The male, in particular, is frequently seen perched on the tops of bushes and posts, in full view of intruders, giving the distinctive 'tak-tak' call. The young, once fledged, also adopt this habit, making them easy to observe.

The nest is a loosely woven cup of grass and leaves, typically low down in thick scrub. Incubation is carried out by the female alone, but the young are fed and attended by both parents. Up to four broods in a season have been recorded but two or three attempts are more normal.

The behaviour of this species makes it particularly easy to obtain atlas records and it is unlikely that any breeding pairs were overlooked. The Stonechat was a common breeding species in the county in the early part of the century but since the 1940s it has become very scarce. Indeed, since that time it has only been proved to breed five times, with a small number of records of probable breeding. Nationally there is evidence of a similar decline, which has been exacerbated by cold winters.

Stonechats are very vulnerable to cold weather and whole populations can be virtually wiped out in severe winters. The high breeding output allows a rapid recovery. However, where populations have been fragmented by habitat loss, the re-colonisation following winter extinction is a chance affair which has become less likely as the population on the east coast and inland counties has declined. Habitat loss has occurred by development, as well as succession of heathland by birch scrub and woodland. The national population now has a strong southerly and westerly bias in areas where habitat loss has been less marked and the winters are more moderate.

In the case of this rare breeder the population may be accurately assessed: there was one breeding record in one year of the new atlas period.   J & CD

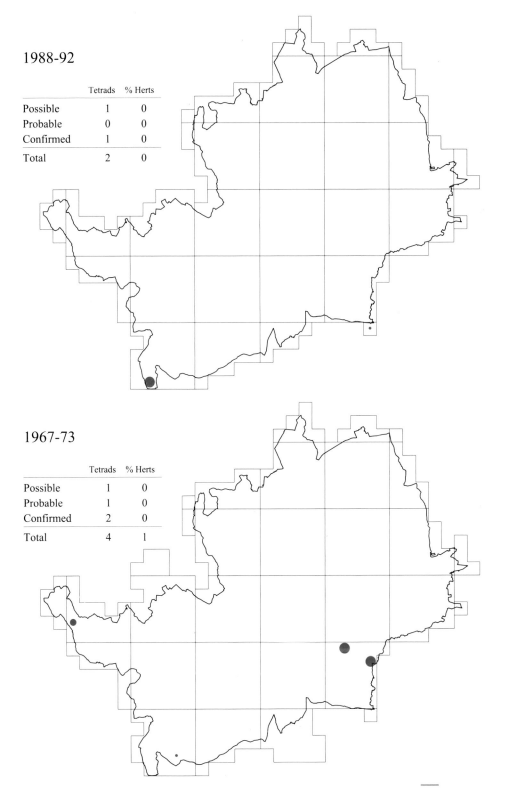

1988-92

	Tetrads	% Herts
Possible	1	0
Probable	0	0
Confirmed	1	0
Total	2	0

1967-73

	Tetrads	% Herts
Possible	1	0
Probable	1	0
Confirmed	2	0
Total	4	1

Blackbird

Turdus merula

National population 4.4 million territories, Hertfordshire 40,000-63,000 territories, static.

Blackbirds are certainly one of, if not the most familiar of the county's birds. Their mellow, flute-like song is instantly recognised and is a major component of the dawn chorus. Their abundance is confirmed by the fieldwork for the old and the new atlases; it is one of only ten species found in every tetrad in this atlas. Also, the Blackbird is the only common species in the new atlas for which all the records are of probable or confirmed breeding. Nationally, Blackbirds maintain their densest populations in woodland, followed by suburban areas and farmland and there is no reason to believe that this is not the case in Hertfordshire, with the main towns harbouring larger numbers than the more rural areas of the north and east. There is a tendency to form small flocks outside the breeding season with the numbers of local birds being supplemented by continental visitors. Gladwin & Sage (1986) recorded the bird's preference for single-sex flocks during this period.

Nest-building is chiefly by the female who constructs a solid cup of dry grass, dead leaves, twigs and moss, lined with dried grass and some mud. A variety of locations are chosen in a hedge or bush, low tree, ledges of buildings or even on the ground in suitable cover. Every year, most local papers will print a picture of an occupied Blackbird's nest in an unusual location such as a tractor or a fire-engine, adding to the species' charm. The young, which hatch after 12-14 days incubation by the female only, are fed by both parents and leave the nest after another 14 days but remain dependent on their parents for food for a further 20 days or so.

Proof of breeding is exceptionally easy to obtain. The male's courtship behaviour is conspicuous, the nest is not difficult to locate and the obvious feeding of the fledged young are all contributory factors. Indeed, the 463 records of confirmed breeding in the new atlas is exceeded only by the Starling with 484 and Blue Tit with 466.

Given that it was found in every tetrad, it has not been possible to detect a change in the distribution of this bird, one of the county's most ubiquitous and numerous residents, between atlas periods. The national CBC indices indicate a shallow downward trend following the severe winter of 1976 and the trends guide notes lower densities in counties dominated by winter cereals – as parts of Hertfordshire have become. As the atlas is a measure of distribution only, it is not possible to confirm if the county trend reflects the national picture.   EWF

1988-92

	Tetrads	% Herts
Possible	0	0
Probable	28	6
Confirmed	463	94
Total	491	100

1967-73

	Tetrads	% Herts
Possible	8	2
Probable	22	4
Confirmed	474	94
Total	504	100

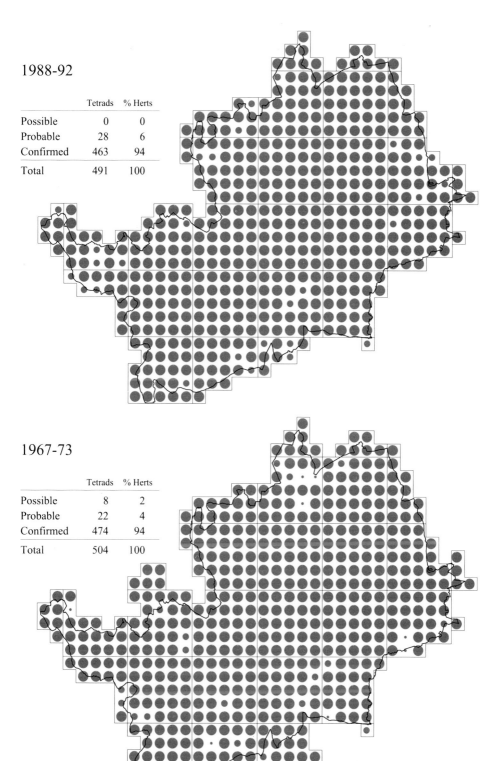

Song Thrush

Turdus philomelos

National population 990,000 territories, Hertfordshire 11,000 territories, decreasing.

With its repetitious song, close relationship with human habitation and familiar snail and anvil feeding method, the Song Thrush is well known to all birdwatchers. Probably originally a bird of the woodland edge, Song Thrushes now breed in almost any habitat with trees or bushes for nesting. Advantage is taken of suburban gardens and parklands and, with their obvious ground feeding habits, the presence of the species is easily proven. Nesting takes place over a long season with the neat, mud-lined nest usually placed within two metres of the ground. Two or more broods are raised, each consisting of an average of five eggs.

The new atlas map shows a position almost identical to the old one. Song Thrushes occur in every tetrad in Hertfordshire as they did 20 years ago but confirmed breeding records have dropped from 91% to 84%. A further survey in 20 years time may well show a rather different position for the Song Thrush is currently under going a long-term decline. The population is still high enough to fill all tetrads in the county but this may not be so for many more years.

Fifty years ago, Song Thrushes outnumbered Blackbirds 3:1 but this position has now reversed as the population of Song Thrushes has declined and that of Blackbird's increased. From being a familiar bird of garden, field and park, the Song Thrush is disappearing from many of its previous haunts. The national CBC indices have been falling since the mid 1970s so they are now less than 50% of their peak. Other monitoring work such as the Garden Bird Survey confirms the decline is across all habitats but is particularly noticeable in cereal farming areas.

The smallest of our breeding thrushes, it has always been susceptible to cold winters which have reduced the population. Baillie (1990) has modelled trends in Song Thrush numbers and found that changes are indeed related to severity of winter weather but that in recent years another factor has resulted in bigger declines than predicted by the model. Magpie predation and agricultural use of molluscicides have been suggested as the reasons. However, the decline is not a result of reduced nesting success, which has actually improved, but is thought most likely to be the result of reduced survival of juvenile and adult birds (Baillie 1990). This tends to rule out Magpie predation as the cause but the increased use of molluscicides is a possibility. Although Song Thrushes are not dependent on snails all year, they do form a major part of the diet in dry summer periods and late spring when berries and fruits have finished. This latter time is the period when molluscicides are used most and this may well be having a substantial impact upon Song Thrushes.   RNS

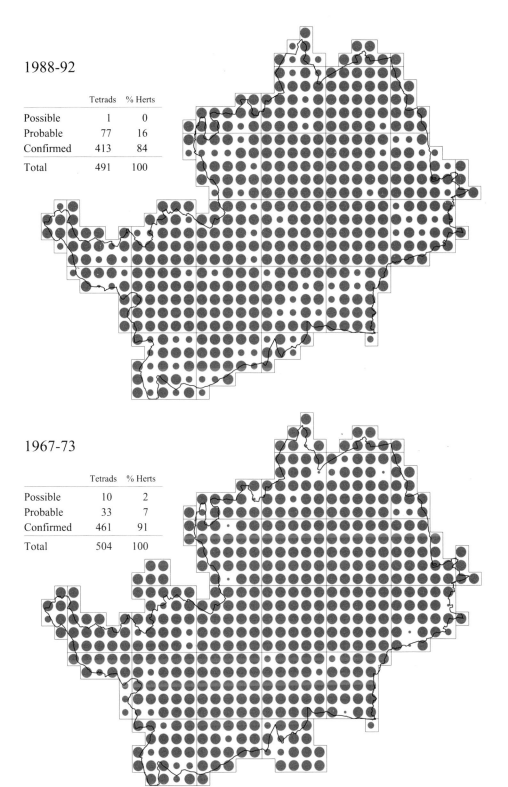

1988-92

	Tetrads	% Herts
Possible	1	0
Probable	77	16
Confirmed	413	84
Total	491	100

1967-73

	Tetrads	% Herts
Possible	10	2
Probable	33	7
Confirmed	461	91
Total	504	100

Mistle Thrush

Turdus viscivorus

National population 230,000 territories, Hertfordshire 2400-4300 territories, static.

This, the largest of our regularly breeding thrushes, proclaims its presence early in the breeding season by singing from the most exposed positions available long before other birds are in song. A very early breeder with eggs frequently in the nest in February, the Mistle Thrush has earned its colloquial name of Storm Cock. Despite its relatively large size and apparently vigorous nature, the Mistle Thrush is susceptible to hard weather and severe winters can substantially reduce the population.

A feeder on grassland invertebrates, it has benefited from the spread of ornamental parks and grasslands which supplement the traditional feeding areas such as grazing land. Winter food is augmented by berries and pairs will defend suitable berry bearing bushes during winter months (Snow & Snow 1988).

The nest is built high in a tree, next to the trunk, with an average clutch of four eggs. Early nests are more often built in coniferous trees than deciduous, presumably to avoid predation and as protection from the poor spring weather conditions. Young Mistle Thrushes are loud and obvious birds so that proof of breeding is fairly easy to obtain. Although the long breeding season, with up to three broods, means that records of breeding could be obtained throughout the fieldwork period, in general they are much easier to find early in the season.

The new map shows the Mistle Thrush to be widely distributed across Hertfordshire with the exception of the north and east. However, even here the range has expanded since the old atlas. Gladwin (1983) considered that Mistle Thrushes benefited from the establishment of verges and parks in towns during the 1950s and 1960s together with the planting of berry bearing trees and shrubs. This is a trend which has continued in the last ten years with much tree and shrub planting carried out by local authorities and this may account for the improvement in the number of tetrads with confirmed breeding.

The habitat associations are positive for woodlands, parklands and built-up areas and in general negative for all agricultural crops. In the first atlas there were positive associations for grasslands and cattle but this is no longer the case.

National populations increased during the 1970s but have levelled out or declined slightly since the mid-1980s. The species is susceptible to freezing conditions and CBC data clearly show the effect of the hard winters of the mid 1980s. The population has apparently declined unevenly. Numbers, fledging success and brood size have reduced in cereal growing areas but in areas with large amounts of grazing land the trend has been more stable (O'Connor & Shrubb 1986). In Hertfordshire the Mistle Thrush appears to have spread into cereal growing areas but still shows an aversion for cereal crops themselves.   RNS

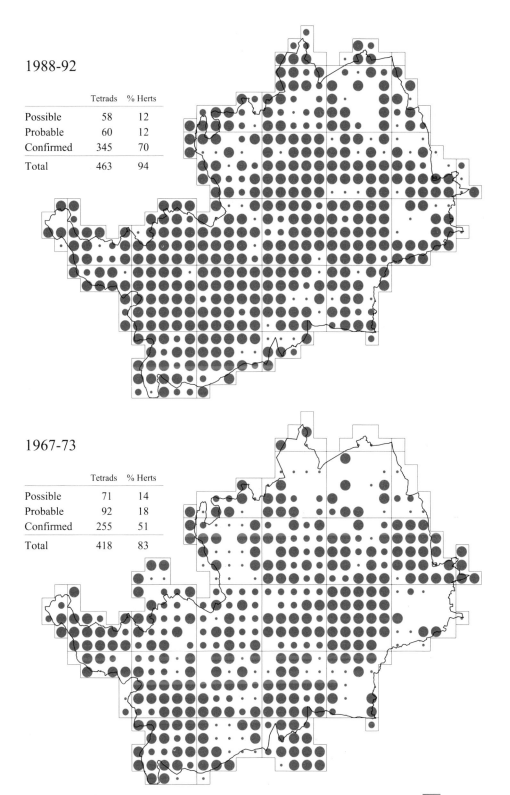

1988-92

	Tetrads	% Herts
Possible	58	12
Probable	60	12
Confirmed	345	70
Total	463	94

1967-73

	Tetrads	% Herts
Possible	71	14
Probable	92	18
Confirmed	255	51
Total	418	83

Grasshopper Warbler

Locustella naevia

National population 10,500 pairs, Hertfordshire 20-50 pairs, major decrease.

Grasshopper Warblers are so named because of their diagnostic, continuous grasshopper-like reeling song, best heard at dawn or dusk and sometimes even at night. Although no British grasshopper makes the sound, it is very similar to certain continental crickets. The two oft quoted comparisons are with the ratchet of an angler's reel or a free-wheeling bicycle. Claims for the bird's power of ventriloquism are explained by it turning its head in mid-song, the length of which can be several minutes with just perceptible breaks for breath (the current record is 110 minutes by a bird in Luxembourg!). It is a particularly elusive bird which skulks amid tangled grass, brambles, bushes and all types of low cover. If disturbed it will tend to creep away rather than fly. People lucky enough to achieve a brief glimpse should see its rounded tail and streaked upper-parts.

The nest of small twigs and grass on a foundation of dead leaves and lined with hair is built on, or very close to, the ground with large grass tussocks being especially favoured. It is exceptionally well concealed. Four to six eggs are incubated by both adults for 14 days and the young leave the nest after ten to twelve days, often before they can properly fly.

It is not surprising that 80% of the atlas records were of singing birds, indeed breeding was confirmed in only a single tetrad. It is possible that some of the singing birds did not find a mate and breed but, for such a secretive species, the low numbers of confirmed breeding records are not surprising. Perhaps more worrying is the fact that the distribution is cumulative for the period 1988-92 and certainly overstates the number of birds present in any one year. A review of the annual bird reports for 1988-91 shows records from between eight and eleven sites each year. The true annual position probably lies somewhere between the atlas picture and that of the bird reports, but tending toward the lower figure.

Irrespective of the actual number of breeding pairs, it is very evident that the population has crashed since the old atlas. It has been suggested that the species may have suffered in its winter quarters during the prolonged Sahelian drought and indeed populations fell in 1971, a few years after the well reported decrease in Whitethroat numbers. However, in addition to this there has no doubt been a chronic general decline over the last few decades, probably related to loss of breeding habitat.

In the old atlas Grasshopper Warblers were associated with broad-leaved and mixed woodlands where they nested in overgrown clearings and young plantations. This is no longer the case in Hertfordshire and as these woodland habitats have become unsuitable the birds are now found only in wetland areas.   EWF

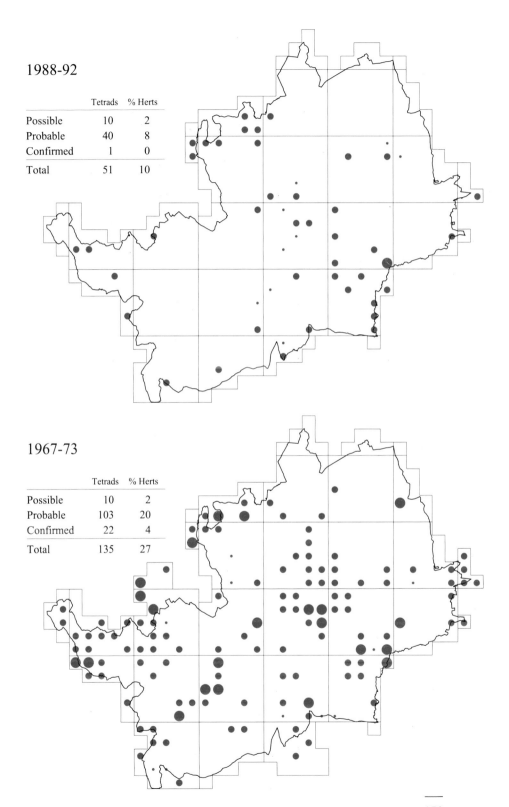

1988-92

	Tetrads	% Herts
Possible	10	2
Probable	40	8
Confirmed	1	0
Total	51	10

1967-73

	Tetrads	% Herts
Possible	10	2
Probable	103	20
Confirmed	22	4
Total	135	27

Sedge Warbler

Acrocephalus schoenobaenus

National population 250,000 territories, Hertfordshire 260-580 territories, considerable decrease.

The Sedge Warbler traditionally favours low, rank vegetation, such as reed and osier beds, adjacent or near to water but it can also be found in young forestry plantations and in standing crops – impenetrable oilseed rape being a recent addition to its catholic choice. It is often difficult to see, hunting insects low down in dense vegetation but gives itself away with its attractive rattling song, which is similar to the Reed Warbler's. It is a good mimic, often introducing parts of other species' songs into its chatter. Even a fleeting glimpse should show a distinct creamy supercilium and its buffy red rump and spread tail are conspicuous in flight, readily separating it from the Reed Warbler. The male has an attractive courtship flight during which he will fly vertically upwards, singing throughout, followed by a descent when wings and tail are spread.

The nest is well concealed in low, dense vegetation and is usually close to water. The female undertakes most of the incubation and the young hatch after about 13 days, leaving the nest 14 days later. There is sometimes a second brood.

It is fairly easy to locate singing males and although nests are difficult to find, the adults are not secretive when carrying food to the young. Almost 90% of the records were of probable and confirmed breeding. The new atlas shows a considerable decrease in the number of tetrads occupied, with over half of the loss being of records of confirmed breeding. There is no discernible loss in any particular area of the county but rather a general contraction throughout the range shown in the old atlas. Nationally, the CBC indices show an all time peak in 1968 followed by sharp falls in 1969, 1971 and 1972 so the old atlas could be viewed as representing the distribution during a period of particularly high populations. There was a further, even greater, plunge in 1985 bringing national indicies to an all time low. These declines are thought to be closely related to the droughts in the birds' wintering range in the Sahel and savanna zones of Africa (Peach *et al* 1991). For the last few years the trend has been one of an increasing population with numbers roughly equal to the figures of the early 1980s.

Sedge Warblers prefer to be close to water but have also demonstrated their tolerance of a wide variety of locations so long as there is rank, dense vegetation for nesting. The 1991 Hertfordshire Bird Report notes a territorial male in a field of oilseed rape four kilometres from the nearest water.

In both atlases Sedge Warblers were associated with wetland habitats: open water, marsh, mineral workings, rivers and streams. In spite of the reports of breeding in oilseed rape this has not happened on a scale sufficient to appear on the habitat preferences in the new atlas.

EWF

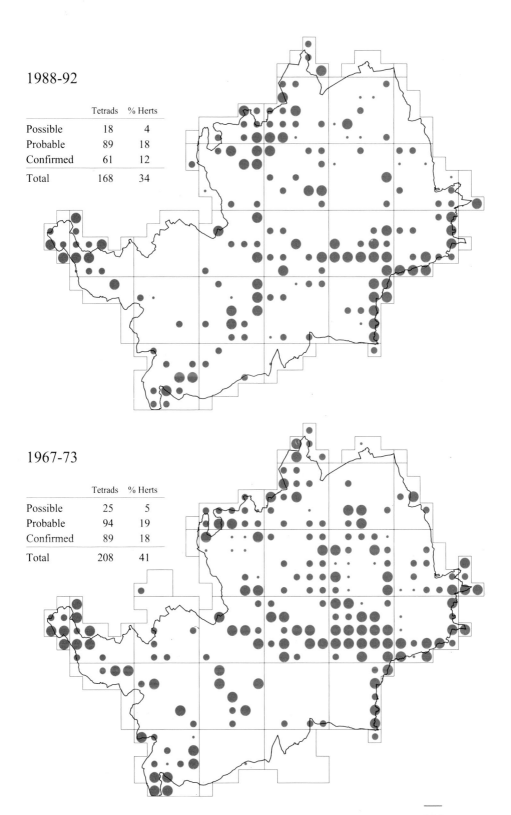

1988-92

	Tetrads	% Herts
Possible	18	4
Probable	89	18
Confirmed	61	12
Total	168	34

1967-73

	Tetrads	% Herts
Possible	25	5
Probable	94	19
Confirmed	89	18
Total	208	41

Reed Warbler

Acrocephalus scirpaceus

National population 40,000-80,000 pairs, Hertfordshire 120-240 pairs, stable.

Reed Warblers are summer visitors which winter in central west Africa. The name is apt as the very large majority of the birds breed in stands of the common reed *Phragmites*. However, their dependence on this plant is not total as they have been found sporadically among osiers and other dense vegetation, but always close to water and even then there are usually some reeds nearby. They have a characteristic harsh song which can be confused with that of the Sedge Warbler. It is similar to the noise made by clicking two stones together and this is one way of enticing the birds from dense cover. Compared with Sedge Warblers, they are long lived and return to the same sites from year to year. There are many instances of ringers re-trapping the same bird over many successive years. The most notable example was of a bird caught at Rye Meads in July 1991 that had originally been ringed as a nestling in June 1980.This constituted a new national longevity record for the species and it was calculated that the bird had travelled in excess of 110,000 kilometres in its lifetime.

The birds arrive from the middle of April onward and build an intricately woven cup-shaped nest which is slung between reed stems up to a metre from ground level. It has a relatively deep cup which helps prevent the eggs or young from being ejected during high winds. Three to five green-white, grey marked eggs are incubated by both adults and hatch in about 12 days. The young fly in 11 or 12 days but will leave the nest before this time, moving nimbly around nearby stems. Reed Warblers nest in loose colonies and are one of the major hosts of the Cuckoo.

The birds are very vocal and it is simple to establish that they are present. Absolute confirmation of breeding is more difficult and best achieved by observing parents carrying food to the nest.

The distributions in the two atlases are very similar with 81 tetrads occupied in the new compared with 78 in the old. There were less records of confirmed and possible breeding in the new atlas but these were matched by increased numbers of records of probable breeding.

The Reed Warbler's affinity for *Phragmites* beds is reflected by their distribution along the Lee and Colne valleys and Tring Reservoirs. Reference to both atlas maps shows only a scattered existence away from these areas. The habitat associations are similar in both atlases; positive for mineral workings, open water, marsh, rivers and built-up areas.

Nationally, Reed Warbler populations appear to be stable or increasing. Unlike Sedge Warblers they have not been affected by the Sahelian drought – presumably because their wintering quarters lie further south. EWF

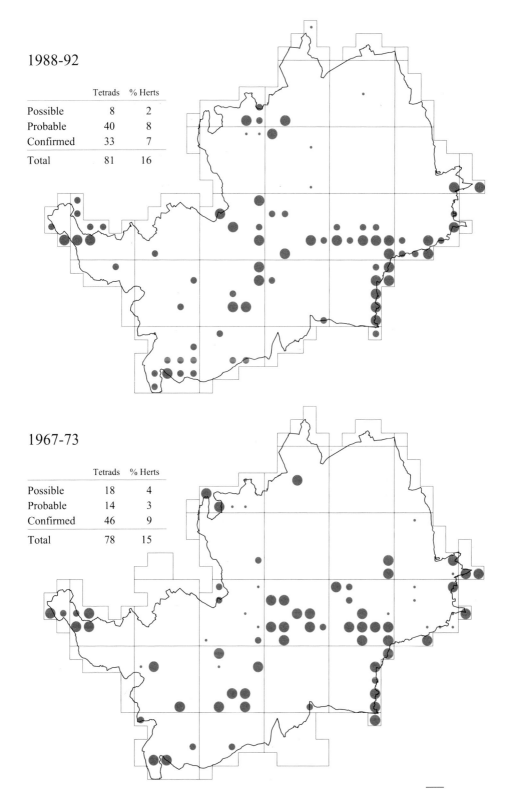

1988-92

	Tetrads	% Herts
Possible	8	2
Probable	40	8
Confirmed	33	7
Total	81	16

1967-73

	Tetrads	% Herts
Possible	18	4
Probable	14	3
Confirmed	46	9
Total	78	15

Lesser Whitethroat

Sylvia curruca

National population 80,000 territories, Hertfordshire 730-2000 territories, increasing.

The Lesser Whitethroat is a rather attractive warbler with neat grey and white plumage and black facial mask. However, because of its rather skulking behaviour it is more often heard than seen. The song period may only last a few days, particularly if the male succeeds in finding a mate, so the species can be easily overlooked. As the current survey shows, it is a relatively widespread warbler but is by no means common. It prefers mature, usually dense, hedgerows most commonly hawthorn and blackthorn. Habitat is often similar to that of its close cousin, the Whitethroat, including mature scrub in gravel pits, overgrown railway embankments and occasionally gardens.

Lesser Whitethroats are slightly smaller than Whitethroats with a noticeably shorter tail. Despite this, and differing plumages, there is a possibility of confusion, although voice is a good way of differentiating the two. The song is a soft chattering warble followed by a quicker louder rattle on a single note, often compared to that of the Cirl Bunting. The loud 'teck-teck' call and a scolding 'tcharr' can indicate close proximity to a breeding territory.

The nest is normally in low, shrubby growth about half to one metre from ground level, occasionally up to three metres. It is made from dead grass, leaf litter and roots and lined with hair, plant down and catkins. Both sexes incubate the four to six eggs for approximately ten days. The young then fledge after a further ten or eleven days. Double brooding has been recorded.

The Lesser Whitethroat is extending its range, particularly into Devon and Cornwall and, latterly, into Scotland. Due to its south-easterly migration route to Sudan and Ethiopia the Lesser Whitethroat has avoided the problems encountered in the Sahel region, although it is surprising that the drought conditions in its wintering area over the last ten years again appear to have had little effect.

Within the county, the survey results show a marked increase in probable and confirmed records. Lesser Whitethroats now appear to breed in and around some urban developments. In the predominantly arable areas the distribution appears, as reflected in the national population, to show a slight expansion.

Very few habitat associations emerged: positive for built-up areas and negative for wheat in this atlas; positive for broad-leaved woodland and permanent grass in the old. It is doubtful whether any of these are particularly related to the ecology of the species. Factors such as hedgerow's length and quality, both likely to affect populations of Lesser Whitethroat, have not been measured.   JD

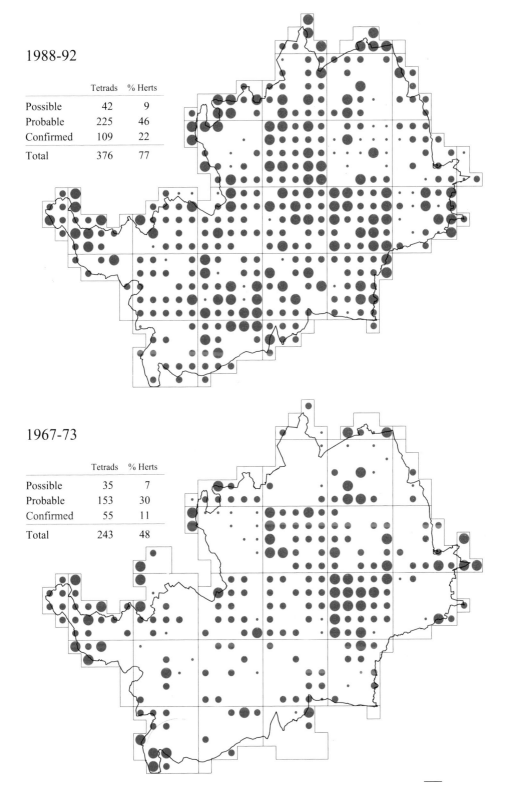

1988-92

	Tetrads	% Herts
Possible	42	9
Probable	225	46
Confirmed	109	22
Total	376	77

1967-73

	Tetrads	% Herts
Possible	35	7
Probable	153	30
Confirmed	55	11
Total	243	48

Whitethroat

Sylvia communis

National population 660,000 territories, Hertfordshire 2100-6300 territories, increasing.

The Whitethroat is a common and widely distributed summer visitor arriving during April and May and departing from its breeding territories from July to September. It is usually detected by its fast, harsh scratchy chatter. This is often presented from prominent perches such as telegraph wires, tall bushes and occasionally buildings, but also during brief song flights. The song and dancing display flight continue well into summer.

Various habitats are selected, ranging from mature hedgerows to relatively 'reduced' or severely cut hedges. Scrubland, woodland edges and clearings, railway embankments, gravel pits, allotments and mature gardens indicate the versatility of this *Sylvia* warbler. Nettle and bramble patches are often used for nesting and give the reason for its country name 'Nettle Creeper'.

Nest building normally begins in May, usually started by the male. After the female arrives she either completes the nest or builds her own. The nests are usually in low shrubs approximately 30-40 centimetres off the ground. They are loosely built, cupped and wedged onto twigs or stems, but not bound to them. The frame is made of dry grass and roots, lined with hair, plant down and wool. Eggs, varying from three to seven, are pale blue or green with finely spotted or speckled light green and grey markings. Incubation is by both sexes and lasts 11 to 13 days. The chicks spend a further 10 to 12 days in the nest before fledging. The species is usually double brooded.

The dramatic crash of Whitethroat numbers after the winter of 1968/69 has been attributed to the drought in the Sahel region of sub-Saharan Africa (Winstanley *et al* 1974). Numbers have recovered somewhat but have yet to return to the levels recorded in the early 1960s.

The fact that there are increased numbers of occupied tetrads in the new atlas is, given the major population crash in 1969, surprising. However the fieldwork for the old atlas would have been done largely after 1969 and the distribution was therefore most like that after the crash.

The habitat associations are not particularly enlightening. In the old atlas they were positive for broad-leaved woodland, oats, field beans, fallow, grass leys and cattle. In the new atlas this had changed to positive for wheat, barley, oats and field beans and negative for built-up areas. JD

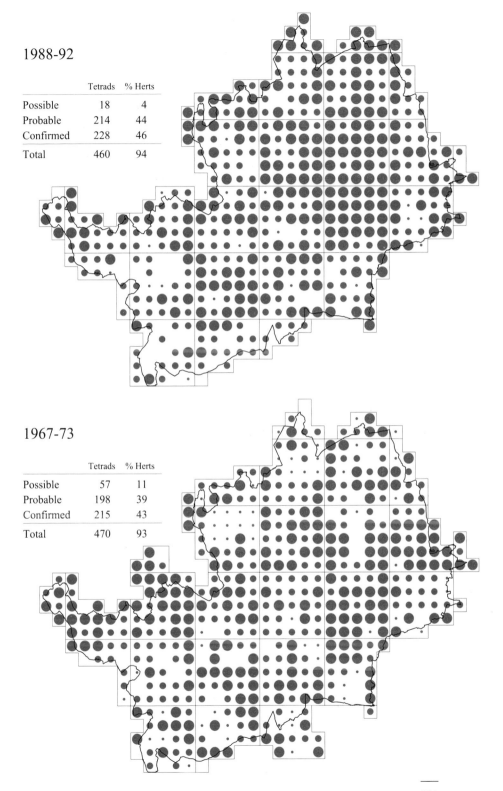

1988-92

	Tetrads	% Herts
Possible	18	4
Probable	214	44
Confirmed	228	46
Total	460	94

1967-73

	Tetrads	% Herts
Possible	57	11
Probable	198	39
Confirmed	215	43
Total	470	93

Garden Warbler

Sylvia borin

*National population 200,000 territories,
Hertfordshire 1200-2500 territories, increasing.*

The Garden Warbler is an inconspicuous
and skulking bird of woodland, woodland edge and scrub. Unlike the Blackcap, which has broadly similar habitat
preferences, this species may be found
in scrub habitats without tall trees. The
song of the Garden Warbler is also similar to that of the Blackcap and even the
most experienced observers can have difficulty distinguishing the two. As it is
often delivered from the midst of low,
dense vegetation, this can sometimes
make confirmation of identity difficult
to obtain. Garcia (1983) has shown that with similar habitat requirements and song there
is evidence of competition between Garden Warbler and Blackcap.

The nest is built close to the ground in brambles or nettles, with the single clutch of
four or five eggs being laid in late May. Around four young are raised from each
successful nest (Mason 1976).

The combination of the lack of positive identification features and its secretive
behaviour make the presence of a breeding pair difficult to establish early in the
breeding season but once the nestlings reach about a week old, the frequent visits by
both parents can make the presence of a nest quite obvious. Caution in deciding between
Garden Warbler and Blackcap for birds with less characteristic songs may have resulted
in the loss of a few records.

The new distribution map shows the species to be absent from the main areas of
urbanisation and from the more open habitats in the north-east of the county. Compared
to the old atlas, there has been an increase of probable and confirmed breeding records
from 47% of the county tetrads to 71%, showing a spread from the main areas of
woodland into smaller woods and, presumably, less favoured habitats such as farmland.

After a ten year decline, the national CBC indices for Garden Warbler reached a low
point in the mid-1970s, since when there has been a slow but steady increase. Between
the two atlas periods the CBC indices for farmland have decreased whilst those for
woodland have increased. It is thus difficult to understand how these relate to the overall
increase in Hertfordshire.

In both atlases the Garden Warbler was associated with woodlands. In the old atlas
there were negative associations with wheat, potatoes and field beans but these are no
longer significant, presumably as a result of the current wider distribution of the species
in the county.   CWD

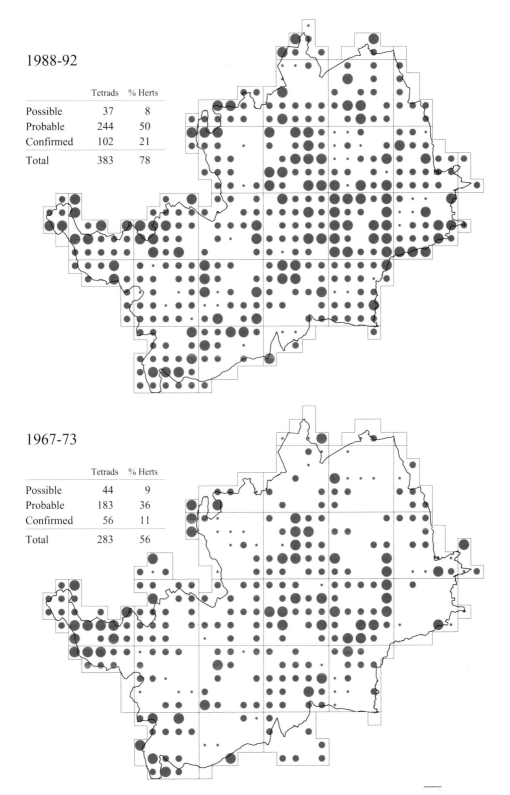

1988-92

	Tetrads	% Herts
Possible	37	8
Probable	244	50
Confirmed	102	21
Total	383	78

1967-73

	Tetrads	% Herts
Possible	44	9
Probable	183	36
Confirmed	56	11
Total	283	56

Blackcap

Sylvia atricapilla

National population 580,000 territories,
Hertfordshire 5800-18,000 territories,
increasing.

The Blackcap is the most abundant and
widespread of the *Sylvia* warblers which
breed in Britain. It is primarily a bird of
high-canopy woodland, but also breeds
in less densely wooded scrub and hedgerow habitats where mature trees exist for
use as song posts. As one of the first
migrant warblers to arrive each spring
from its wintering grounds in the Mediterranean basin, the attractive song of
the Blackcap is easily detected. It is often delivered from a high perch, although
locating the bird as it moves amongst the
fresh foliage is rarely easy. The female, and the male when not singing, are skulking and
secretive birds, although the harsh 'tack' of the anxiety call is distinctive once recognised.

Like the other three common *Sylvia* warblers, the Blackcap nests most frequently in
bramble where it forms the woodland ground cover. It may also utilise small shrubs
such as hawthorn, elder and elm. The first clutch of four or five eggs is laid in the first
half of May and generally four young are raised per successful nest (Mason 1976). A
small proportion of pairs may make a second breeding attempt.

The highly territorial behaviour of this species means that records of probable
breeding are relatively easy to obtain and the combination of alarm calls with family
groups of brown-headed juvenile birds later in the season makes confirmation of
breeding straightforward. The similarity of the Blackcap's song to that of the Garden
Warbler may have resulted in some incorrect registrations, but these are thought to be
few in number.

The Blackcap is now almost ubiquitous in Hertfordshire, absent or only possibly
breeding in just a few of the poorly vegetated tetrads in the north-east of the county. The
increase in the number of probable and confirmed records since the old atlas reflects a
national and European increase in the Blackcap population. The national CBC indices
show a steady increase over the past 30 years, with that for farmland showing a greater
increase than that for woodland.

It has been suggested that the high population levels are now causing a spread of the
species into sub-optimal non-woodland habitats. This view is supported by the habitat
association analyses for Hertfordshire. At the time of the old atlas, there was a highly
significant association between the distribution of breeding Blackcaps and that of
woodland. With the spread of the species across the whole county, it is not surprising
that there is no longer any association with habitat or agricultural variables at the tetrad
level.   CWD

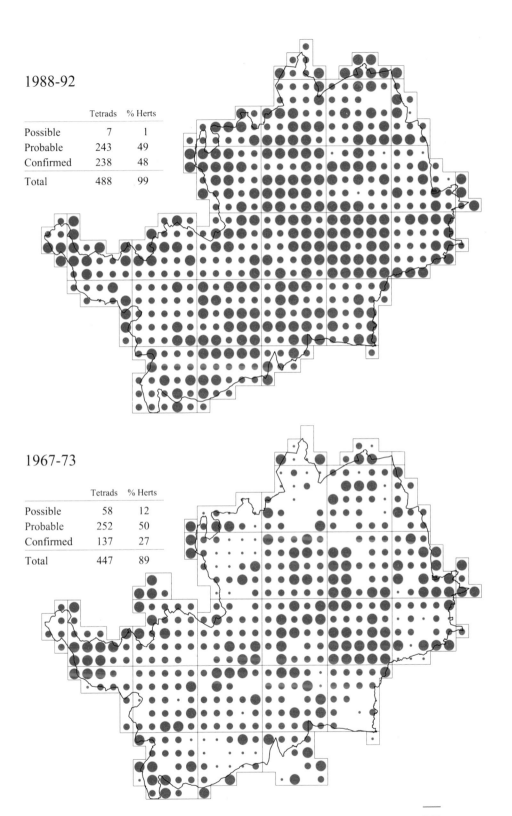

1988-92

	Tetrads	% Herts
Possible	7	1
Probable	243	49
Confirmed	238	48
Total	488	99

1967-73

	Tetrads	% Herts
Possible	58	12
Probable	252	50
Confirmed	137	27
Total	447	89

Wood Warbler

Phylloscopus sibilatrix

*National population 17,200 males, Hert-
fordshire 0-9 pairs, declining.*

The Wood Warbler is more brightly coloured than its close relatives the Willow
Warbler and Chiffchaff. It has a contrasting plumage of yellowish green
upperparts with a broad golden eyestripe,
sulphur stained breast and throat, and a
pure white belly and under tail coverts.
However, the most reliable way to tell
the species apart is by their distinctive
songs. 'A sibilous shivering noise in the
tops of tall woods' was how Gilbert White
described Wood Warbler song in his letters to Thomas Pennant. In fact the male
has two different versions to its song.
The typical one is a repetition of a single note 'sip' which quickens into a trill. The
second consists of several plaintive notes 'piew...piew...piew'. The song is delivered
from a perch or when in flight from tree to tree.

The Wood Warbler is a true forest bird preferring closed canopy woodland with
sparse shrub cover and, in Hertfordshire, is found in acid oak-birch woodlands (James
1981). The domed nest is built by the female alone in a hollow amongst bracken,
brambles or herbs and is relatively easy to locate by watching the adults back. Although
there have always been regular Wood Warbler sites in Hertfordshire, most notably the
Ashridge woodlands, males often sing in odd sites for some days without attracting a
mate, so that singing birds do not necessarily constitute proof of breeding.

There has clearly been a reduction in the number of occupied tetrads between the two
atlases. Support for the view that this reflects a genuine decline in the Wood Warbler
comes from the numbers of birds in the Ashridge woodlands which have hardly changed
in character in the period. Up to 20 singing males were recorded there in the 1950s and
60s falling to 12 in 1980, four in 1990 and only two in 1992. There have been two
surveys of Wood Warblers in Hertfordshire in the last two decades; 1978-79 (James
1981) and as part of the national survey in 1984-85 (Bibby 1989). It is interesting that
neither survey produced as many occupied tetrads as the two atlases. Clearly the Wood
Warbler's habit of turning up in different sites from year to year results in the
accumulation of more records in an extended atlas than would be obtained in a single
year. However, comparing the two atlases, both surveyed over an extended period, is
likely to be a fairly reliable indication of change. There is no reliable national index of
Wood Warbler numbers with which to compare the Hertfordshire situation.

The Wood Warbler is on the eastern edge of its range in Hertfordshire with the main
British populations in the upland woodlands of the north and west. Bibby (1989)
discussed the common factors between lowland and upland sites and concluded they
were both woodlands on relatively poor soils often with some grazing pressure.
Ungrazed woodlands on more fertile soils tend to develop dense shrub layers making
them unsuitable for Wood Warblers.   JET

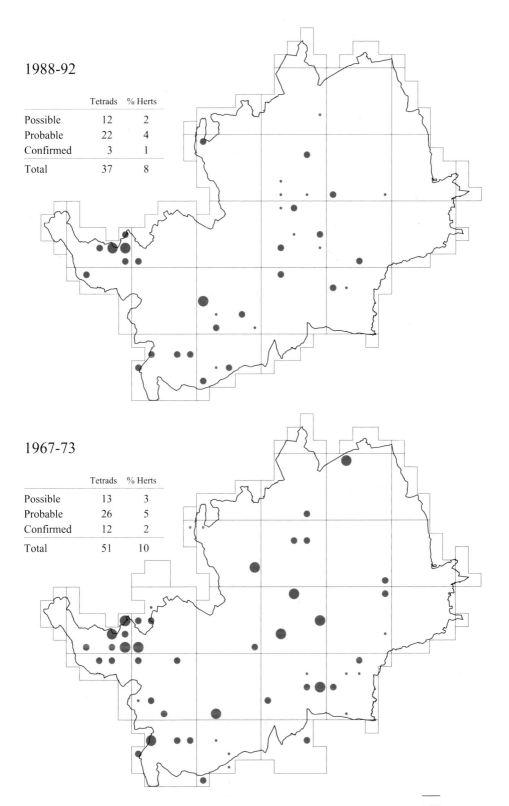

1988-92

	Tetrads	% Herts
Possible	12	2
Probable	22	4
Confirmed	3	1
Total	37	8

1967-73

	Tetrads	% Herts
Possible	13	3
Probable	26	5
Confirmed	12	2
Total	51	10

Chiffchaff

Phylloscopus collybita

National population 640,000 territories, Hertfordshire 4700-14,000 territories, increasing.

The Chiffchaff can be found commonly throughout Hertfordshire during the summer months where it can be heard uttering it distinctive 'chiff-chaff chiff-chaff' song from high amongst the leaf canopy or seen flitting from branch to branch constantly flicking its wings and tail as it searches for food. As well as having a distinctive song, it can be separated from the very similar Willow Warbler by its dumpier appearance, shorter primary projection and generally darker legs. It can be found in a variety of habitats, consisting primarily of deciduous or mixed woodland but also commons, parks, heaths, coppiced woods, hedgerows with standard trees and well grown forestry plantations.

Chiffchaffs winter both north and south of the Sahara and around the Mediterranean basin with a small percentage of birds (probably birds from the continent) choosing to spend the winter in Britain.

Being one of the earliest harbingers of spring, Chiffchaffs generally start to arrive during the latter part of March with passage continuing into early April, with the majority of breeding birds having arrived by the middle of the month. Early in the season birds tend to favour wetland habitats such as reservoir edges and gravel pits before moving on to their chosen breeding site.

The domed nest is built in low vegetation usually within one metre of the ground and is constructed of dead leaves, grasses and moss and lined with feathers. Nest construction, incubation of the clutch of approximately six eggs and the majority of the feeding of the young is carried out by the female. The breeding season lasts from May to July and one or two broods are raised.

The distinctive far-carrying song enables birds holding territory to be located easily, although singing birds on passage can possibly lead to some spurious breeding records. The nest is more difficult to find, partly due to its location and partly to the difficulty in watching adult birds back to it. This is reflected in the high percentage of probable breeding records.

The distribution of the species in Hertfordshire has increased significantly since the old atlas with a small increase in the number of occupied tetrads, mainly due to extra records from the north and east of the county. Nationally there have been several population slumps during the mid-1970s and 1980s in line with Sahelian rainfall deficits and the overall trend shows a small decline.

In the old atlas the Chiffchaff was associated with woodlands, grasslands and cattle. The woodland associations remain but not the others.   GE

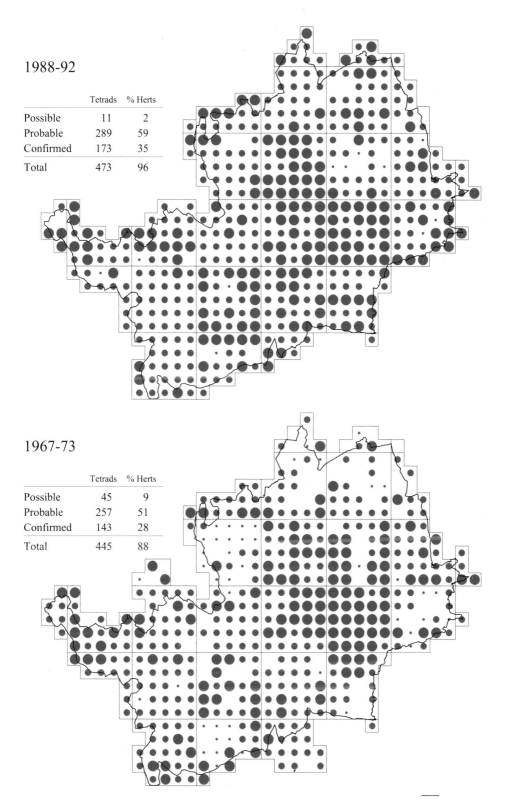

1988-92

	Tetrads	% Herts
Possible	11	2
Probable	289	59
Confirmed	173	35
Total	473	96

1967-73

	Tetrads	% Herts
Possible	45	9
Probable	257	51
Confirmed	143	28
Total	445	88

Willow Warbler

Phylloscopus trochilus

National population 2.3 million territories, Hertfordshire 8500-17,000 territories, stable.

The Willow Warbler is the most numerous and widely distributed of our summer migrants, rated ninth in the national league table of abundance, and is the only summer visitor in the 'top' 15 of Britain's most numerous breeding species.

It is primarily a bird of young woodlands, woodland edge and scrub, and avoids areas of mature woodland with a closed canopy. A small olive and yellow warbler, appearing neater and sleeker than the very similar Chiffchaff, it is often encountered flitting restlessly from branch to branch, occasionally flycatching and hovering as it searches for insects.

Willow Warblers winter well to the south in tropical Africa, an area that has enabled them to avoid the worst of the drought related problems that have affected several other trans-Saharan migrants (Lack 1989). However, increased drought in sub-Saharan Africa may now be adversely affecting the species. They return to Britain in early April, when the distinctive downward cascading song of both birds on passage and breeding males marking their territories can be heard from virtually every area of suitable habitat throughout the county. The domed nest is constructed entirely by the female, well concealed either on or near the ground and built mostly of grasses and moss. The eggs are laid at a rate of one a day until the clutch is complete, usually six or seven eggs, which are then incubated by the female only for about 13 days. The young birds are fed by both parents, although the female does the larger share, and the young fledge after 13-14 days.

The Willow Warbler's distinctive song enables breeding birds to be located easily and this, coupled with the large numbers of birds involved, has resulted in breeding birds being recorded in all but two of the county's tetrads. This is a slight but significant increase compared with the previous atlas and, in addition, there is a substantial increase in the number of confirmed records, possibly reflecting improved coverage. Nationally numbers have been stable or have slightly decreased over the same period.

The Willow Warbler is essentially associated with woodlands, but given the high number of occupied tetrads, it is not surprising that few other associations have emerged.   GE

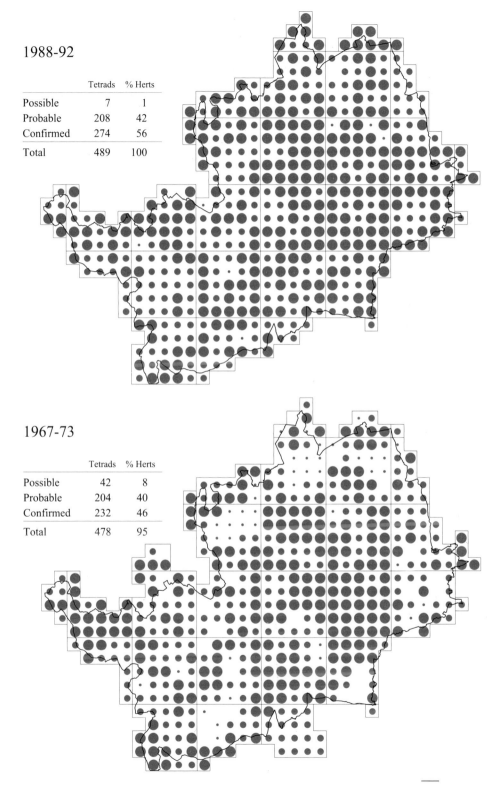

1988-92

	Tetrads	% Herts
Possible	7	1
Probable	208	42
Confirmed	274	56
Total	489	100

1967-73

	Tetrads	% Herts
Possible	42	8
Probable	204	40
Confirmed	232	46
Total	478	95

Goldcrest

Regulus regulus

National population 560,000 territories, Hertfordshire 3700 territories, increasing.

The Goldcrest is a typical bird of coniferous woodland throughout Britain. It also occurs less commonly in mixed and deciduous woodland, but even there, is often associated with small clumps or individual conifers. It is tiny, constantly active and most often detected by its 'zee-zee' contact call or its distinctive high pitched song which is given throughout the year. A resident species, the British population is much increased in winter by birds of continental origin. Being insectivorous it is susceptible to cold winters and this seems to be the factor limiting the population size and also results in large fluctuations in numbers from year to year.

The nest is usually placed 1 to 23 metres above the ground in a conifer tree. It is a tiny mass of lichen and spiders' webs, lined with feathers and may be attached to twigs or placed in small holes in branches. The clutch size varies from seven to ten eggs which are incubated by the female alone. The young are fed by both parents and fledge in 16-21 days. Two broods are normal.

Although Goldcrests sing frequently, the high pitched song is inaudible to some people, so the bird may be overlooked. In addition, the nest is not easy to locate, particularly if it is high above the ground. It is possible that the Goldcrest is under-recorded in marginal habitats but in prime habitats the population density is sufficiently high to ensure that it is not missed.

Comparison of the two maps shows an obvious increase in distribution, perhaps a result of the recent run of warm winters. This reflects the national situation, where the national CBC index is now considerably higher than in the last atlas period. However, the scale of the increase is not just a result of an increasing population. Other factors are the greater area of mature conifer plantations and a move into marginal areas. It is interesting that, even with a higher number of occupied tetrads, some of the major gaps in the distribution have remained in both atlases, which is presumably the result of a lack of suitable habitat in these areas.

In the old atlas the Goldcrest was associated with broad-leaved and mixed woods and parkland but surprisingly not coniferous woodland. It is not clear why this should have been so but it is suspected that because of the way woodlands are recorded on Ordnance Survey maps, coniferous woodland has been under-estimated. Interestingly in the new atlas, coniferous woodland and built-up areas have been added to the list of habitats selected by Goldcrests. This presumably reflects the species' use of a wider spectrum of habitats now that the population levels are high.   J & CD

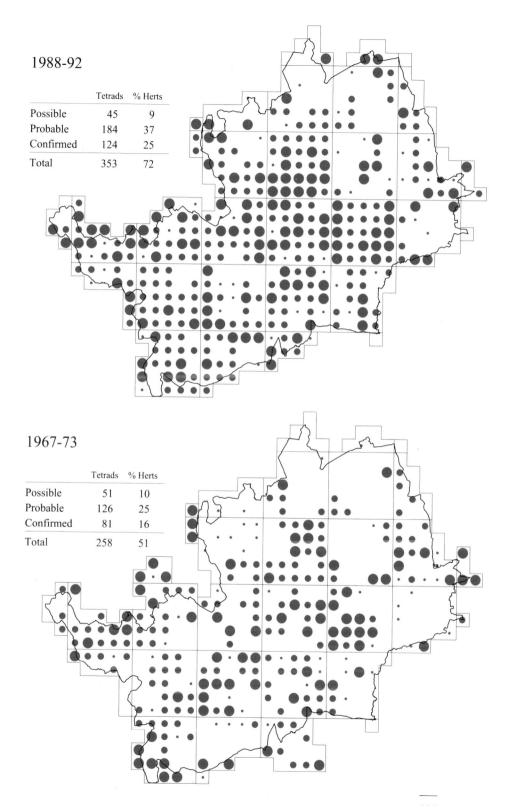

1988-92

	Tetrads	% Herts
Possible	45	9
Probable	184	37
Confirmed	124	25
Total	353	72

1967-73

	Tetrads	% Herts
Possible	51	10
Probable	126	25
Confirmed	81	16
Total	258	51

Firecrest

Regulus ignicapillus

National population 80-250 males, Hert-
fordshire 0-10 pairs, increasing.

A good view of the striking face pattern
of the Firecrest immediately separates it
from the plain unmarked face of the otherwise similar Goldcrest. The paler un-
derparts and the bronze green upper parts
also give the Firecrest a more contrasting plumage than the Goldcrest. Seen in
the right lighting conditions the male's
brilliant crown feathers make it clear
why the species got its name.

It is a bird of conifers, particularly
Norway spruce, but can be found in deciduous woods with yew or holly. It is a
passage migrant, winter visitor and a
breeding bird but it is not clear whether the British breeding birds winter here or
migrate. Nationally they appear at regular breeding areas in early May and disappear in
August.

The nest is similar to the Goldcrest's, usually suspended from a conifer branch or in
an ivy covered trunk. Juniper bushes have also been used. The tightly woven cup of
mosses and spiders' webs is placed up to 20 metres above the ground. The clutch of
seven to 12 eggs is incubated by the female and the young are attended by both parents.
They fledge in 19-20 days. In this country two broods are common.

Although the nest may be difficult to observe, the song is distinctive and is frequently
given early in the season. As with the Goldcrest, proof of breeding is often obtained by
seeing adults carrying nesting material or food. Since considerable areas of potentially
suitable habitat exist within the county it is possible that individuals or pairs were
overlooked during the fieldwork.

Comparison of the maps shows an increase in total distribution; the Firecrest was not
even a confirmed breeding bird at the time of the old atlas. The two records of singing
males in the old atlas were situated close to the well established colony in Buckinghamshire and it is surprising that there are not more records from this area in the new atlas.
Most of the records in the new atlas came from the centre of the county and relate to
singing birds.

Whilst it is likely that the possible and some probable records relate to migrant birds
or un-paired males, the single confirmed breeding record should be regarded as a
minimum. These circumstances reflect the national status. The Firecrest is a new
colonist to Britain with breeding first confirmed in 1961 since when the national
population has grown to its present level. In recent years the population has fluctuated
around 80 pairs but is probably under-recorded (Spencer *et al* 1993). Its spread in
Britain appears to be part of a general range expansion in Europe.

With such small numbers of records no meaningful analysis of habitat associations
was possible.

J & CD

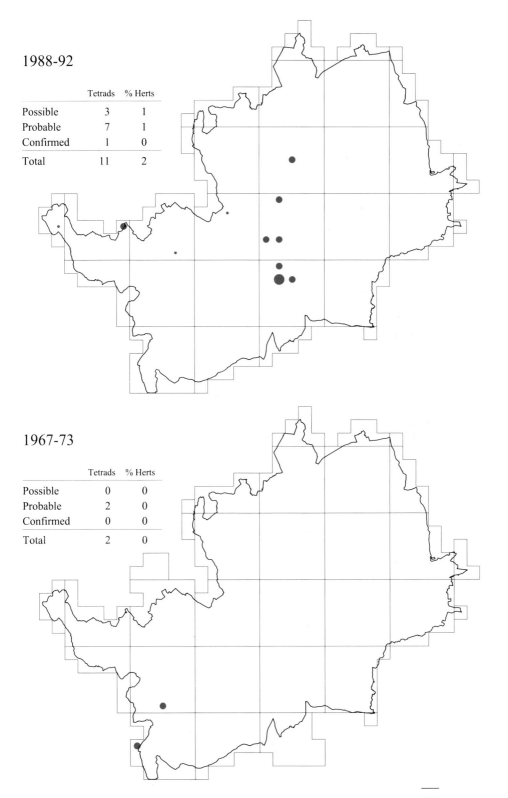

1988-92

	Tetrads	% Herts
Possible	3	1
Probable	7	1
Confirmed	1	0
Total	11	2

1967-73

	Tetrads	% Herts
Possible	0	0
Probable	2	0
Confirmed	0	0
Total	2	0

Spotted Flycatcher

Muscicapa striata

National population 120,000 territories, Hertfordshire 1100 territories, decreasing.

The Spotted Flycatcher is a small, sparrow sized bird with an upright stance which, as its name suggests, catches insects on the wing. The plumage is greyish brown above, white below with faint streaking on the breast and the sexes are similar. A summer migrant, it is found in gardens, parks and open woodland from May onwards. With its quiet behaviour and inconspicuous plumage this bird can easily be overlooked. It is normally first drawn to one's attention by its quick darting flights as it sallies after passing  insects with great agility; it often feeds from a favourite perch to which it returns after each feeding attempt.

The nest is built on a ledge, natural or man-made, or a hollow of a tree, especially where a branch has been removed. In gardens a variety of sites are used: a wall covered in creepers, hanging baskets and open-fronted nest boxes. Incubation of the four to five eggs is carried out by both sexes for about two weeks with the chicks leaving the nest approximately two weeks later.

The presence of birds in the early part of the season is not easy to detect. Males sing for a few days after arrival in early May but subsequently are very quiet. It is often only when the birds are feeding young that they are noticed. It is therefore possible that several breeding pairs may have gone undetected.

Although the Spotted Flycatcher is still a fairly widespread species, the new atlas shows a bias towards the central and eastern half of the county and since the first atlas there has been a marked loss from the west of the county. Overall, it is probable that a significant decline in numbers has taken place, in line with national trends.

In the first atlas the Spotted Flycatcher was associated with woodland but in the new atlas it is associated with built-up areas and rivers. Clearly many woodland areas which used to hold birds no longer do so, whilst there has been greater use of urban environments such as gardens. DM

1988-92

	Tetrads	% Herts
Possible	83	17
Probable	81	16
Confirmed	214	44
Total	378	77

1967-73

	Tetrads	% Herts
Possible	73	14
Probable	121	24
Confirmed	213	42
Total	407	81

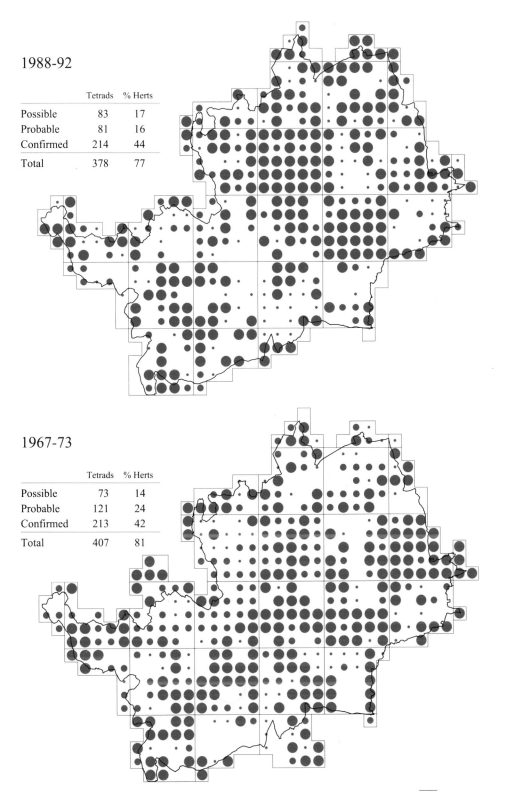

Long-tailed Tit

Aegithalos caudatus

National population 210,000 territories, Hertfordshire 2600 territories, increasing.

As its distinctive pink plumage would suggest, the Long-tailed Tit is not a true member of the tit family but is in a sub-family of its own. It is unique amongst the British tits as the only species to live and breed in family groups. Often first detected by their soft 'chirrup' calls, a flock will move through areas of scrub and bushes, the members pecking rapidly as they search for small food items amongst the buds and shoots. The Long-tailed Tit cannot hold seeds or nuts with its feet, does not feed on the ground and only occasionally uses garden bird feeders, although this habit appears to be on the increase.

The principal breeding habitats are overgrown hedgerows, scrub, bramble patches, woodland edge and rural gardens. Nest building starts in early March, the nest being an oval ball of moss and hair held together with interwoven spider's webs and lined with feathers; the outside is skilfully camouflaged with grey lichen. The small entrance hole is on or near the top. The site is either high up in a fork or branch ends of deciduous or coniferous trees, or lower down in a bush, creeper or patch of bramble.

Although staying in family parties during the winter, in spring the birds form pairs to start nesting (Glen & Perrins 1988). Nests are very vulnerable to predation and failed pairs either re-nest or join other nearby nesting pairs as helpers. The breeding success of nests with helpers is significantly higher than those without. After nesting, family groups will join together forming flocks numbering anything up to 40 or more birds and range over the combined breeding territories of the participating families (Perrins 1979).

The Long-tailed Tit is far more widely distributed in the new atlas than the old with many of the formerly blank areas filled. The numbers of occupied tetrads increased approximately in line with the change in the national CBC index over the same period. It is probable that the increased distribution in Hertfordshire is related to the series of mild winters in the late 1980s which are also thought to have been responsible for the national increase. Severe winters can cause big reductions in populations, particularly when ice glazing and hoar frost coat the small branches and make food inaccessible.

In both atlases the major habitat associations were with broad-leaved and mixed woodlands.   JHT

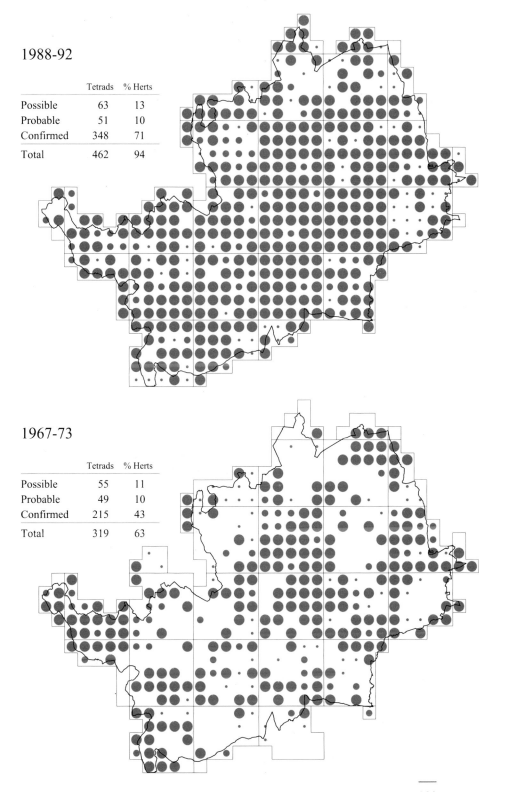

1988-92

	Tetrads	% Herts
Possible	63	13
Probable	51	10
Confirmed	348	71
Total	462	94

1967-73

	Tetrads	% Herts
Possible	55	11
Probable	49	10
Confirmed	215	43
Total	319	63

Marsh Tit

Parus palustris

National population 60,000 territories, Hertfordshire 450 territories, slight decrease.

This bird's name is a misnomer as it usually inhabits deciduous woodlands, especially those with large oaks, birches, ashes and alders. It is readily confused with the very similar Willow Tit and, in much of Hertfordshire, the ranges of both species overlap. There are subtle plumage differences such as a glossy rather than a sooty crown and the absence of a pale patch on the closed wing of Marsh Tits, but birds seen only briefly are liable to be confused. Once heard, however, the birds are far easier to separate as both the calls and songs differ. Pairs remain faithful to each other and to their breeding range. Even in winter they will readily join a mixed tit flock feeding in their own territory but will not follow it when it leaves.

The nest – a foundation of moss with a cup of hair or down – is built by the female in an existing natural cavity, usually a tree-hole, but the birds will nest amongst tree roots and will occasionally use man-made sites such as nest boxes, dry stone walls and even hollow metal posts. The territory is violently defended against other pairs but the nest site may be surrendered to larger tits and other hole nesting species such as Nuthatch. Incubation is undertaken entirely by the female, fed on the nest by her partner. The young remain dependent on their parents for about a week after leaving the nest and there is normally only a single brood.

The major problem associated with obtaining atlas records was that of confusing the bird with its close relative, the Willow Tit, and it is possible that uncertainty over identification has led to the loss of a few records. Whereas singing birds pose no problems, it has already been noted that the visual identification of adults can be difficult for the less experienced fieldworker and the separation of juvenile birds is virtually impossible.

Nationally, Marsh Tit populations roughly halved between 1970 and 1990. In Hertfordshire there was a slight, but not significant, reduction in the number of occupied tetrads between the two atlases. More significantly the distribution of records has changed with more in central and south-east Hertfordshire and a reduction in the west and south of the county.

The reasons for the decline are not clear and cannot be explained solely by habitat changes as the birds have disappeared from areas where no serious loss of habitat has occurred. Neither is there any distinct evidence of a declining food supply. The populations of Coal, Great and Blue Tit have increased and there may be some inter-specific competition for food or nest sites.

The main habitat associations are with broad-leaved and mixed woodlands. In the old atlas parklands and high ground were also favoured but this is no longer so. EWF

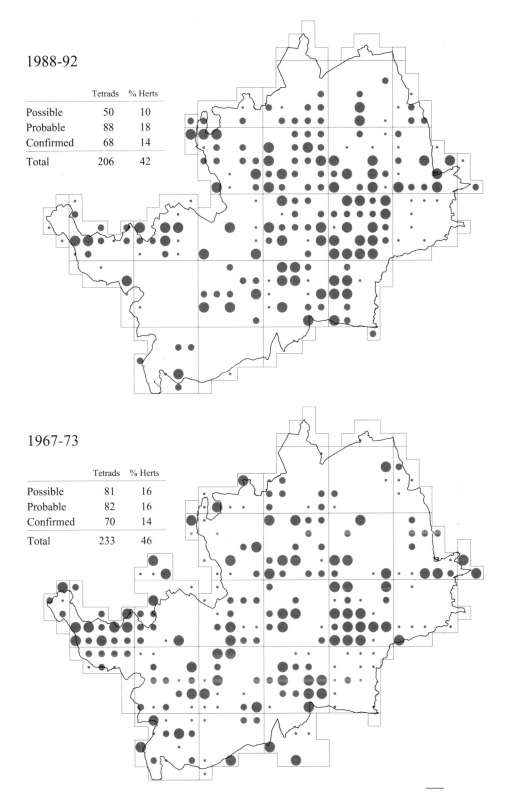

1988-92

	Tetrads	% Herts
Possible	50	10
Probable	88	18
Confirmed	68	14
Total	206	42

1967-73

	Tetrads	% Herts
Possible	81	16
Probable	82	16
Confirmed	70	14
Total	233	46

Willow Tit

Parus montanus

National population 25,000 territories, Hertfordshire 180-500 pairs, decreasing.

Willow Tits are birds of wet woodland and scrub and are probably most easily distinguished from Marsh Tits by their calls. It is not easy to separate them on plumage alone. Even experienced observers will mis-identify birds not seen well – the major differences being the Willow Tit's sooty, rather than glossy cap and the silvery markings on the closed wings, caused by the pale fringes of the secondary and tertial feathers.

Unlike the Marsh Tit, Willow Tits excavate their nest hole in soft, rotten wood. The nest is lined mainly with wood chips, fibres and a pad of hair. Tree species favoured are alder, birch, elder and willow and there is an affinity with damper woodland habitats, such as overgrown, flooded gravel pits which are commonly found along river valleys. Brooding is entirely by the female who is fed by the male whilst on the nest.

The fledged young of both Willow and Marsh Tits are extremely similar and so some of the atlas records will be confused. However, such errors are not deemed to be significant. Also, as Willow Tits excavate their own nest-hole rather than using a natural one, they are easily distinguished at the nest.

The new atlas data show a highly significant decrease in the distribution, particularly in mid-Hertfordshire. However, there is a surprising local trend not indicated by the overall pattern: in the period 1967-82, Mead & Smith had noted a two- to three-fold increase in Hertfordshire and Gladwin (1983) reported an increase of up to 400% in Central Hertfordshire between 1956 and 1980. Although there are no national data going back to 1956, the CBC population index increased from 1966 until the late 1970s and has subsequently decreased to around 70% of the peak. So the decline between the two atlases may represent a return to former population levels. What is not clear is why the recent mild winters have not led to an increase in Willow Tit numbers. It would appear that the series of relatively mild winters in the 1970s led to high numbers then which have subsequently declined.

The main habitat associations are for broad-leaved and mixed woodlands and high ground but, interestingly, there is also an association with the total area of all wetland habitats.

EWF

202

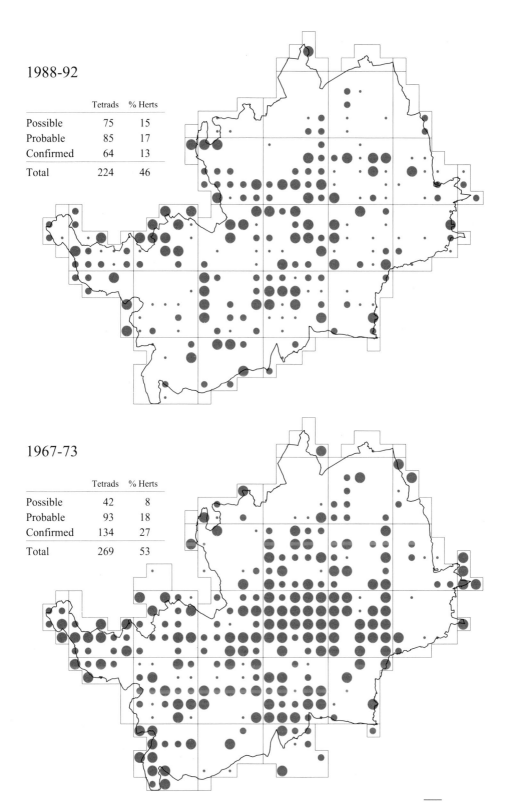

1988-92

	Tetrads	% Herts
Possible	75	15
Probable	85	17
Confirmed	64	13
Total	224	46

1967-73

	Tetrads	% Herts
Possible	42	8
Probable	93	18
Confirmed	134	27
Total	269	53

Coal Tit

Parus ater

National population 610,000 territories,
Hertfordshire 4000 territories, stable.

The Coal Tit is the smallest of the three commonest tits in Hertfordshire, having a distinct preference for coniferous woodland, a habitat in which it heavily outnumbers both Great and Blue Tits. A large headed, short tailed bird with a distinct white nape patch, it has a narrow pointed bill which is perfectly shaped for feeding in amongst bunches of conifer needles. Sedentary in nature, Coal Tits will move only short distances during the winter months when food is in short supply, often in the company of other tits and Goldcrests. The Coal Tit feeds largely on insects, although in late winter, as these become scarce, seeds such as beech mast and food from garden bird tables will be eaten. Being such a small bird it must feed almost continually during the short daylight hours in the winter, with sudden freezes or extreme weather conditions having a profound effect on the availability of food, thus threatening the birds' survival. Coal Tits will busy themselves at bird feeders taking small items and hiding them in convenient crevices, presumably to be recovered later.

Coal Tits generally nest slightly earlier than Great and Blue Tits. They choose nest sites that are generally lower than the other tits, such as holes in the ground, amongst the roots of trees and in suitably placed nest boxes. They nest mainly in areas of coniferous woodland although gardens and parks which only contain one or two conifers are also used. In times of high population Coal Tits can be found in pure deciduous woodlands. Clutch sizes vary between seven and eleven eggs. The clutch is incubated for about 17 days by the female and the young leave the nest a little under three weeks after hatching. Being a very vocal bird the far carrying song makes location of resident breeding birds relatively easy.

A quite substantial increase in distribution is apparent between the two atlas maps, with a notable growth of confirmed breeding records. Although some of this is perhaps a reflection of observer ability to detect nests, there has certainly been a genuine increase of the species in the county. This is in agreement with significant upward trends in the national population indices in the same period. This is thought to be due to a series of mild winters and the greater maturity of many conifer plantations which offer a richer food supply and more potential nest sites for breeding Coal Tits.

Coal Tits were found in tetrads with high areas of mixed and deciduous woodland, parkland and built-up areas. Interestingly, there was no association with coniferous woodland but this probably reflects the difficulty of identifying this habitat on the Ordnance Survey maps.

GE

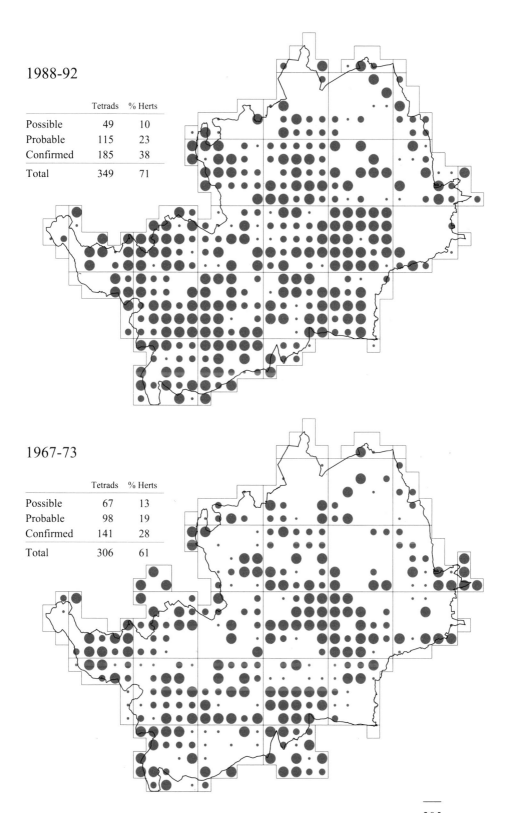

1988-92

	Tetrads	% Herts
Possible	49	10
Probable	115	23
Confirmed	185	38
Total	349	71

1967-73

	Tetrads	% Herts
Possible	67	13
Probable	98	19
Confirmed	141	28
Total	306	61

Blue Tit

Parus caeruleus

National population 3.3 million territories, Hertfordshire 25,000-50,000 territories, static.

The Blue Tit is, perhaps, the most widely known and watched of Hertfordshire's breeding birds. It readily adapts to the suburban environment and frequently uses garden nest sites. Breeding is not, however, reliant on nest boxes and the Blue Tit is the most abundant breeding species of tit in a variety of habitats throughout the county, particularly deciduous and mixed woodlands. The essential components for successful breeding are a suitable cavity and the presence of nearby bushes or trees. Ideally the trees will be broad-leaved, the species' natural preference, to which they are especially well adapted. Whatever the nest site, large clutches of between 7 and 16 eggs are produced. Both parents feed the young in the nest and the families remain together for some time after fledging. It is at this time that the slow and clumsy young may attract the attention of the local feline community or a Sparrowhawk.

Because of their confiding nature, the presence of Blue Tits and evidence of breeding are not hard to obtain. Densities may be lower in more rural areas but birds were recorded in all tetrads during atlas work. The fact that the number of tetrads with confirmed breeding has increased from 86% to 95% over the last 20 years is explained by an increase in population and better coverage. Some of the areas in the north of the county where Blue Tits were not confirmed to breed in the past are probably suboptimal areas into which the population has overflowed over the past twenty years. It has been suggested that the Blue Tit has become dependent on man for both breeding and winter survival. Supplied food is unlikely to become the sole source of sustenance and studies have suggested that it merely provides a safe supply when the natural crop of, for example, beech mast, is poor. There is some evidence that the provision of nest boxes increases the breeding density by removing the constraining factor of lack of nesting holes. The Blue Tit is a great opportunist however, and has also been recorded using old lamp posts (*pers obs*) and the old nests of both Blackbird (Dalton 1989) and House Martin (McNeil 1992). As with food, it is clear that artificial nest sites are used to supplement natural locations.

Given that Blue Tits were found in every tetrad, there are no significant habitat associations.

RY

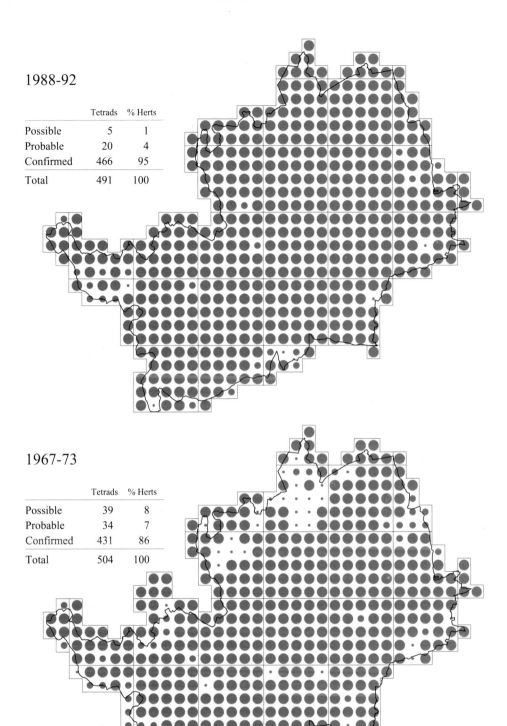

1988-92

	Tetrads	% Herts
Possible	5	1
Probable	20	4
Confirmed	466	95
Total	491	100

1967-73

	Tetrads	% Herts
Possible	39	8
Probable	34	7
Confirmed	431	86
Total	504	100

Great Tit

Parus major

National population 1.6 million territories, Hertfordshire 15,000-25,000 territories, static.

Associated with deciduous trees, parkland and suburban gardens, the Great Tit is a familiar sight and sound. It is the largest British tit; almost twice the size of other tit species, and is one of the commonest British birds. It feeds lower down in trees and more often on the ground than the smaller species, utilising a wide range of food sources – chiefly insects in summer and seeds (especially beech mast) in winter. It can be seen visiting garden bird tables and often aggressively chasing away other species. Males are slightly more colourful than females, with the black breast-band being much wider and extending to the legs and vent. In females this is much narrower and rarely reaches the legs. Apart from the familiar 'teacher-teacher' call, Great Tits produce a wide variety of contact and song notes that has been known to confuse many an expert! This species takes readily to garden nest boxes but in the wild normally uses a hole in a tree. Like other tit species it is also famous for selecting unusual nest sites – cans, pipes, road signs, letter boxes, wall cavities and even bee-hives have all been utilised.

The nesting season begins as early as March, with males being very vocal and holding territory. The nest is built by the female in a suitable cavity and consists of a moss base, (often using large quantities to fill large nest cavities) into which a neat cup of roots and hair is placed. Feathers are very rarely used by Great Tits. The female lays one red-flecked, white egg a day until the full clutch of 8 to 13 is completed. Prior to incubation the eggs are covered by nesting material. During this period the male makes frequent visits to the female with food and this makes nesting very easy to detect. The eggs hatch after 13-14 days and the young are fed very frequently on large numbers of caterpillars, with both parents bringing food. Rearing large numbers of young takes its toll on the parents and only rarely do they attempt a second brood – although birds in the north of Britain sometimes do. The young leave the nest after 16 to 22 days and are totally independent within two weeks – often joining up into large communal feeding parties.

Given its confiding nature and its close association with suburban gardens the Great Tit is one of the most extensively recorded atlas species, with confirmed or probable breeding in nearly every tetrad in the county. CBC indices have shown a gradual increase in farmland populations and this can be seen in the new atlas, where the more open 'prairie' farmlands to the north and west of the county have been more extensively occupied. This is reflected in the habitat associations. In the old atlas there was a positive association with woodlands but with the spread of the species this is no longer the case.

JNT

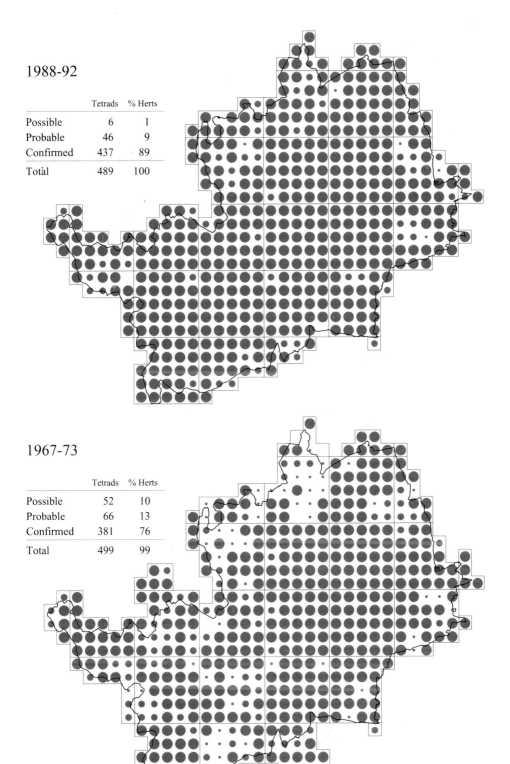

1988-92

	Tetrads	% Herts
Possible	6	1
Probable	46	9
Confirmed	437	89
Total	489	100

1967-73

	Tetrads	% Herts
Possible	52	10
Probable	66	13
Confirmed	381	76
Total	499	99

Nuthatch

Sitta europaea

National population 130,000 territories, Hertfordshire 1300 territories, steady increase.

Nuthatches are sedentary birds of mature broad-leaved woodland, parkland and, increasingly, suburban gardens. Where birds are found it is likely that they breed in the vicinity, so that 'possible' and 'probable' atlas records are good evidence of a nesting area. Nuthatches feed on a variety of hard foods such as acorns, beech mast and hazel, but with a larger proportion of insects during the summer months. They spend most of their time foraging from the larger branches and tree trunks, often loudly hammering at their food – the habit that gives them their name. A number of piercing calls and early spring song make them fairly easy to locate, even in dense woodland.

andrew .P. Chick 93.

Breeding begins in late March when a ready-made nest hole, between three and ten metres from the ground, is selected by both adults. They make use of old woodpecker nests, squirrel holes, and increasingly in recent years, nest boxes in suburban gardens. Adjustments to hole size are made by plastering around the entrance with mud, finishing off with rapid bill prodding to give a stippled finish. The female constructs the simple nest cup from bark fragments and dry leaves (often oak) with a sparse lining of hair and feathers. From late April to May six to nine red-speckled, white eggs are laid and incubated by the female for 14 to 18 days. The male brings food to the nest at this time and both parents feed the young for the two week fledging period. Pairs are usually single brooded, although double broods have been recorded.

The national CBC index has shown a long term gradual increase over the last 20 years and this trend can certainly be seen when comparing the new and old atlas. There has been a marked increase into two new areas, the more sparsely wooded north and east of the county, and also into the more suburban south.

The precise ecological basis for this spread and increase in numbers remains obscure. A number of factors may have played a part – a warmer climatic interlude, a move to occupy suburban gardens and nest boxes and, possibly of greatest significance, the increasing use of garden feeding stations during winter. Hard winters are known to increase Nuthatch mortality greatly and this comparatively new habit must have had a significant effect on survival. Certainly the population has doubled nationally in the last 20 years and extended its range northwards to the Lake District and westward into Wales. The county figures seem to reflect this national increase.

The habitat associations reflect this change in status. In the old atlas there were positive associations with broad-leaved and mixed woodlands, parkland and wetland, but in the new atlas built-up areas have been added. Throughout, there were negative associations with most types of agricultural land except for grassland and cattle in the old atlas.

JNT

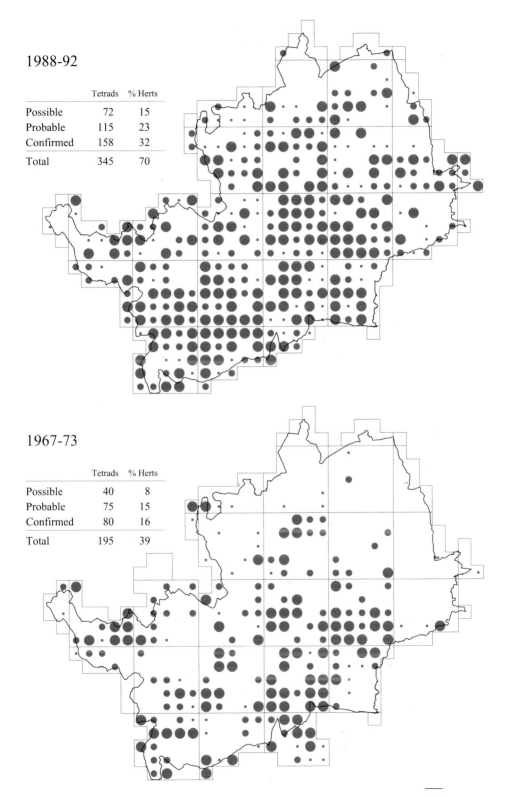

1988-92

	Tetrads	% Herts
Possible	72	15
Probable	115	23
Confirmed	158	32
Total	345	70

1967-73

	Tetrads	% Herts
Possible	40	8
Probable	75	15
Confirmed	80	16
Total	195	39

Treecreeper

Certhia familiaris

National population 200,000 territories, Hertfordshire 1600 territories, static or small increase.

The mouse-like Treecreeper is characteristic of deciduous woodland where it works its way slowly up a tree trunk, probing for small insects with its long curved bill. It is interesting that in continental Europe this species is found mainly in upland coniferous forest, with the Short-toed Treecreeper *C. brachydactyla* occupying lowland deciduous habitats.

Treecreepers have a thin, high-pitched call which some people find difficult to hear. Their habit of hiding from observers behind trunks and branches also increases the difficulty of finding them. However, they remain a fairly common resident, rarely, if ever, moving far from their home territory. Given their small body size and their largely insectivorous diet it comes as no surprise that hard winters with prolonged ice and snow cover cause great mortality. An interesting survival strategy has developed – roosting in hollowed-out depressions in the well insulated bark of giant redwood trees. This has been recorded wherever these trees grow and examples of such roost sites have been found in Panshanger Park, near Welwyn.

Nest sites are usually found behind loose bark or ivy on tree trunks and are fashioned from a loose cup of twigs lined with roots, moss and grass, with a lining of feathers. Both sexes build the nest – usually beginning in April. Four to seven eggs are laid – white with fine red/brown speckles and spots on the larger end only. Incubation lasts two weeks and only the female sits on the eggs. The young fledge in 14 to 16 days, at first flying weakly, but always able to climb well. Treecreepers regularly raise two broods annually – enabling populations to recover quickly from losses caused by hard winters.

Nationally, the CBC index has shown a slight upward trend after the cold winters of the 1960s but periodic cold spells have often caused temporary declines (especially so in 1979). Over the 20 years between the two atlases the national CBC index for woodlands increased by over 50%. The old and new atlas distributions for Hertfordshire show a small but significant increase which could not be readily accounted for solely by increased fieldwork effort. It is likely that there has been a significant increase in the population numbers in the county during the survey period.

In the old atlas Treecreepers were associated with broad-leaved and mixed woodlands and parklands. In the new atlas coniferous woodland and built-up areas have been added to the list – perhaps reflecting the increase and spread of the species to habitats other than its preferred woodlands.

JNT

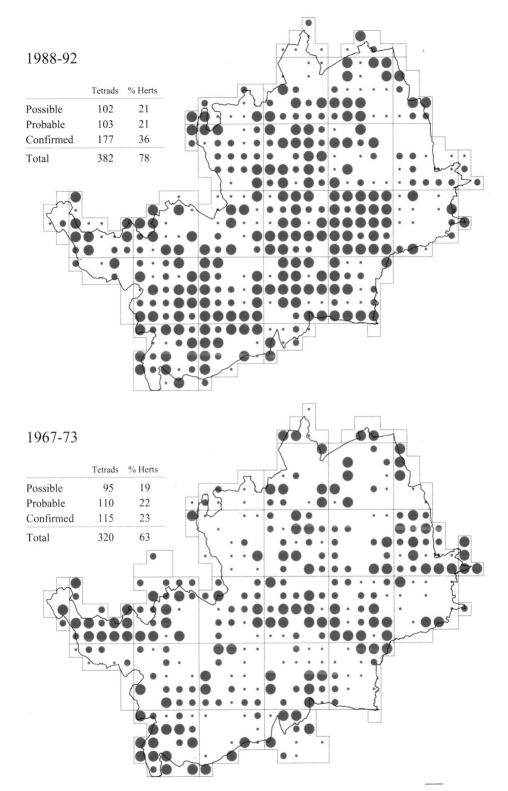

1988-92

	Tetrads	% Herts
Possible	102	21
Probable	103	21
Confirmed	177	36
Total	382	78

1967-73

	Tetrads	% Herts
Possible	95	19
Probable	110	22
Confirmed	115	23
Total	320	63

Jay

Garrulus glandarius

National population 160,000 territories,
Hertfordshire 1100-2000 territories,
static.

The Jay is amongst the most spectacular
of our woodland birds with its pinkish
brown body and flashes of blue and white
on the wing. In the 1880s the attractive
blue wing feathers were collected during
an annual shoot in Oxhey Woods,
Watford and sold in Scotland for the
manufacture of salmon flies. Apart from
autumn and early winter, when it may be
seen in open woodlands feeding on the
ground on acorns, it is most frequently
detected by its raucous call. A white
rump disappearing into deep cover is
often all that is seen. Jays, which in Britain rarely move more than ten kilometres, are
found throughout England, Wales, south-west Scotland and much of Ireland, with an
isolated population north of the Forth-Clyde valleys.

Jays prefer to breed in open deciduous woodlands with a thick shrub layer, especially
those containing oaks, but they do breed at lower densities in conifer plantations. They
play an important role in the dispersal of acorns. In autumn they bury thousands of
acorns for consumption later in the winter but many are overlooked and germinate, thus
spreading oak woods. The single brood of two to four young is fed principally on
caterpillars and beetles. Nests are placed three to six metres high, in tree forks, on
horizontal boughs and in well established ivy. In recent years Jays have colonised
suburban areas with large gardens. With its rather shy habits, breeding is often difficult
to prove as nests are built in thick cover and incubating birds sit very tight. Nests can be
located by cold searching but family groups offer the easiest proof of breeding.

Although the least widely distributed of our crows, it is only slightly less widespread
than the Rook, with 80% of tetrads occupied – an increase from 70% in the old atlas. The
maps show the increase to be by in-filling previous gaps rather than an increase in range.
Although the total number of records has increased, the numbers of tetrads in which
breeding was confirmed or probable have decreased slightly between the two atlases,
perhaps indicating the presence of wandering non-breeding birds.

The population appears to have been little affected by severe winters and has shown
a very substantial increase throughout the 20th century. The doubling of the population
in TL21 and TL31 between 1956 and 1980 was attributed to the extensive re-afforesta-
tion during these years (Gladwin 1983). The national CBC index for woodland indicates
an increase since the old atlas period which may still be continuing. In addition to
increased habitat availability, it is likely that Jays continue to benefit from reduced
levels of persecution nowadays.

In both atlases the Jay was associated with all types of woodland and parkland but in
the new atlas was also significantly associated with built-up areas, a trend that is
apparent for many woodland birds. JM

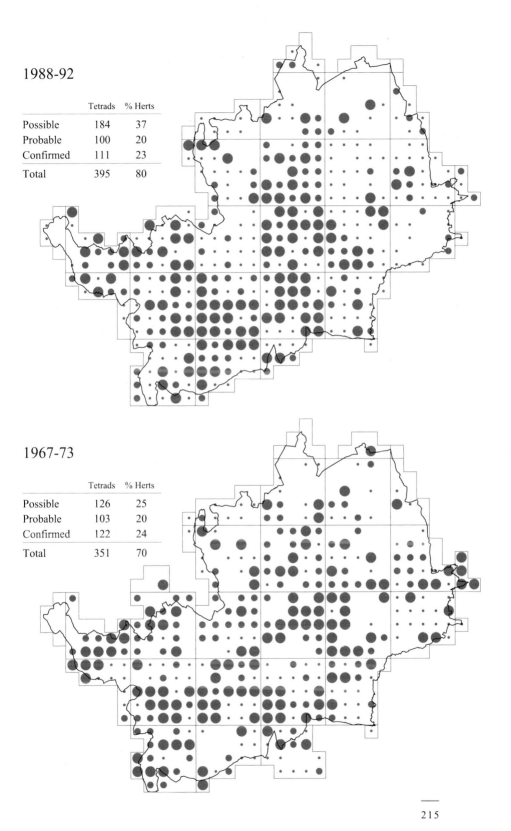

1988-92

	Tetrads	% Herts
Possible	184	37
Probable	100	20
Confirmed	111	23
Total	395	80

1967-73

	Tetrads	% Herts
Possible	126	25
Probable	103	20
Confirmed	122	24
Total	351	70

Magpie

Pica pica

National population 590,000 territories, Hertfordshire 7700-15,000 territories, rapidly increasing.

The Magpie, with its iridescent black and white plumage and its long, diamond-shaped tail, is the most conspicuous and noisy of our crows. Magpies are essentially ground feeders; mainly on insects but other animal items, including carrion, together with some vegetable matter, are taken (Birkhead 1991).

Magpies are single brooded with a typical clutch of five or six eggs. Laying begins in late March or early April, but some pairs start nest building in late December and early January. With its large domed nest in hedgerows and isolated trees, attempted breeding is easily detected as the nest is clearly visible both before the foliage develops and after the leaf fall. Fledged young are also obvious, especially when foraging in family groups on roadsides in the early morning. Magpies occur in all habitats, having invaded suburban and industrial areas from the 1940s, and now breed at higher densities in some cities than in rural areas.

The Magpie's habit of depredating the nests of garden songbirds has made it infamous and in some cases it has been accused of wiping out our songbird populations. Although it is clear that such predation is common and all too visible, there is still insufficient evidence that it is adversely affecting songbird populations on a wide scale (Gooch *et al* 1991).

Magpies were present in all but two tetrads, making it one of our most widespread species, with breeding confirmed in more than 80% of tetrads. Tetrads with no evidence of breeding in the north and east reflect a genuine absence of breeding there, but failure to prove breeding in some parts of the south and west is more surprising.

Magpies have shown a spectacular increase in distribution this century from being very rare between 1880 and 1910. In 1902 they were 'a thing of the past in most parts of Hertfordshire' (Crossman 1902) and were still a noteworthy bird in Hertfordshire in the 1940s. Even in the mid-1950s, Magpies were scarce in many areas of the county. Gladwin & Sage (1986) reported increases of between 400 and 500% between 1956 and 1980, with Ashwell not colonised until 1980. This increase has been attributed to the reduction in gamekeeper pressure but road traffic increases, resulting in improved carrion food supply, may also be a contributory factor.

The national CBC shows an increase in the farmland index since the period of the old atlas and a dramatic increase in the woodland index now appears to be levelling off. Magpies have spread into a variety of habitats. In the first atlas there were positive associations with woodland and parkland but, given the spread of the bird, this is no longer the case. Arable habitats were also avoided in the first atlas and pasture preferred but neither of these is now the case.   JM

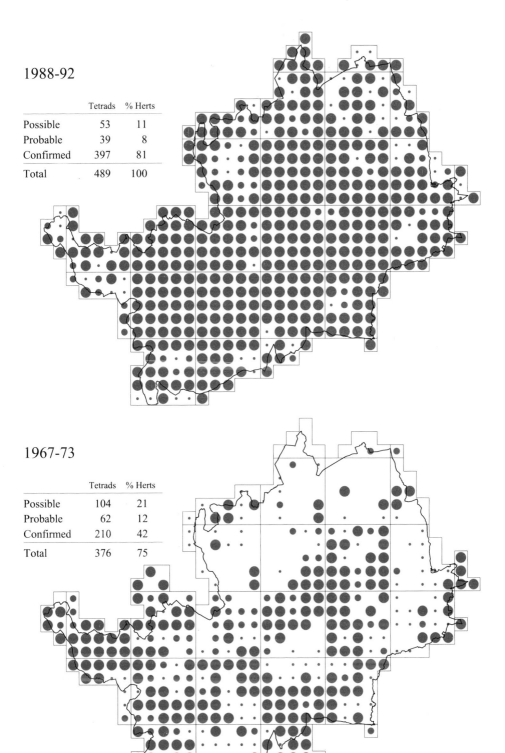

1988-92

	Tetrads	% Herts
Possible	53	11
Probable	39	8
Confirmed	397	81
Total	489	100

1967-73

	Tetrads	% Herts
Possible	104	21
Probable	62	12
Confirmed	210	42
Total	376	75

Jackdaw

Corvus monedula

National population 390,000 territories,
Hertfordshire 2000 territories, stable.

Our smallest common crow is recognised by its grey nape and bright eye, its distinctive call and its jaunty walk. Jackdaws nest in chimneys and other holes in all types of buildings and old trees. Some sites are used successively for many years. The importance of buildings as nest sites means that Jackdaws are a characteristic breeding bird of town and village where they have access to good feeding on playing fields and pasture. Nests are sometimes isolated but are usually in small colonies. In contrast to the Rook, the Jackdaw is less specialised, feeding mainly from the soil surface on the larvae of moths, butterflies and flies as well as spiders, seeds and cereal grains. They also take defoliating caterpillars in May and a wide range of animal items and some vegetable matter. Jackdaws are widespread in Britain and Ireland except for much of north-west Scotland.

Jackdaws are often seen sitting near prospective nest sites before breeding. They are single brooded with a typical clutch of four to six eggs that are not laid before the second half of April. Breeding birds can be seen entering or leaving nest sites, and after fledging dependent young can be identified by their less contrasting nape and duller eye.

The results of the new and old atlases are very similar with the greatest concentration of proved breeding in the centre of Hertfordshire. There has been a small decrease in the numbers of tetrads with proved or probable breeding which, in view of the improved coverage in the new atlas, is highly significant.

The national CBC index for farmland shows a substantial increase from the late 1960s up to 1982 of well over 100% but has subsequently levelled off. The population in TL21 and TL31 was reported to have increased between 1956 and 1980 (Gladwin 1983).

The habitat associations of the Jackdaw are difficult to explain. In the old atlas they were positive for woodland, parkland, barley, oats, grasslands and cattle. This seemed sensible in relation to the bird's nesting and feeding requirements. However the bird now seems to have lost virtually all of these associations which is, to say the least, intriguing.

JM

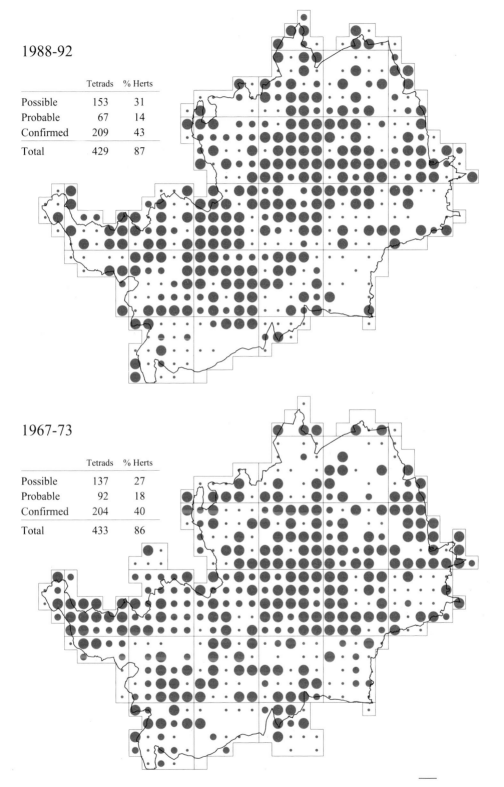

1988-92

	Tetrads	% Herts
Possible	153	31
Probable	67	14
Confirmed	209	43
Total	429	87

1967-73

	Tetrads	% Herts
Possible	137	27
Probable	92	18
Confirmed	204	40
Total	433	86

Rook

Corvus frugilegus

National population 853,000-857,000 pairs, Hertfordshire 7500-10,000 nests, probably declining.

The glossy black Rook is a characteristic bird of mixed farmland and is easily recognised by its white face and feathering around the upper legs, which gives it 'shaggy trousers'. The familiar calls at rookeries in villages and around farmsteads are one of the first sounds of spring. Rooks have a varied diet, feeding on cereal grain, earthworms and other invertebrates. Until at least the late 1950s many rookeries were shot during May with records of up to 600 young birds killed at Ashwell, with doubtless many ending up in Rook pie.

Nest building, usually at traditional sites, starts in late February with colonies ranging in size from two or three nests up to several hundred. The typical clutch is four to six eggs which are laid in March or April. The colonial habit, with nests in the outer branches of tall trees, means that colonies in deciduous trees can be easily detected before the foliage develops. However, it is possible that colonies in conifers or isolated single nests were overlooked. It is also probable that fledged young were reported from tetrads away from the nest site.

Rooks were present in over 80% of tetrads but breeding was confirmed in only half of these. In the old atlas almost exactly the same number of tetrads were occupied but 75% of these held breeding birds. This indicates a significant contraction in breeding range of around one third. The overall figure disguises great variation with decreases concentrated in the south and centre of the county.

There have been regular national surveys of breeding Rooks, the last complete one being in 1975 with a sample census in 1980 (Sage & Whittington 1985). In Hertfordshire there were 10,708 nests in 1971 which by 1975 had decreased to 8685. There were no counts during the atlas period but a county survey was completed in 1993 and the results will be published in the Hertfordshire Bird Report. Although the reasons for these population changes are obscure, modern farming has probably reduced food availability with a move away from mixed farming systems.

In spite of building their nests in trees, Rooks showed little association with woodland in either atlas. Their main associations were with cereals (wheat, barley, oats), field beans and fallow land. Surprisingly, grasslands did not feature in spite of detailed work indicating that Rooks need a mixture of cereals and grassland in which to forage (Brenchley 1984).

JM

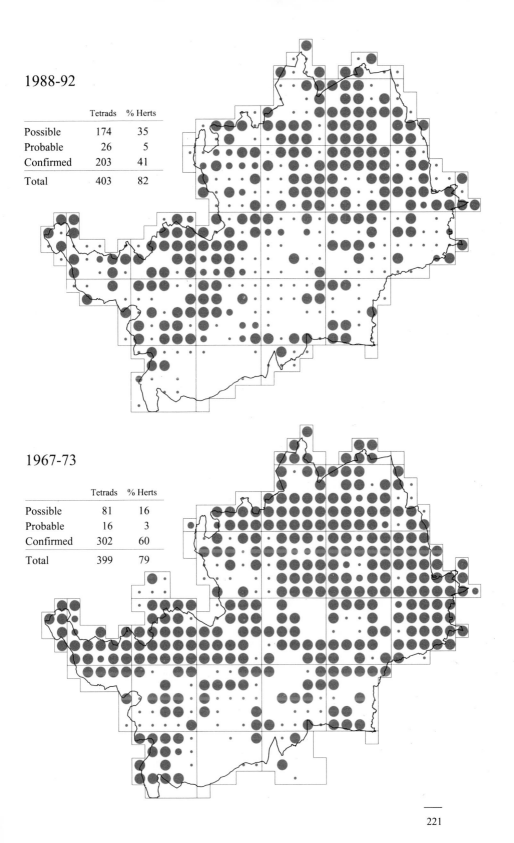

1988-92

	Tetrads	% Herts
Possible	174	35
Probable	26	5
Confirmed	203	41
Total	403	82

1967-73

	Tetrads	% Herts
Possible	81	16
Probable	16	3
Confirmed	302	60
Total	399	79

Carrion Crow

Corvus corone

National population 790,000 territories, Hertfordshire 5200 territories, increasing.

The all black Carrion Crow, which is easily recognised by its distinctive croaking call, feeds on a wide range of animal and vegetable food and, as its name suggests, partly on carrion. Together with the conspecific Hooded Crow, it is the second most widespread species in Britain and Ireland (after the Skylark), breeding in all types of open country including woodland and urban environments with trees.

Carrion Crows are single brooded with typically four to six eggs laid in April or May in nests built in a range of sites from isolated hedgerow trees to dense woodland. Some nests are well hidden in ivy covered trees. Old nests may be used, sometimes later in the same season, by Hobbies and Kestrels. In isolated trees, nests, usually in a fork, are obvious early in the year but it is not always easy to confirm the status of the breeding attempt. The most frequent way in which breeding was confirmed was by the sight of recently fledged young in family groups.

Carrion Crows were found in 99% of tetrads and proved to breed in 64%. Both figures were up slightly on the 95% and 53% in the old atlas. Increases in confirmed breeding in central Hertfordshire were offset by losses in the extreme west and in parts of the east.

Because of intense persecution by gamekeepers, Carrion Crows were a rare bird in Hertfordshire and elsewhere at the end of the 19th century. Since the First World War, and especially since 1940, there has been an increase over the whole of the British range as a result of a relaxation of persecution pressure. Carrion Crows were not common breeding birds in the Bishop's Stortford area in the early 1950s and were still comparatively scarce in Ashwell, Stevenage and Baldock in the mid-1950s. They were apparently unaffected by the use of organochlorine pesticides in the 1950s and early 1960s. National farmland and woodland CBC indices have almost trebled in the period since the old atlas though the increase may not have begun until 1970-72 in eastern England. Locally, the population in TL21 and TL31 was said to have trebled between 1956 and 1980 (Gladwin 1983). Because virtually all tetrads were occupied in both atlases, it would not have been possible to record an increase of this magnitude in the new survey.

In the old atlas Carrion Crows were associated with woodlands, grasslands, cattle and sheep. Twenty years later, in the new atlas, they were associated with parklands and built-up areas and the grassland associations had gone entirely. It is interesting to speculate whether this change is related to a reduction in levels of persecution allowing the birds to occupy a wider range of habitat types.

JM

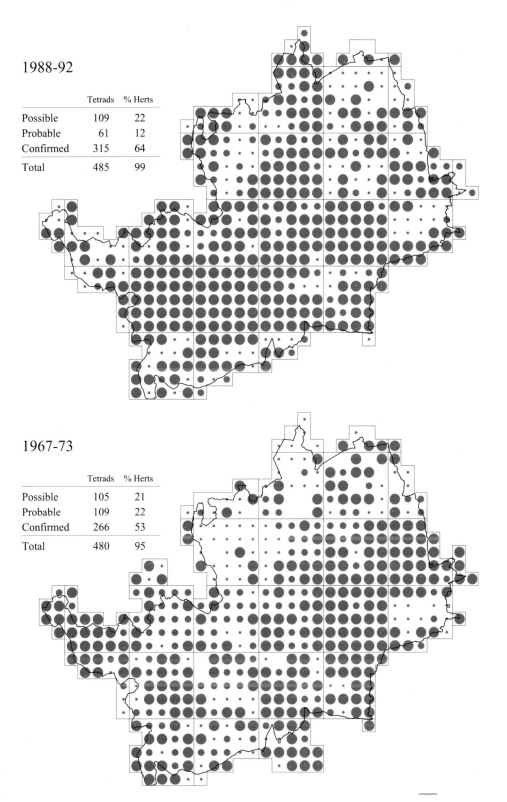

1988-92

	Tetrads	% Herts
Possible	109	22
Probable	61	12
Confirmed	315	64
Total	485	99

1967-73

	Tetrads	% Herts
Possible	105	21
Probable	109	22
Confirmed	266	53
Total	480	95

Starling

Sturnus vulgaris

National population 1.1 million territories, Hertfordshire 13,000-25,000 territories, declining.

The Starling is a common and conspicuous bird throughout the country. A lone male on a late spring afternoon proclaiming ownership of a nearby nest site uses a repertoire of mimicry second to none, ranging from a favourite wader to practically any other species. These natural sounds may be interspersed with hoots, whistles or metallic noises good enough to deceive the human ear.

Starlings sometimes breed semi-colonially with nests placed in cavities, lined with straw or grasses and feathers. Holes and crevices of all kinds are used: in walls and roofs of houses, factories or farm buildings, frequently between the beams in concrete and asbestos cement structures. In woodlands, nests are often in old woodpecker holes and, when Starling numbers are high, there can be competition between them and woodpeckers for nest sites. Censusing is fairly easy as adults returning from foraging trips fly direct to the nest and noisy young confirm breeding. Fledging of the young is synchronised to mid-May, the juveniles then noisily follow the parents to feeding areas, which can be some distance from the nest and often in woodlands where they feed on caterpillars.

In rural areas grazed livestock pastures or recently mown fields are favoured feeding sites as are the grass of parks, golf courses and wide roadside verges in urban areas. Soil invertebrates, primarily leather jackets, are the principal food. Research in Holland showed that a pair fed their brood from 118 to 255 times a day, bringing between 16,000-27,000 items of which leather jackets were 14-26% (Simms 1971).

Although still recorded in every tetrad in Hertfordshire, the Starling has undoubtedly declined in numbers since the old atlas. A similar well documented decline has occurred all over northern Europe (Feare 1984) and this is evident in Hertfordshire from the reduced wintering population. Counts recorded in the mid 1970s of as many as a million roosting birds are now unheard of, with the largest numbers in recent years in the order of 50,000.

The exact reason for the Europe-wide decline is not clear and there are probably different reasons from place to place. Agricultural and climatic changes no doubt have a part to play. In Hertfordshire the loss of permanent grassland, the move to rotational leys and the reduction of livestock numbers are all likely to have had an adverse effect on Starling numbers. Unfortunately, as Starlings are present in all tetrads the analysis of habitat associations in this atlas could not provide any useful insights. JHT

1988-92

	Tetrads	% Herts
Possible	3	1
Probable	4	1
Confirmed	484	99
Total	491	100

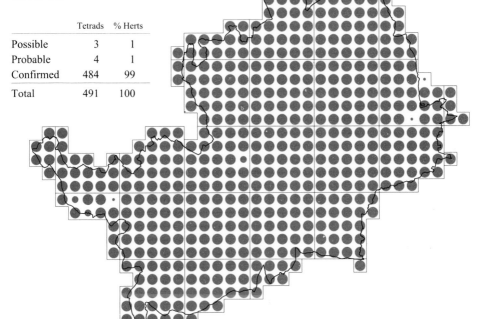

1967-73

	Tetrads	% Herts
Possible	24	5
Probable	12	2
Confirmed	468	93
Total	504	100

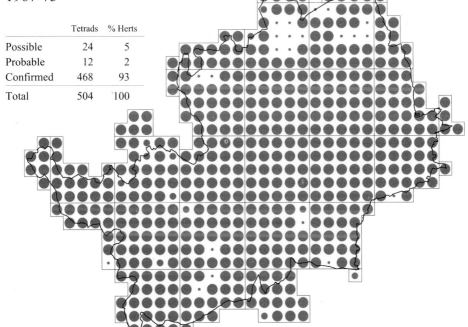

House Sparrow

Passer domesticus

National population 2.6-4.6 million pairs, Hertfordshire 27,000 pairs, declining.

Because of its close association with man, the House Sparrow requires very little introduction; it is the small brownish bird seen almost everywhere and is probably familiar to everyone over the age of five. The female is a drab looking bird, but the male can be told by its grey crown and black bib.

Found in small social groups, it is usually present anywhere there is human habitation, from farmyards to busy city centres. As a colonial nester the House Sparrow is rarely seen on its own. In rural areas it forms noisy parties, chirping loudly and flitting backwards and forwards between a food source and some form of cover, such as a hedge or low bush. It is a favourite prey of the Sparrowhawk, which will pop over a hedge to make a surprise attack on such a group or crash around in the hedge in the hope of intimidating an unfortunate House Sparrow to break cover.

The nest is placed in a hole or crevice of a building, often under loose tiles or even behind creepers, and occasionally in nest boxes. The nest itself is an untidy collection of grasses, hay, straw and string and is lined with feathers. The eggs are normally incubated by the female for about two weeks. Although the male has no brood patch he will, for short periods while the female is away, keep the eggs from cooling. The young fledge about two weeks after hatching. Because of the House Sparrow's close association with man, proof of breeding is relatively easy to obtain, especially whilst the parents are feeding their offspring. The long breeding season, which lasts from March to September, during which up to three broods are raised, gives the observer an extended period in which to obtain results.

In the old atlas, more than 99% of the tetrads were occupied with proof of breeding in 92%. This compares with the new atlas in which 100% of tetrads were occupied, with proof of breeding in 93%. As the House Sparrow is so ubiquitous it is not possible from the tetrad data to assess the change in total population in the county over the last twenty years. Summers-Smith (1988) suggested that the dispersion of suburban populations of House Sparrows is maintaining the rural populations which are thought to be in decline due to changes in modern agricultural practices. Nationally the CBC index has fallen during the 1980s.

With virtually all tetrads occupied, it is not surprising that no significant habitat associations were found in either atlas.   DM

1988-92

	Tetrads	% Herts
Possible	14	3
Probable	22	4
Confirmed	455	93
Total	491	100

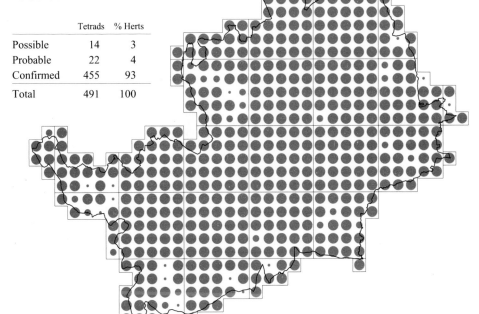

1967-73

	Tetrads	% Herts
Possible	24	5
Probable	12	2
Confirmed	466	92
Total	502	100

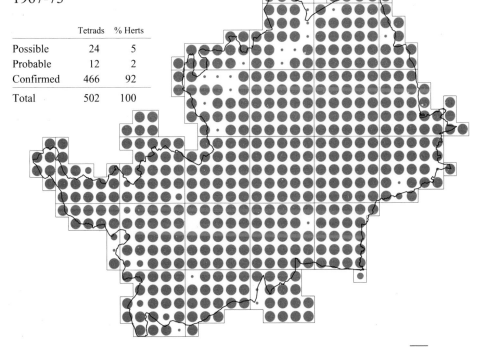

Tree Sparrow

Passer montanus

National population 110,000 territories, Hertfordshire 320 territories, dramatically declining.

The Tree Sparrow is somewhat similar in appearance to the male House Sparrow and indeed can sometimes be overlooked in winter when it may occur in mixed sparrow flocks. The main distinguishing features are its completely chestnut-brown crown, black spots on the ear coverts and neat, black bib which give it a much cleaner appearance than that of the House Sparrow. Unlike that species, the sexes are similar. Found during the breeding season in parks, orchards and open woodlands, especially areas with old trees, attention is often first drawn to a Tree Sparrow's nesting site by the metallic 'chip chip' of the male as he stands guard close to the nest hole. Proof of breeding is relatively simple to obtain once the male has been located.

The nest is usually built in a hole in a tree, a crevice of a building or even loosely in the branches of a bush; nest boxes are also readily used. The untidy construction is made of straw or hay and lined with an abundance of feathers. Eggs are incubated by both adults for about two weeks and the chicks, which are also fed by both adults, take about a further 14 days to fledge. The species is multi-brooded, raising up to three broods in a season. Tree Sparrows are normally colonial in their nesting habits, however, since their decline it is now more usual to find only one or two nests at a site.

In the old atlas the Tree Sparrow was widespread in the county with 88% of the tetrads occupied. Over the last 20 years the distribution has been massively reduced and now only 35% of the tetrads are occupied. A similar decline has been noted nationally with the CBC index now around a third of its 1970 level. The reasons for the collapse are not clear. There have previously been several long-term fluctuations of populations and Summers-Smith (1989) proposed that the upsurge of the British population in the 1960s was due to irruptions from the continent following high populations there, with the British numbers falling when immigration was over. It is also probable that changes in agricultural practices in Britain have had adverse effects on Tree Sparrows.

When the old atlas was published in 1982 the Tree Sparrow was already starting to decline. This trend has definitely gained momentum and the large nesting colonies once seen are no longer found in the county. At Rye Meads the breeding population of around 50 pairs in the early 1970s had become extinct by 1985 (Leader & Melling 1989).

The habitat associations are confused. In the old atlas there were positive associations for woodland, wheat, oats, field beans, clover leys and cattle. With the contraction of range in the new atlas, these associations have become weaker and changed to oats, oilseed rape, fallow, cattle and sheep. It is difficult to relate the changes in Tree Sparrow numbers to any of these, although both the area of oats and the number of cattle have decreased between the two atlases. DM

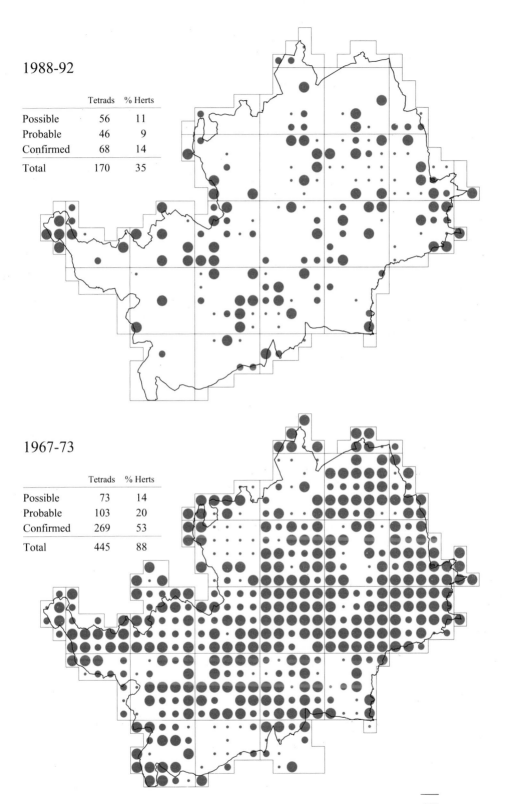

1988-92

	Tetrads	% Herts
Possible	56	11
Probable	46	9
Confirmed	68	14
Total	170	35

1967-73

	Tetrads	% Herts
Possible	73	14
Probable	103	20
Confirmed	269	53
Total	445	88

Chaffinch

Fringilla coelebs

National population 5.4 million territories, Hertfordshire 27,000-51,000 territories, stable or increasing.

Chaffinches are one of only ten species recorded in every tetrad in Hertfordshire. Even in the atypical urban and industrial areas, Chaffinches do occur at low densities. The familiar colourful male is invariably accompanied by the drabber female and pairs are regularly seen feeding in close company prior to breeding. Although a common bird of parks and suburban gardens, the highest concentrations are to be found in mature broad-leaved woodland and open farmland. The bird's song, with its exuberant flourish at the end, is well known but, in fact, does vary slightly between birds and locations. The Hertfordshire population is greatly increased in winter by the influx of large numbers of birds from the continent which stay until late March or April.

The nest is usually built by the female and is made from lichen and moss, lined with wool, hair or feathers. It has a characteristic cup shape and is placed in a bush, hedge or tree-fork and is well camouflaged, often making it difficult to find. Incubation, lasting 12-14 days, is solely by the female and the young, fed on a protein-rich diet of insects, aphids and caterpillars, fly after 12-15 days. There is a fairly long period of post fledging care so second broods are the exception rather than the rule and probably occur only after loss of nest or young (Newton 1972).

Although the nests are not easy to locate, the birds themselves, with their distinctive call and song, are very evident. Parents gathering food for nestlings are also not difficult to spot later in the season and this has led to the high numbers of confirmed breeding records.

The distribution of this ubiquitous and abundant breeding bird appears to have increased between the two atlas periods and is now at least a probable breeding species in almost every tetrad. The national CBC indices indicate that there may be periodic minor decreases after particularly hard winters but in general there has been a steady increase since the 1960s with around a 20-30% increase since the last atlas.

In the old atlas there were weak positive associations with woodland and built-up areas, but with the increased distribution it is not surprising that these have disappeared in the new atlas.

EWF

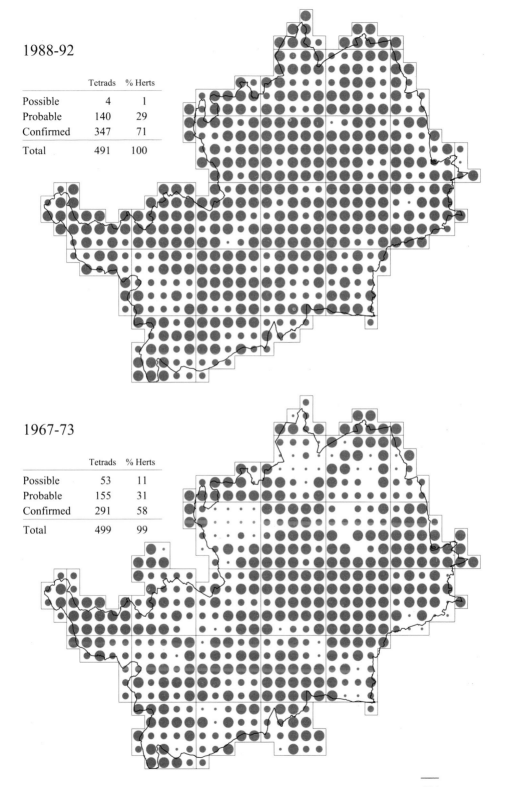

1988-92

	Tetrads	% Herts
Possible	4	1
Probable	140	29
Confirmed	347	71
Total	491	100

1967-73

	Tetrads	% Herts
Possible	53	11
Probable	155	31
Confirmed	291	58
Total	499	99

Greenfinch

Carduelis chloris

*National population 530,000 territories,
Hertfordshire 5800-15,000 territories, increasing.*

A slight misnomer, being basically green
but with conspicuous yellow patches on
the wings and tail, noticed especially in
flight, Greenfinches have become so ac-
customed to association with man that
they are now rarely found far from human settlement. Even in the more rural
areas they will tend to favour mature
gardens and are attracted particularly to
the evergreen shrubs in vicarages and
churchyards. They have thrived on the
increasing habit of people providing sup-
plies of bird food in gardens in winter; so
much so that their aggressive behaviour towards other finches and tits is beginning to
earn them a bad name. In winter, they readily form single species flocks, or join other
species of finches and buntings, to feed on stubble or waste land. Aggregations of
several hundred are not unusual. If disturbed, a feeding flock explodes with a sudden
whirring of wings and disappears in a bobbing flight.

Greenfinches are sociable birds and breed in loose colonies with nests in adjacent
bushes or even in the same bush if it is sufficiently large. Most nests are between 1.5 and
5 metres above ground level, in suburban gardens and farmland hedgerows, especially
where there are thorn or evergreen shrubs. The nest, built chiefly by the female, is a
bulky cup of twigs, plant stems and moss, lined with rootlets, hair and feathers.
Incubation is by the female only and the four to six eggs hatch after two weeks. The
young are fed on regurgitated food by both parents and fly after 12-15 days. A second
brood is common and a third is sometimes raised in favourable conditions.

Fieldworkers found no difficulty in locating Greenfinches throughout the county.
Males exhibit a variety of display flights, including a weaving song flight between
treetops or across clearings, with exaggerated slow and deep wing beats. The bulky nest
is fairly easy to find, more so if a colony has been formed, and the parents can be fairly
readily watched back, so the proportion of confirmed breeding records was relatively
high.

There was a small, but not significant, increase in the distribution of this already very
widespread bird. This echoes the findings of the national CBC which has been stable
since the 1970s. There has, however, been some redistribution with more records in the
north-west of the county. Oilseed rape is exploited in late summer and autumn as are
cereal grains. By feeding in gardens, Greenfinches appear to have found an alternative
winter food source to the traditional stubble fields.

Given that Greenfinches were found in virtually every tetrad, it is not surprising that
no significant habitat associations were found. EWF

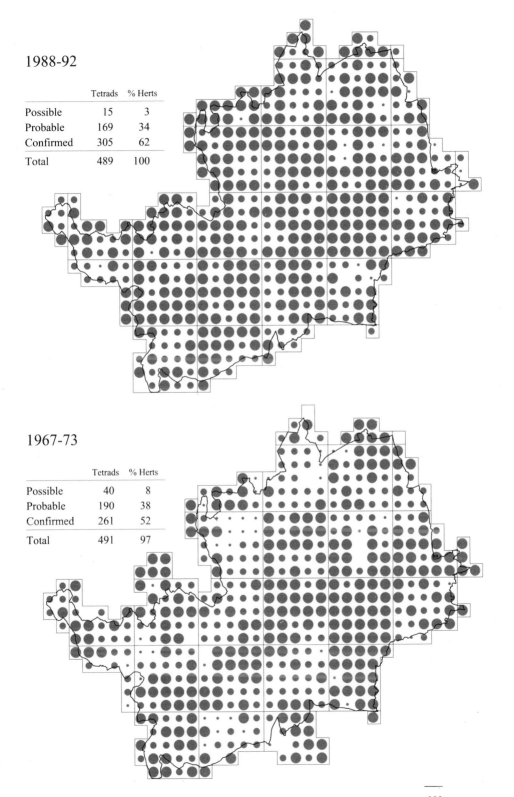

1988-92

	Tetrads	% Herts
Possible	15	3
Probable	169	34
Confirmed	305	62
Total	489	100

1967-73

	Tetrads	% Herts
Possible	40	8
Probable	190	38
Confirmed	261	52
Total	491	97

Goldfinch

Carduelis carduelis

*National population 220,000 territories, Hertfordshire 2000
territories, slight decline.*

The Goldfinch is a small, brightly coloured finch commonly
found in country areas. It is particularly fond of areas of scrub
where its characteristic twittering flight calls are an aid to
location and identification. The light and undulating flight is
typical of small finches. It feeds on or near the ground on
thistles and other compositae, flitting from plant to plant and
feeding 'tit like' on the actual seed heads, extracting the seeds
with its bill which is rather long and thin for a finch. In winter
the Goldfinch can often be found in small flocks feeding on
alder and birch. Small feeding flocks of adults and young are
commonly seen in late summer.

During the breeding season, it is a bird of large gardens,
orchards and open cultivated land with scattered trees and
hedgerows. The nest is generally built higher than those of
other finches, up to 15 metres from the ground. It is particularly
fond of chestnut and fruit trees. The nest is neatly built by the
female using moss and roots, interwoven with wool. She lays
between five and six eggs and incubates them alone for about
12-13 days. The young are fed by both parents and fly when
about 14 days old. There are normally two or three broods per
season.

During the breeding season, its pleasing, liquid song, which
is an elaboration of the call note, makes the Goldfinch an easy
bird to detect. It can be heard between mid-March and mid-
July.

Goldfinches are widely distributed throughout Hertfordshire, being found in more than 90% of tetrads in both atlases.
Overall, there has been a small but significant decrease in the distribution. This is in
accordance with Gladwin & Sage (1986) who reported that the Goldfinch was only a
little less numerous in 1982 than 25 years previously.

However, the overall picture masks distributional changes. The distribution has
declined in the eastern arable half of the county but increased in the central areas.
Gladwin (1983) suggested that a decline in rural areas due, amongst other factors, to a
change in agricultural practices such as the control of weeds, may have been compensated by increases in new urban areas as gardens and trees matured. There is evidence to
suggest that this has, in fact, occurred since some of the tetrads in which the Goldfinch
has increased are those in urban areas.

The habitat associations also support this hypothesis. In the old atlas Goldfinches
were positively associated with wheat, oats and clover leys. Twenty years later the
positive associations were for built-up areas, parkland and rivers and, amazingly, the
association with wheat had become a negative one.   RD & JM

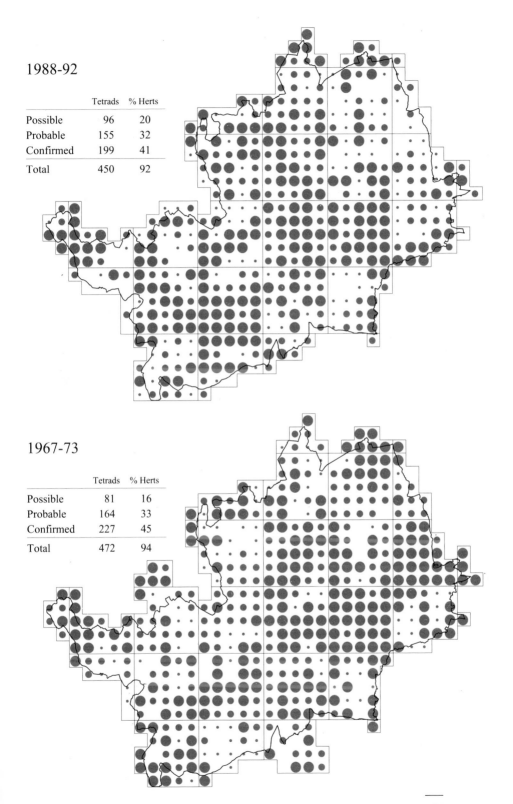

1988-92

	Tetrads	% Herts
Possible	96	20
Probable	155	32
Confirmed	199	41
Total	450	92

1967-73

	Tetrads	% Herts
Possible	81	16
Probable	164	33
Confirmed	227	45
Total	472	94

Siskin

Carduelis spinus

*National population 300,000 pairs, Hert-
fordshire 0-3 pairs, static.*

This attractive and confiding little finch
is familiar to most birdwatchers in Hertfordshire as a regular visitor to garden
bird feeders, particularly in late winter.
The Siskin's well known preference for
peanuts offered in red feeders is much
alluded to in popular garden bird books.

Primarily a bird of the northern spruce
forests, the Siskin feeds on the seeds of
spruce, larch, birch, alder and other trees.
It is currently undergoing a major expansion of its range and breeding populations
have grown in Britain following increases
in the area of coniferous woodlands, prin-
cipally in the uplands, where the birds now breed in large numbers. Siskins were always
known as breeding birds of the Scottish highlands (Thom 1986) but, starting around
1950, as conifers planted during the previous two decades became sufficiently mature to
bear cones, they expanded their breeding distribution. They have now spread southwards through Galloway, the northern Pennines, the Lake District, the Peak District and
Wales to reach the Norfolk Brecklands, the New Forest and Devon. There is also a
scattering of breeding records spread throughout other southern counties.

In spite of the increase in wintering numbers in the county, there appears to be little
evidence of an increase in breeding over the last twenty years. Reports of breeding birds
are still few and far between. The confirmed breeding record in the old atlas in fact
referred to two males singing in Bramfield Forest in May and June. Despite thorough
investigations by several observers no further evidence of breeding was obtained, so the
record should be demoted to probable breeding. In 1982 breeding was confirmed when
a pair reared four young near Hemel Hempstead. In 1987 newly fledged young were
seen on 14 June in Sherrardspark Wood. The confirmed breeding record during the new
atlas period was a sighting of recently fledged young being attended by adult birds in a
garden at Ringshall, close to suitable breeding habitat.

In the new atlas there were eight records of birds being present in the breeding season.
These were probably birds remaining from winter flocks which in any case do not
normally leave until March or early April. There is no evidence that they resulted in
breeding in the county.

Given its readiness to come into suburban gardens, the Siskin will continue to be a
most welcome part of the county's avifauna. However, because of the limited extent of
available breeding habitat, it is only likely to breed in small numbers and then probably
only irregularly.   JET

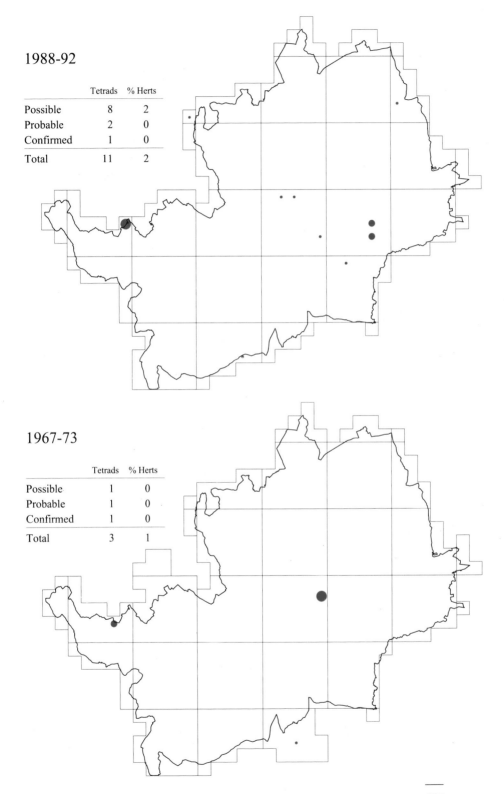

1988-92

	Tetrads	% Herts
Possible	8	2
Probable	2	0
Confirmed	1	0
Total	11	2

1967-73

	Tetrads	% Herts
Possible	1	0
Probable	1	0
Confirmed	1	0
Total	3	1

Linnet

Carduelis cannabina

National population 520,000 territories, Hertfordshire 2100-6100 territories, decreasing.

Linnets are streaked brownish in colour with forked tails, short broad bills and red patches in their plumage. Cock birds, with their attractive red crown and breast and persistent twittering song were one of Victorian England's favourite cage birds. Linnets breed from just below the arctic circle south to the desert fringes of north-west Africa and the middle east, and winter in the south of their range. A semi-colonial species, they are widespread in Britain and found in open farmland, heaths, downs and coastal flats. They feed exclusively on seeds: chickweed, charlock and other brassicas, persicaria, fat hen, dandelions and thistles are particular favourites.

Linnets breed in small colonies of four to six pairs and are one of the first finches to start nesting in spring. Eggs are laid from mid-April when fresh seeds become available, and breeding can continue until August, giving time for multiple broods. Early in the season nests are sited in gorse and other evergreens and in deciduous bushes once the leaves have opened. The nests of dry grass, moss, twigs and roots are lined with hair or wool. The four to six eggs are incubated by the female alone. From a few days after hatching the young are fed by both parents. They form large post breeding flocks in late summer.

Linnets were recorded in 96% of tetrads in the old atlas and 95% in the new. The striking difference is that 80% of old atlas tetrads had firm evidence of breeding but this had fallen to 76% in the new atlas. This probably indicates a decline in overall numbers across the whole county and reflects the national picture.

Linnets, persecuted last century, recovered in the 1920s and 1930s when arable weeds were abundant during the agricultural doldrums. Latterly the national CBC has shown a steep decline since 1977 and Linnet populations are now at an all time low. This has been attributed (O'Connor & Shrubb 1986) to reduced breeding success linked to food shortages for nestlings. Seeds of arable weeds are now relatively scarce due to modern chemical control. Recent observations have shown Linnets exploiting the increased acreage of oilseed rape and holding territories near rape fields. They take seed as soon as it is set in June and continue to feed until the post-harvest stubble is exhausted. However, no evidence of an association between Linnets and the area of oilseed rape in each tetrad in Hertfordshire is evident. The increased consumption of rape seed does not alleviate the food shortage in the difficult late winter period both here and in France. It will be interesting to see how the latest European community 'set-aside' policy affects the Linnets' fortunes.

In the old atlas Linnets were associated with woodland, oats and permanent grass. In the new atlas the only positive associations were with built-up areas and rivers. LMS

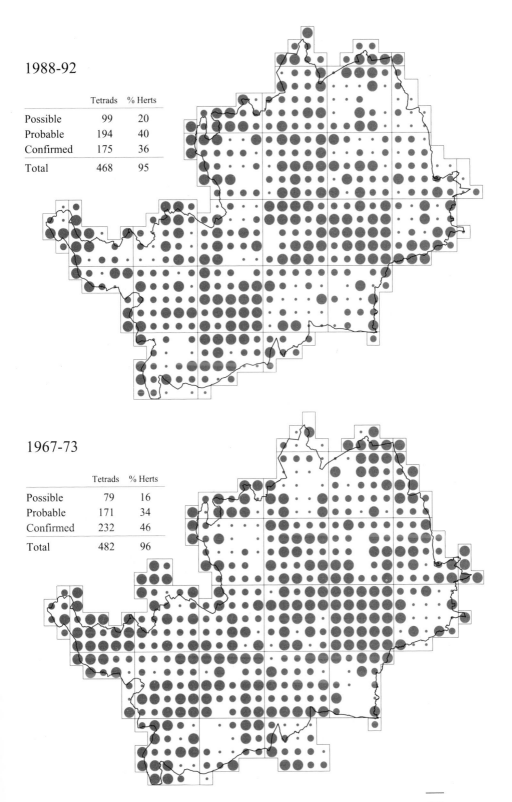

1988-92

	Tetrads	% Herts
Possible	99	20
Probable	194	40
Confirmed	175	36
Total	468	95

1967-73

	Tetrads	% Herts
Possible	79	16
Probable	171	34
Confirmed	232	46
Total	482	96

Redpoll

Carduelis flammea

National population 160,000 pairs, Hertfordshire 74-150 pairs, declining.

Redpolls are lively sociable birds, their presence often first indicated by their distinctive metallic call and bouncy undulating flight. Their red forehead and black chin are distinctive at close range and some males are very colourful in spring with a pink flush to the throat and chest. Redpolls occur mainly in open northern forests around the world and races vary more in size and colour than in most other species. The British race, 'Lesser Redpoll', is on the edge of the world distribution, and is smaller, darker and less variable than Redpolls elsewhere.

They breed mainly in birch scrub and thickets of alder, sallow and hawthorn and in overgrown hedgerows, and are now also exploiting commercial conifer plantations nesting in trees up to six metres high. They often breed in small groups and have a distinctive display flight. Nests are placed two to four metres high in tall bushes and are usually well concealed. Confirmation of breeding is thus most likely from sightings of family parties with newly fledged young.

The main food in spring is flowers and seeds of sallow and insects on conifer buds, followed by weed and grass seeds; from July the mainstay is birch seeds supplemented by alder. The availability of birch seeds also seems to determine how many birds remain in England in winter rather than move to the continent.

Redpoll numbers show significant short and long term fluctuations. They have historically been relatively scarce in the south-east of England, but populations increased in Scotland in the 1930s and spread southwards in the 1950s. They were still largely absent from central southern England at the time of the first breeding atlas. In Hertfordshire, on the eastern edge of this area, increasing populations had been noted in the 1950s and the original atlas map records breeding in the wooded central and eastern areas of the county. Numbers continued to increase through the 1970s , mirroring the national trend, where the population index in 1977 was four times that 10 years earlier. Latterly breeding numbers have declined in England and slumped in Hertfordshire. The new atlas has firm evidence of breeding in only 18% of tetrads compared with 29% previously. The main losses have been in the central band right across the county.

Population fluctuations and density changes are attributed to variations in seed crops and changes in the suitability of conifer plantations as they mature. The long term decline remains unexplained, but probably relates to factors outside Hertfordshire.

In the old atlas Redpolls were positively associated with broad-leaved and mixed woodland. Twenty years later they were just significantly associated with mixed woodlands but strongly associated with built-up areas and rivers. There is a strong negative association with a range of agricultural variables. LMS

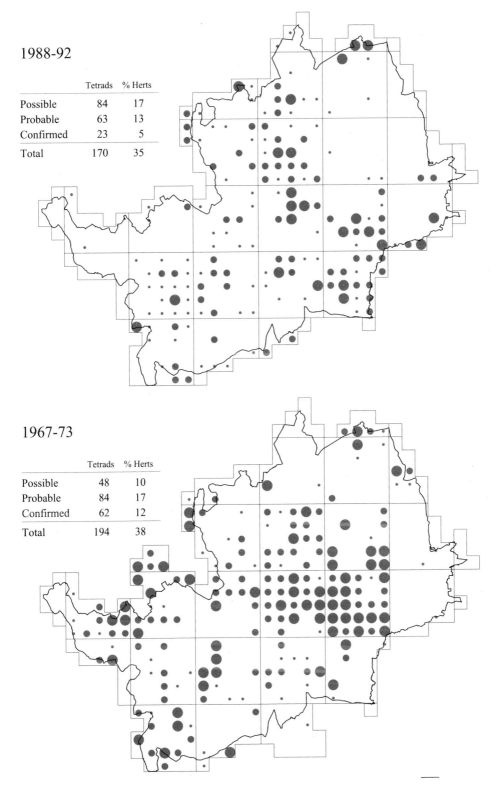

1988-92

	Tetrads	% Herts
Possible	84	17
Probable	63	13
Confirmed	23	5
Total	170	35

1967-73

	Tetrads	% Herts
Possible	48	10
Probable	84	17
Confirmed	62	12
Total	194	38

Crossbill

Loxia curvirostra

National population 500-5000 pairs, Hertfordshire 0-9 pairs, no change.

The Crossbill is a highly specialised, powerful and colourful species of finch. Its curious bill is used to extract the seed from the cones of coniferous trees, particularly spruce. During 'irruption years' huge numbers cross the north sea from Scandinavia. These influxes occur, usually between June and September, when there is limited food supply due to crop failure or during times of over population in the core range. After such irruptions small numbers stay here to breed for a year or two.

Breeding occurs in mature coniferous stands. Activity is timed to utilise fully the ripening of the cone seeds and consequently Crossbills breed very early, typically between January and April. Nests of pine needles interwoven with moss and lichen and lined with softer material are constructed in the tops of high conifers. Three or four eggs are laid with the young being tended for 17 to 21 days prior to leaving the nest.

The spread of coniferous afforestation is widely held to be unhelpful to the majority of bird species. However with the associated increase in suitable habitat, the Crossbill has been able to expand its breeding range and exploit new areas by opportunistic breeding, following irruptions.

The presence of birds is relatively easy to record with individuals often being detected by their loud 'chip chip' flight call or seen when visiting drinking pools and puddles. However, breeding of Crossbills is not easy to establish. They nest largely outside the normal breeding season and potential nesting habitats include extensive areas of tall and often dense conifers, although any patch of conifers may attract the more ambitious birds. Given the number of tetrads in which Crossbill were found it seems possible that breeding occurred in more than one.

The maps give an interesting comparison of the populations over the two atlas periods. Whilst the irruption of 1972 may have occurred too late to influence the original atlas, many of the recent records will relate to birds involved in the huge irruption during 1990 (Nightingale & Allsopp 1991). It is interesting to note that the occurrences overlap in only one tetrad, in which only possible breeding was recorded during both studies.

There is probably no native population of Crossbills in Hertfordshire. Birds were reported to have bred in Bramfield Forest between 1944 and 1975 but there have been no recent records there. Because of the difficulties in obtaining confirmation, breeding may have occurred in any of the 16 tetrads shown on the new map and, given suitable habitat and conditions, small populations may become established. It is clear, however, that much of the breeding resulting from irruptions is short-lived and, without the support of a further influx, the Crossbill may again cease to breed in Hertfordshire. RY

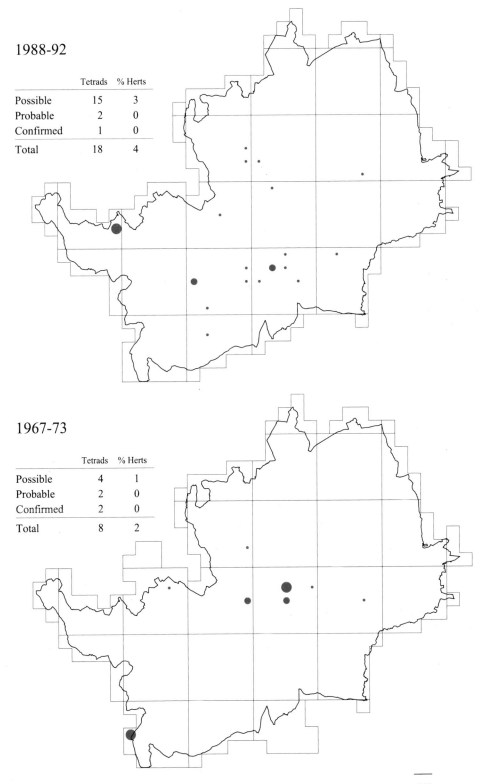

1988-92

	Tetrads	% Herts
Possible	15	3
Probable	2	0
Confirmed	1	0
Total	18	4

1967-73

	Tetrads	% Herts
Possible	4	1
Probable	2	0
Confirmed	2	0
Total	8	2

Bullfinch

Pyrrhula pyrrhula

*National population 190,000 territories,
Hertfordshire 1800 pairs, decreasing.*

Bullfinches are one of the largest and
most handsome finches, although somewhat secretive. They frequent woodland
edge, scrubland and hedgerows. Basically sedentary in Britain, they seldom
join large flocks and are usually found in
pairs or family parties. In winter they
feed on flower and fruit buds and have
for this reason been widely persecuted in
orchards and other fruit growing areas.

They breed in woodland undergrowth,
thickets, hedgerows and shrubberies including those in parks and gardens in
towns. The nest consists of a shallow
base of twigs with an inner cup of rootlets. It is usually placed in thick scrub, one or two
metres above ground. The male leads the female to suitable sites, she builds the nest and
incubates the four or five eggs. Laying starts in early May and breeding can continue
until mid-September. Two clutches are normal, but there can be up to four attempts
depending on the level of predation. Incubation takes 12-14 days and the young fledge
in 15-17 days. They are fed on insects and seeds by both birds and are fully independent
by 35 days.

Although they have conspicuous plumage, Bullfinches can easily be overlooked in
the breeding season. They frequent thick scrub and rarely feed on open ground. Both
birds are quiet and secretive, the soft creaky song carries only a few metres and they
have no display flights. The male only approaches the vicinity of the nest when bringing
food. The difficulty of proving breeding is apparent in the records. The results from both
atlases have presence recorded in over 90% of tetrads but a low percentage with
evidence of breeding.

The Bullfinch is one of a number of birds of agricultural land that has declined in the
last 20 years. In the new atlas, confirmed breeding is concentrated in a band running
from the north-west to the south-east and in the south-west sector. Although birds were
still present in over 90% of tetrads, the number with firm evidence of breeding has
declined markedly since the old atlas. This indicates that although Bullfinches are still
widely distributed the overall population has declined and evidence of breeding is less
likely to be detected. This is consistent with the national picture.

A link between the increasing numbers of Sparrowhawks and the decline of Bullfinches has been suggested. This is not substantiated in Hertfordshire, where the main
losses of Bullfinches are in areas not yet recolonised by Sparrowhawks. The decline is
more likely to be linked to hedgerow and scrub loss and intensive farming which
provides poor conditions for Bullfinches.

In the old atlas Bullfinches were weakly associated with broad-leaved woodlands,
altitude, oats and sheep. The only positive association in the new atlas is with rivers with
negative associations with wheat, field beans, fallow and poultry.   LMS

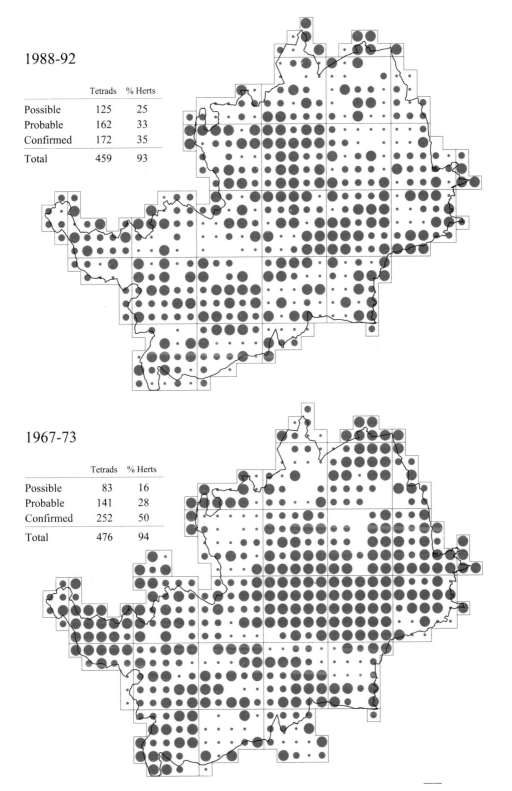

1988-92

	Tetrads	% Herts
Possible	125	25
Probable	162	33
Confirmed	172	35
Total	459	93

1967-73

	Tetrads	% Herts
Possible	83	16
Probable	141	28
Confirmed	252	50
Total	476	94

Hawfinch

Coccothraustes coccothraustes

National population 3000-6500 pairs,
Hertfordshire 43-130 pairs, declining.

The Hawfinch is a large, heavy-billed
bird of mature broad-leaved woodlands
– especially those with good stands of
hornbeam or cherry. Generally it is an
elusive species; easily disturbed, it disappears rapidly into dense canopy before most observers are aware of its presence. Hertfordshire remains one of its
national strongholds and it is regarded
by some as a contender for our 'county
bird'. Split cherry stones, cracked by the
massively powerful bill may be one of
the few signs of birds in the area. In
winter they often form loose flocks and
disperse locally, sometimes visiting mature gardens and orchards. An observer must
become familiar with the explosive 'tzic' contact call before the birds can be easily
located.

The nesting habitats follow two distinct strategies (Mountfort 1956), some breeding
in loose colonies of three to six pairs – often nesting within a few metres of each other
– whilst other pairs remain strictly solitary and strongly defend their nesting area. They
also return to the same area of woodland to breed each year, pairs being formed in late
March. The male usually selects the nest site and lays a twig foundation and the female
completes the task, lining the nest with roots and grasses. The final structure is usually
several metres from the ground and placed in a group of thin branches and can be
mistaken for a small pigeon's nest. The eggs, usually four to five, are laid by late April.
They have a buff, bluish-grey ground colour, covered with irregular spots and blotches
of purple, brown and pale grey. Unusually, the young are fed on a mixture of regurgitated seeds from the crop and large numbers of caterpillars, carried in the beak. Nest-
visiting by the parents is very frequent, every eight minutes on average. It is known that
Hawfinches regularly produce two broods, and sometimes even three (Mountfort 1957).

Finding birds is never easy and obtaining proof of breeding can be very difficult.
Hawfinches do not have a display flight, although an elaborate display takes place at the
nest.

The Hawfinch remains an elusive and enigmatic species and has always been difficult
to monitor. It may be seriously under recorded, given its shy and retiring nature. The
new atlas shows a decline in confirmed breeding, especially to the west and south-west
of the county. This is perhaps surprising given the number of exceptionally warm
summers – a situation which should favour a species with a distinctly continental
distribution. In both atlases the species is associated with all types of woodland but
particularly mature semi-natural. This habitat has not significantly declined in area
during the census intervals and therefore the current changes may indicate subtle
differences in the woodland habitat or that the birds have been overlooked. Given the
improved coverage in the new atlas the latter is not likely.   JNT

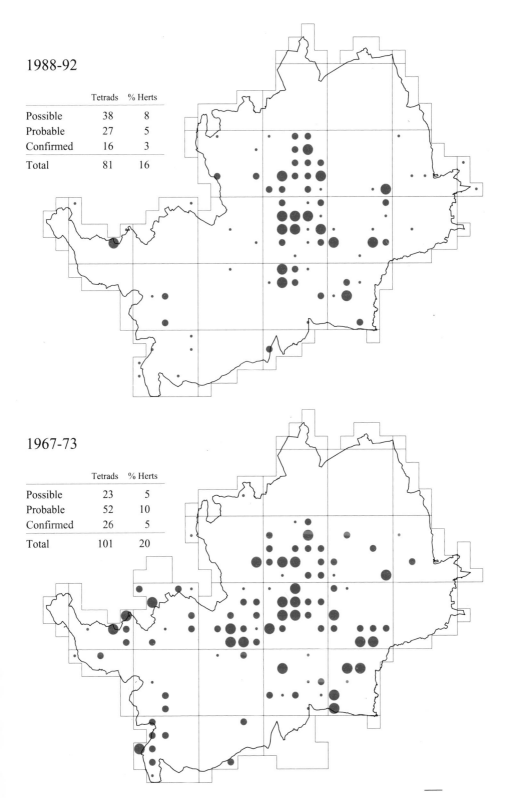

1988-92

	Tetrads	% Herts
Possible	38	8
Probable	27	5
Confirmed	16	3
Total	81	16

1967-73

	Tetrads	% Herts
Possible	23	5
Probable	52	10
Confirmed	26	5
Total	101	20

Yellowhammer

Emberiza citrinella

National population 1.2 million territories, Hertfordshire 9100-18,000 territories, static.

The Yellowhammer is the most numerous and widely distributed bunting breeding in Hertfordshire, being a typical bird of farmland and scrub. Its '...little bit of bread and no cheeeeze...' song is one of the most familiar and evocative sounds of summer. In times of high populations, Yellowhammers expand onto scrubby commons, young plantations and even motorway embankments.

Andrew. P. Chick 93.

The breeding season is very long, with males first starting to sing on territory on warm days in February and pairs nesting from April to September. With such a long season, double and triple broods are normal. Nests are substantial: built of straw, grass, weed stems and moss, lined with hair and fine grass. There is often a characteristic 'doorstep' built out in front. A very wide range of nest sites are used including hedges, small trees, bushes and banks with the nest usually less than two metres above the ground.

Their long breeding season and easily recognisable song made Yellowhammers relatively easy to find during the atlas fieldwork. Confirmation of breeding usually relied on finding adults feeding young and was obtained in approximately half of the records.

As a seed eating bird, the Yellowhammer was one of the key species to suffer from the effects of organochlorine seed dressings in the 1950s. A decline in the predominantly cereal growing eastern counties was attributed to this cause (Parslow 1973) and lasted well into the 1960s. Since the period of the first atlas the national population index has, with minor fluctuations associated with harsh winters, remained remarkably constant. In Hertfordshire there is no evidence of any change in the distribution between the two atlases. However, with over 95% of tetrads occupied it would be difficult to detect anything but a major decline.

The Yellowhammer seems to be better able than other buntings to exploit whatever opportunities are offered by modern agriculture. Even the most intensively managed cereal fields are likely to have Yellowhammers nesting in the adjacent hedgerows. As to be expected for such an adaptable bird, the habitat associations are for all agricultural landuse: cereals, grasslands, field beans, fallow and all types of animal husbandry. Occupied tetrads have lower areas of urbanisation, wetlands and parkland than unoccupied ones.

JHT

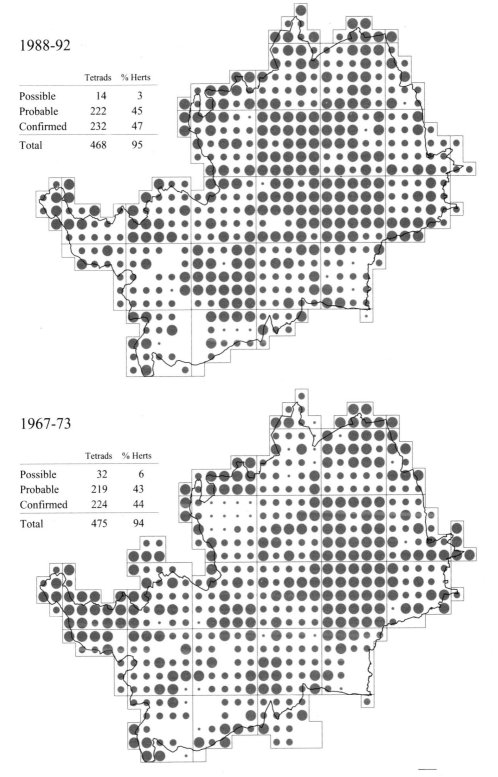

1988-92

	Tetrads	% Herts
Possible	14	3
Probable	222	45
Confirmed	232	47
Total	468	95

1967-73

	Tetrads	% Herts
Possible	32	6
Probable	219	43
Confirmed	224	44
Total	475	94

Reed Bunting

Emberiza schoeniclus

National population 220,000 territories, Hertfordshire 1100-1500 territories, declining.

The Reed Bunting is primarily a wetland species in Hertfordshire. Males, with their striking plumage and three or four note call, delivered from a low exposed perch, can be found in spring in any roughly vegetated areas adjacent to wetlands. At some sites they are found in quite high numbers, for example 34, 17 and 14 singing males at Rye Meads, Cheshunt and Amwell gravel pits respectively in 1990.

The nest, built of grasses and moss, is usually situated fairly close to the ground in a clump of grass or rush. Confirmation of breeding is not particularly difficult to obtain although the hen will sit more tightly than other buntings. If accidentally flushed from the nest she usually leaves making an injury feigning display.

Nationally, the Reed Bunting population index increased to high levels in the 1970s but has subsequently decreased significantly. In Hertfordshire there has been a significant decline in the numbers of occupied tetrads since the last atlas. When the population levels were high in the late 1960s and early 1970s Reed Buntings were found to be nesting in a more diverse range of habitats which included dry farmland as well as wetlands (O'Connor & Pearman 1987). However, the habitat associations found in the two Hertfordshire atlases provide no evidence that this was happening locally. In both the only significant associations were with wetland habitats.

Lack (1992) has recently reported territorial Reed Buntings selecting oilseed rape fields. The area of rape was very low in the first atlas and one would not have expected to be able to detect any selection for the crop from the atlas data. However, significant areas were being grown at the time of the new atlas fieldwork but even then there was no evidence of an association with oilseed rape.

Being resident, seed eating birds which collect most of their food from the ground, Reed Buntings are particularly vulnerable to severe weather conditions in winter. Numbers were very low after the 1962/63 winter but were also hard hit by the severe winters of the early 1980s. It is probable that, in recent years, changes to the management of agricultural land, particularly the loss of agricultural weeds to herbicides and the shift to autumn cultivations, have depleted winter food resources for Reed Buntings.

JHT

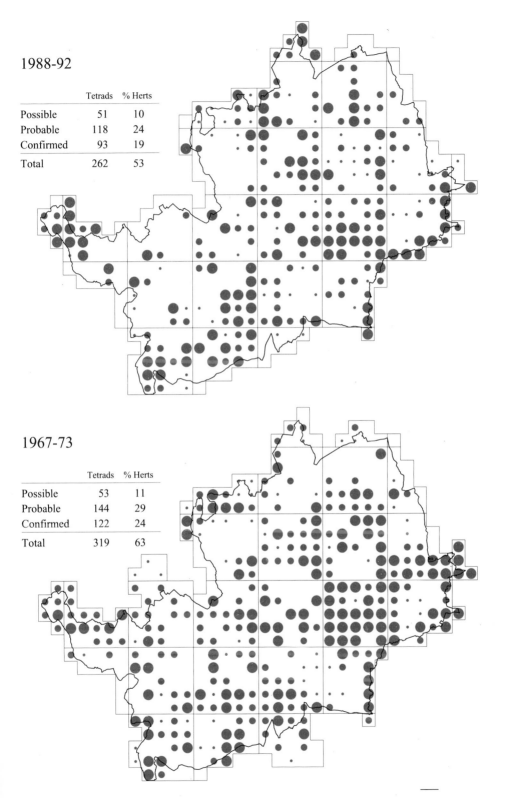

1988-92

	Tetrads	% Herts
Possible	51	10
Probable	118	24
Confirmed	93	19
Total	262	53

1967-73

	Tetrads	% Herts
Possible	53	11
Probable	144	29
Confirmed	122	24
Total	319	63

Corn Bunting

Miliaria calandra

National population <160,000 territories, Hertfordshire 300-730 territories declining.

In summer, the Corn Bunting singing its unmistakable jingle from a commanding song post shares the wide arable acres of Hertfordshire with the Skylark. This, our largest bunting, has drab plumage, without any of the flashes of yellow or white of the other buntings. From October to late April flocks frequent rough grassland and arable fields but males may leave to sing in potential territories as early as February, returning to the communal roosts in reedbeds or dry scrub. Nesting does not start until May and males are frequently polygynous, having more than one female nesting in their territory. It is therefore always difficult to estimate true breeding numbers and surveys of singing males may underestimate the numbers of nesting females.

Historically, Corn Buntings have always been known as birds of arable farmland and have probably expanded or declined in step with the fortunes of agriculture. For instance, Morris in 1863 noted the Corn Bunting had become more common following the agricultural revolution of that period! After the agricultural depression of the 1920s and 1930s there was a wartime resurgence in arable farming which probably benefited Corn Buntings. It was not until the 1970s that the population began to decline; the CBC index shows a decline steepening after 1981 to today's figures of roughly one third of that 20 years ago.

In Hertfordshire the expansion into the south and centre of the county which took place in the 1950s and 1960s (Gladwin 1983) is now in reverse and, as the two atlas maps show, there has been a significant reduction of the range over the last 20 years.

In 1985 the Herts Bird Club organised a sample survey of breeding Corn Buntings (Terry 1986). This too found evidence of a decline, particularly in areas with heavy clay soils. The numbers on the light chalk and gravel soils appeared to be faring better. The total Hertfordshire population was estimated as between 700 and 1400 singing males in 1985 but, when the Bird Club repeated the survey in 1992, this estimate had fallen to 300-730 singing males (Dee *in prep*).

The decline is almost certainly related to changes in cereal production. Corn Buntings have been shown to be associated with barley (O'Connor & Shrubb 1986, Thompson & Gribbin 1986) which has declined in area in Hertfordshire, but more subtle changes such as the increased intensity of management and the shift from spring to autumn cultivations are also likely to be involved.

In the first atlas tetrads with breeding Corn Buntings had larger areas of cereals, field beans, fallow and temporary grasslands. In the second atlas the association with cereals and field beans remained but those with fallow and temporary grasslands were no longer significant. JHT

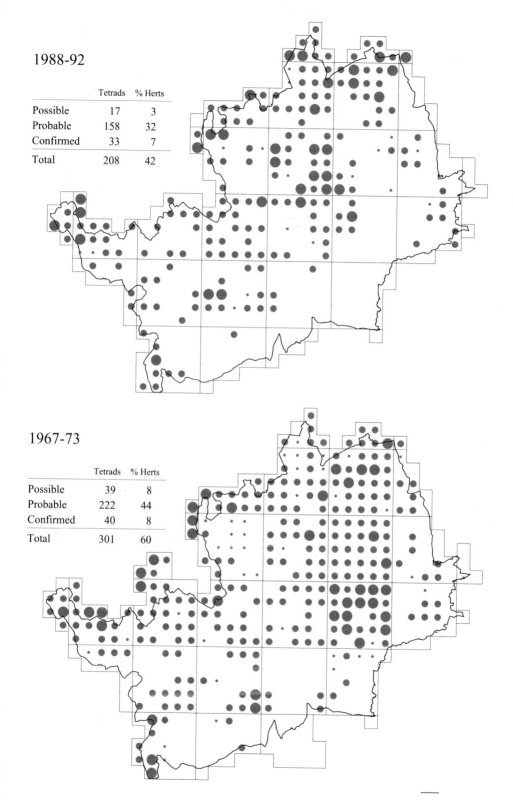

1988-92

	Tetrads	% Herts
Possible	17	3
Probable	158	32
Confirmed	33	7
Total	208	42

1967-73

	Tetrads	% Herts
Possible	39	8
Probable	222	44
Confirmed	40	8
Total	301	60

Additional species

The first line of text for each species gives the number of tetrads in which the species was recorded in the first atlas (1967-73) and new atlas (1988-92), each in the order: possible, probable and confirmed breeding.

Black-necked Grebe

Podiceps nigricollis

1967-73: 0, 0, 0; 1988-92: 0, 0, 1.

The first proven breeding of this species in England was at Tring Reservoirs in 1918 (three pairs) where breeding continued until 1928. Since then the Black-necked Grebe has been a scarce winter visitor and passage migrant to Hertfordshire and, as such, there have been records each year during the last decade, with the exceptions of 1986 and 1988. The number of birds seen has not exceeded single figures in any year. The bird is a very rare breeding species nationally with around 25-40 pairs breeding each year. Central England and Scotland are the birds' chief centres of population with the RSPB's reserve at the Loch of Kinnordy the best site to see them without creating unwarranted disturbance.

It was therefore both surprising and exciting when a pair bred at Hilfield Park Reservoir during 1990. The birds were initially seen at the beginning of June when they began to display. A well hidden nest was eventually discovered in a *Typha* bed at the end of the month. The birds were observed throughout the 21 day incubation and three young were hatched around the 22 July. Feeding, as with incubation, was by both parents and all three chicks were raised successfully. The family departed individually between the middle of August and mid-September.

This was the first confirmed breeding in the county since 1928. A single calling bird was at the same location in 1991 but water levels were too low for breeding to take place and a juvenile was also seen in mid-July although there was no reason to suspect breeding. In 1992 a pair displayed in spring but no breeding took place. The regular use of Hilfield Park Reservoir, plus Tring Reservoirs and the Lee valley gravel pits by wintering and passage birds does give real promise that further breeding could occur in the future.

Cormorant

Phalacrocorax carbo

1967-73: 0, 0, 0; 1988-92: 4, 0, 0.

Traditionally a bird of coastal habitats, the Cormorant was a scarce passage migrant and winter visitor at the time of the old atlas. Since then a dramatic change has taken place and Cormorants are now present in substantial numbers during the winter months, with birds occasionally staying for the summer.

In 1984 a pair built a nest at Stockers Lake but did not use it and the following year birds were seen displaying and collecting nesting material at Tring Reservoirs.

The pattern of summering birds continued throughout the duration of the atlas fieldwork when between two and five birds could be found in the Lee valley (TL21B, TL30S, TL31V). An isolated report of a single bird present in the breeding season was also received from TL21F and it is possible that other birds were not reported. Interestingly, breeding was established in 1991 when six young were raised at Walthamstow Reservoirs at the south end of the Lee valley – but regrettably several miles outside Hertfordshire.

Although no definite evidence of breeding was obtained during the atlas fieldwork, the existence of the Walthamstow colony, coupled with the activities at Stockers Lake before the atlas period and the regular presence of small numbers of adult birds in the breeding season, suggests that it will not be too long before breeding is proved within the county.

Egyptian Goose

Alopochen aegyptiacus

1967-73: 0, 0, 0; 1988-92: 0, 0, 1.

The Birds of Hertfordshire described Egyptian Goose as a very rare visitor to the county, noting that only 16 birds (including a party of five in the Lee valley in 1979) had been recorded between 1966 and 1982.

They are not true geese, being more closely related to Shelduck, and were not admitted to the British List until 1971, previously being regarded as ornamental waterfowl not able to sustain a viable independent population without assistance. The main concentration of the true feral breeders is now north Norfolk and Suffolk. Their status, especially outside these two areas, remains confused as they continue to be widely kept in wildfowl collections where they breed freely.

This is certainly the case in Hertfordshire where it has not always been easy to decide whether sightings relate to wild birds. Notable among records in the early 1980s was a single bird that remained all year on the Hertfordshire/Essex border in 1984, followed by a pair in the same area all the following year. Six birds at Kings Langley from January to July 1990 were thought to be of captive origin. More recently in 1992 a pair, confidently considered not to have escaped from any maintained stock, laid two eggs at Amwell gravel pit (TL31R). Although the eggs were incubated for several weeks, no young were raised and it was assumed that the eggs were infertile. This constituted the first breeding attempt in the county since 1938.

The recognised gradual growth of the numbers of Egyptian Geese in East Anglia does mean that some birds may seek fresh breeding grounds away from their traditional areas.

Wood Duck

Aix sponsa

1967-73: 0, 0, 0; 1988-92: 0, 0, 1.

This bird is classified as in 'Category D' by the British Ornithologists' Union Records Committee which indicates that its feral breeding population may not be self-supporting and is sustained by assistance from man. This would normally exclude it from the atlas but the event of 1992 is considered sufficient reason for inclusion.

Wood Ducks have been seen regularly in the county in the last decade with between one and six birds per year, mostly in winter, although there were records of individual males in the 1986 and 1987 breeding seasons. All these birds were deemed to be of captive origin. In 1992, a pair raised young in TL20P. One instance of successful breeding is certainly not evidence that these birds are now truly feral (both parents may, themselves have originated in collections – or their forebears...) but the circumstances can be added to the historical database of the species to assist the next evaluation of its status.

Honey Buzzard

Pernis apivorus

1967-73: 0, 0, 0; 1988-92: 1, 1, 0.

This bird is a very rare summer vagrant to the county, with only six records this century. It is by nature very secretive and most sightings in the UK are of birds on the wing. Its distinctive 'sky-dancing' display is diagnostic and this is usually the manner by which lucky observers make a positive identification. Its stronghold is the New Forest where several pairs nest, encouraged by suitable habitat and enlightened conservation. It is probably more widely distributed but under recorded (Spencer *et al* 1993). Another well-publicised site is the Forestry Commission's controlled viewing at Haldon Forest, close to Exeter.

In one tetrad displaying birds were seen on more than one occasion and in another one was simply present in 1991. Both sightings were in areas suitable for breeding and, as it is now accepted that Honey Buzzards do attempt to breed away from their usual strongholds, this unobtrusive nester should be regarded as a potential addition to the county breeding list and observers be accordingly aware of the possibility and act with suitable discretion.

Buzzard

Buteo buteo

1967-73: 5, 0, 1; 1988-92: 8, 0, 0.

The old atlas showed a pair of Buzzards as definitely breeding, possibly in successive years, in the western part of the county. Additionally, single birds were present in the breeding season in five other tetrads (SP91V; TL01A; TL10D; TL22R and TL32V). During 1988-92 birds were seen in eight tetrads in the breeding season but no real evidence of success was gathered and the bird's status as a breeding species can be no higher than possible. Prior to the atlas period single birds were present in suitable habitat in 1982, 1984, 1986 and 1987 and a pair were also seen circling near Digswell in 1984.

Buzzards probably bred regularly up to 100 years ago from which time their incidence has gradually tailed off until now they cannot be regarded as other than intermittent breeders with many years between confirmed nesting. Hertfordshire is well to the east of their normal range in the UK. Although habitat factors are probably involved, their absence is probably also related to the high levels of persecution in the lowlands (Elliott & Avery 1992). However, observers should not be surprised to see birds outside the breeding season as it remains a regular winter visitor, though never in large numbers.

Chukar

Alectoris chukar

1967-73: 0, 0, 0; 1988-92: 2, 1, 1.

The Chukar is a partridge widely distributed from the eastern Mediterranean to Manchuria. It has been released elsewhere, notably in the USA, where it has become established in the west. It is closely related to the Red-legged Partridge but does not meet that species in the wild, their ranges being separated by a third closely related species, the Rock Partridge *A. graeca*. In captivity Red-legged Partridges and Chukars freely hybridise; large numbers of hybrids have been released for sporting purposes in this country along with smaller numbers of pure Chukars.

It is likely that a number of the records of Red-legged Partridge in the new atlas refer to hybrids, either released or less likely, wild stock. Probably because of the identification difficulties, only four records were submitted referring specifically to hybrids or Chukars, including one of Chukars with fledged young.

With the release of Chukar illegal after 1992 we should be grateful that the species will not be a permanent addition to the county's avifauna, though the problem of hybrids (whose release is also illegal) is likely to remain for some years.

Golden Pheasant

Chrysolophus pictus

1967-73: 0, 0, 0; 1988-92: 1, 0, 0.

Although small feral breeding populations of Golden Pheasants are established elsewhere there has never been any evidence of breeding in Hertfordshire. The first record in the county was of a male seen in Knebworth Park in September 1974. Prior to the new atlas fieldwork, there were three further sightings in the breeding season – all of males – at Batchwood, Amwell and Wallington in 1977, 1978 and 1984. During the atlas period birds were seen in Hatfield Park in February and Stevenage on 1 April 1991. The only breeding season record during the period was of a male resident in the Luffenhall area continuously from early 1989 until at least 1992.

Obviously, none of the above records constitute breeding and the origins of the individuals are uncertain, but were probably the result of casual or accidental releases. The persistence of the Luffenhall bird indicates that individuals are well able to survive. Also, it is worth considering that whereas a male Golden Pheasant is readily recognisable, a female could very easily be dismissed as just another strange looking 'common' Pheasant. Thus the possibility of breeding in the past or the future should not be regarded as completely untenable.

Lady Amherst's Pheasant

Chrysolophus amherstiae

1967-73: 1, 2, 1; 1988-92: 2, 0, 1.

In Hertfordshire, Lady Amherst's Pheasants tend to be overspill birds from the major concentrations which are centred in Bedfordshire and they are accordingly found less than annually, in very small numbers in the west of the county only. It is suspected that some birds could go unobserved as the species is notoriously shy. Once seen, invariably by chance at the edge of thick undergrowth, it is puzzling to accept that the multi-coloured males can ever remain inconspicuous. Nevertheless, the most usual method of establishing presence is the knowledge of their call.

There were four atlas records in 1967-73, confirmed breeding in TL01Z, probable breeding in SP91X and TL01B and a sighting in TQ09U. The current fieldwork established breeding just outside the county boundary in TL11J, and there were isolated views of birds in TL11D and TL13F. The latter record is far enough away from the bird's Hertfordshire base to pose the question of whether it was a truly feral bird as these ornamental fowl are known to be kept by collectors. Whilst the Bedfordshire population continues to be viable, there is yet to be any definite proof of breeding within Hertfordshire itself.

Spotted Crake

Porzana porzana

1967-73: 0, 0, 1; 1988-92: 0, 0, 0.

The Spotted Crake is one of the UK's most elusive and rare breeding birds. Even now, apart from the Ouse washes and the Spey valley in Scotland, there are no areas where it nests with any regularity. It is rarely seen in the breeding season and the chief indication that it is present in the thick marshland vegetation that it favours is its diagnostic and repetitious 'h-whit, h-whit, h-whit...' whiplash-like call. It was totally unexpected, therefore, when an adult and young were seen by the River Lee near Wheathampstead in 1967.

Birds are very occasionally seen on passage in autumn and winter (less than one per year) although even these records have petered out since 1984. There were no records at all during the new atlas fieldwork, the last record of a bird present in the breeding season being one calling on Ickleford Common in May 1979.

The 1967 and 1979 records are the only instances of confirmed or possible breeding in the county. They must be considered as opportunistic only and the future status should reflect this.

Corncrake

Crex crex

1967-73: 3, 3, 0; 1988-92: 0, 1, 0.

There were six records of Corncrake in the old atlas, three of probable breeding (TL01F and TL12P and W) and three of possible (SP91K, TL12T and TL21M). At that time it was noted that the species was declining nationally from being a fairly common summer visitor (including Hertfordshire) to a very rare breeding bird confined mainly to the Western Isles and Ireland. This sad decline has continued (Hudson *et al* 1990). Changes in agriculture are the reasons for the massive decrease; hayfields – the major breeding habitat – have been converted to silage or are being cropped earlier. This either destroys the young directly or leaves them exposed to predation.

There have been only two breeding season records since the old atlas. A bird was calling all summer at Gosmorebury, near Hitchin, in 1977 and a pair were resident at another site in the north of the county in 1990. These birds were identified by non-birdwatchers. A couple living in Hare Street had watched a television programme about Corncrakes and realised that the distinctive call was exactly the same as one they had heard regularly all summer. They contacted the county recorder who spoke at length with them and established that the birds had been present in June and July, preferring a field with long grass but emerging sporadically into a field occupied by grazing sheep. It is regretted that no young were ever seen.

Stone Curlew

Burhinus oedicnemus

1967-73: 2, 4, 6; 1988-92: 0, 0, 0.

Stone Curlews are now extinct as a breeding species in Hertfordshire. Although one was sighted in 1990 it was not near any breeding habitat and must be assumed to be a bird on passage. The last time breeding was definitely established was 1981 and although birds were seen in the same locality and elsewhere the following year, and lone pairs occurred in 1983 and 1984, nesting was never confirmed. Single birds were seen in suitable habitat in 1986 and 1987 since when the traditional locations have been barren. Changes in farming practice are considered to be the main influence – Stone Curlews prefer long distance all round vision throughout incubation so that they can slip away rather than fly if danger approaches and, with autumn sown crops growing too tall, this has become a rare commodity in Hertfordshire.

At the time of the old atlas, it was still a regular breeder on open farmland in the north of the county where breeding was confirmed in six tetrads, probable in four and possible in a further two.

The bird does still breed in Cambridgeshire, not too distant from the border with Hertfordshire (Spencer *et al* 1993) and with recent initiatives for farmers to set-aside land it is possible that the fluty, haunting cry may be heard in future years and successful breeding occur once more.

Curlew

Numenius arquata

1967-73: 0, 3, 0; 1988-92: 1, 0, 0.

The old atlas included the Curlew as a probable breeder. There were just three records of territorial birds (SP81S, SP91D and TL21U), one of which was in a tetrad including part of Hertfordshire, although the birds spent some of the time in Buckinghamshire. Breeding was never confirmed and Gladwin & Sage (1986) are unequivocal in stating that there had been no definitive evidence of successful breeding in the county.

A review of the annual bird reports since 1982 indicates that Curlews can be seen in Hertfordshire in every month of the year, more commonly in flight but also feeding, virtually anywhere away from the main towns. It is just possible that a pair could linger as did those noted during the old atlas and recently just such sightings in TL11X might indicate an attempt to set up a territory.

The birds do breed on farmland in Oxfordshire and Buckinghamshire and there have been suggestions of a slow eastward spread and, as such, there remains an outside possibility of nesting in Hertfordshire in the future.

Ring-necked Parakeet

Psittacula krameri

1967-73: 0, 0, 0; 1988-92: 1, 0, 0.

This bird is a regular visitor to the county, having been absent in only three years since 1974. There are usually one or two records of individuals each year (one instance of a flock of seven in 1976) and they occur chiefly in winter. There has been a marginal increase in numbers since 1987 along with breeding season records in four of the five years up to 1991.

There are substantial feral breeding populations in Middlesex and Kent and the London Bird Report for 1991 predicts breeding in Essex. The bird's continued expansion around London should lead to confirmed breeding in Hertfordshire in the not too distant future.

Wryneck

Jynx torquilla

1967-73: 2, 1, 1; 1988-92: 0, 0, 0.

When the fieldwork for the original atlas was carried out the Wryneck was regarded as barely clinging on as a breeding species in Hertfordshire. There were only four records noted – confirmed breeding in TL31F, a territorial bird in TL01F and two 'possibles' in TQ09I and TL20X. Since then, the status as a breeding bird in Hertfordshire has echoed the national decline. The last confirmed breeding in the county was at Ringshall in 1977. Two single birds were present in spring in 1982 and one was seen in May 1984. There have been no further breeding season records, although ones or twos are still seen on passage in most years.

The number of pairs breeding nationally does not usually exceed single figures (Spencer *et al* 1993) and so it would represent superb good fortune for the bird to breed in the county again, even though there is an abundance of large gardens and orchards which were the preferred habitat.

Woodlark

Lullula arborea

1967-73: 3, 0, 7; 1988-92: 0, 0, 0.

The Woodlark ceased to be a breeding species in Hertfordshire in the latter part of the 1960s when it was recorded in very small numbers. There were just seven records of confirmed breeding in the old atlas mostly centred around Kings Langley and Ashridge areas.

When the old atlas was published early in 1983 it was suggested that the Woodlark might make a comeback, albeit in small numbers. This was expected to mirror the then national trend and reflected the availability of the preferred habitat of scrubby grass and heathland with scattered trees, which still existed in several places.

Sadly, this prediction proved to be incorrect. National numbers have declined (Sitters 1986) and there were only three records of Woodlark in Hertfordshire in the 1980s (1984, 1985 and 1988), all of them outside the breeding season. There is now a better understanding of the Woodlark's habitat requirements and unless heavy grazing is restored to some of the heaths and grassland areas it is unlikely that the bird will return. Increased rabbit numbers probably offer the best chance.

Wheatear

Oenanthe oenanthe

1967-73: 12, 1, 1; 1988-92: 7, 0, 0.

The 1968-73 fieldwork established just one instance of confirmed breeding in tetrad TL02Z. This was, in fact, over the county boundary in Bedfordshire but valid for atlas recording purposes. A 'probable' record came from TL42M in 1970 and there were 12 other 'possibles' from widespread locations. The current fieldwork turned up seven sightings – all of single birds in reasonable breeding habitat but none in any of the tetrads noted 20 years ago.

The problem with categorising records of Wheatears in the breeding season is, of course, that of separating genuine attempts from the considerable numbers of birds which are passing through on passage. Wheatears are common passage birds, the spring migration persists until well into May and it is not unknown for early returning birds to appear in July. It has not been possible to establish any detailed information about any of the seven records noted above and it would be natural to classify them all as birds on passage. However, the observers submitted them in good faith with knowledge of the guidelines about care being taken over migrating species and they have therefore been retained.

Birds last bred for certain in Hertfordshire in 1954 and there were suspicions of nesting in 1961 and 1967.

Cetti's Warbler

Cettia cetti

1967-73: 0, 0, 0; 1988-92: 0, 2, 0.

This species' gradual colonisation of southern Britain has been one of the more delightful ornithological events of the last two decades. Unknown on the mainland prior to the winter of 1967-68, the first confirmed breeding was in Kent in 1972. The first Hertfordshire record came from Rickmansworth in 1975-76. Although there were birds present in suitable habitat in the breeding season in both 1976 and 1977, the first attempted breeding was not established until the following year when a nest with infertile eggs was found at Rye Meads. The definitive confirmation of local breeding had to wait until 1980 when a pair reared two broods at Stanstead Abbots gravel pit and a second pair was successful elsewhere in the county (Sharrock *et al* 1982). Three pairs raised young in 1981.

Although initial colonisation of the UK was by way of the south-east, these birds have been greatly reduced by cold winters and the main populations are now in the south-west (Spencer *et al* 1993). The severe winters in the 1980s undoubtedly affected the bird in Hertfordshire. The numbers seen in the traditional areas in the Lee valley declined considerably after these cold winters. The pattern of records for the last ten years has been for at least two birds to be seen every year during the winter months with a peak of six at Amwell gravel pit in September 1989. Singing males have been present in suitable breeding locations in 1982, 1983, 1985 and twice during atlas fieldwork. Strangely, breeding has not been confirmed since 1981 in spite of the preferred sites being very regularly watched by some of the county's most experienced birdwatchers. It is possible that breeding has been unobserved, or observed and not reported but this is considered improbable.

Cetti's Warblers will surely be confirmed again as a breeding species and hopefully echo the national trend of slowly increasing where suitable habitat occurs.

Savi's Warbler

Locustella luscinioides

1967-73: 0, 0, 0; 1988-92: 1, 0, 0.

Savi's Warbler is a very rare species in Hertfordshire with only occasional breeding season records. However there were two most interesting records during 1989. A male singing at Rye Meads between 2-5 May was trapped and ringed on the 3rd. A second bird was caught at the Wilstone Reservoir constant effort ringing site on 14 July. This bird had been ringed at Brandon Marshes, Warwickshire on 9 May that year and constituted the first ever control (retrap) of a Savi's Warbler in Britain.

The species is now breeding annually in very small numbers in south and south-eastern Britain (Spencer *et al* 1993) so the appearance of isolated individuals in the county's reed-beds will always be a future possibility.

Marsh Warbler

Acrocephalus palustris

1967-73: 0, 0, 0; 1988-92: 1, 0, 0.

This bird is a very rare vagrant to the county. There were only two records between the two atlas periods, a bird singing at Stockers Lake in summer 1978 and one caught and ringed near Wheathampstead in June 1980. During the new atlas period, a bird was heard singing from a raspberry thicket at Northchurch, Berkhamsted on 5 June 1988. It was caught and ringed but left the area on the following day.

With a small and apparently stable breeding population in south-east England (Spencer *et al* 1993) there is always the possibility of this species breeding in Hertford-shire in the future.

Pied Flycatcher

Ficedula hypoleuca

1967-73: 0, 0, 0; 1988-92: 4, 3, 1.

Historically, Pied Flycatchers have been regarded as annual spring and autumn migrants which occur in small numbers. There was a claim of successful breeding in 1917 but subsequent review placed considerable doubt on the event and led to it being reclassified as insufficient to establish confirmed breeding.

As with Wheatear, evidence of breeding attempts must always be treated with real caution, bearing in mind the difficulty of discounting spring migrants. Presence in a suitable environment does not really justify a claim of possibly breeding. However, an event during the atlas period was totally unambiguous.

On 25 May 1988, a female was seen at Lemsford Springs nature reserve. She laid six eggs in a nestbox, although no male was ever seen. The bird was present until 12 June but not thereafter. The eggs proved to be infertile and were removed under licence, along with the nest, to North Herts Museum. This constituted the first definite breeding attempt by the species in Hertfordshire. Birds have also been sighted prospecting nest boxes and holes, one at Rye Meads in 1986, one in Ashridge Forest in 1990 and one in Sherrardspark Wood in 1992.

Pied Flycatcher is traditionally thought of as a species of western oak woods but the events in Hertfordshire over the last few years suggest that it may eventually manage to breed successfully in the county.

Bearded Tit

Panurus biarmicus

1967-73: 0, 0, 1; 1988-92: 0, 0, 0.

The previous atlas showed that Bearded Tits had successfully bred in just one tetrad (TL21F). This disguised the true position as the record actually referred to two pairs in Stanborough Reedmarsh in 1968, 1971, 1972 and one pair in 1973. (Two pairs had also bred there in 1966). The 1966 and 1968 attempts were all successful but no young fledged in 1971 and the 1972 and 1973 attempts were thwarted when the reedbed was destroyed by fire.

There have not been any further breeding attempts since 1973. In most years small numbers of birds are seen, generally in the Lee valley or at Tring Reservoirs. The majority of these originate from the thriving East Anglian populations but mainland European birds have also been trapped.

It is difficult to predict the future but the balance of logic must be that Bearded Tits are now completely extinct as Hertfordshire breeders – but it would be delightful to be proved wrong.

Golden Oriole

Oriolus oriolus

1967-73: 2, 0, 0; 1988-92: 1, 0, 0.

Two records of birds present in suitable habitat occurred during the old atlas fieldwork (TL10F and TL21Y). In the early 1970s a pair nested at a secret site in the west of the county and newly fledged young were seen. Individual singing males were recorded in 1977, 1979, 1980 and 1984, two birds were noted in 1982 and 1985 and five were seen in 1981, including a pair at Little Gaddesden.

There have been no sightings at all notified to the county recorder since 1985; the one atlas record, in TL13S, was not in Hertfordshire.

Golden Orioles nest in small numbers in south and east England particularly favouring poplar plantations in East Anglia. It is unlikely that they will ever become a regular Hertfordshire breeding species although they will continue to be recorded occasionally.

Red-backed Shrike

Lanius collurio

1967-73: 6, 1, 8; 1988-92: 1, 0, 0.

The decline of the Red-backed Shrike in Hertfordshire has echoed the national pattern. Fairly common in Hertfordshire in the 1930s, it was still regular in the 1940s and 1950s but decreased in the 1960s when only one or two pairs nested in most years. The original atlas showed confirmed breeding in eight tetrads with possible attempts in six more. Most of these records were close to the county boundary in the north-west. These records reflected the cumulative sightings from 1967 to 1973 and in any single year there were probably no more than one or two pairs.

The last probable breeding was in 1974 when a pair present at Oughtonhead Common was said to have bred (Gladwin & Sage 1986). Since then there have only been four breeding season records – all of single birds (1979, 1980, 1981, and 1992) – and three other records (August 1977, August 1981 and September 1984). The 1992 record was of a male singing for some days in suitable habitat and was found only as a result of atlas fieldwork.

The national decline of the species has been relentless (172 confirmed pairs in 1960, 48-64 in 1977, none in 1989 and one in 1990 (Spencer *et al* 1993)). There is speculation that the species is about to stage a comeback but only time will tell.

Cirl Bunting

Emberiza cirlus

1967-73: 4, 3, 1; 1988-92: 0, 0, 0.

The original atlas showed one confirmed breeding record (SP90E), plus three probable and four possible attempts, but, by the time the old atlas was published, the Cirl Bunting was long extinct as a breeding species in Hertfordshire. The only additional sightings since that time have been one at Moor Park golf course in June 1977 and an immature at Bricket Wood in September 1981. The single record of confirmed breeding was actually outside the county border so it is not clear when breeding ceased in Hertfordshire – a singing male near Kimpton in 1967 was probably the last.

The contraction of the breeding range of the Cirl Bunting has been one of the most spectacular changes of status of a British breeding species seen over the last 50 years (Sitters 1982). Breeding birds are now restricted to a small area of south Devon, having disappeared from most of southern England (Sitters 1985, Evans 1992). The decline is almost certainly related to changes in agricultural practices, particularly the intensification of cereal farming and loss of weed rich feeding sites (Smith *et al* 1992). Thanks to a series of actions, numbers are currently increasing in south Devon although it is likely to be many years before the birds are restored to their former range.

ALL EWF, EXCEPT CHUKAR (PJW)

IV: Changes in bird distributions between the two atlases

In the individual species texts the changes in the bird distributions have been discussed in some detail. In this chapter these changes are examined for groups of birds associated with particular habitats. Using the habitat associations described in the next chapter, birds have been divided into four groups: those associated with wetlands, woodlands, farmland and built-up areas. For each species in each of these groups the numbers of tetrads with confirmed and probable breeding in each atlas have been counted, the changes in these totals examined and compared with the national trends in populations where these are known.

COVERAGE IN THE TWO ATLASES

Any changes in the numbers of occupied tetrads can only be judged in relation to the coverage achieved for the two atlases. The methods and categories of breeding were the same in both surveys but the duration of the fieldwork period was shorter for the new atlas (five years as opposed to seven for the first atlas). In spite of this shorter duration the coverage was better for the new atlas largely because the results were computerised as they were collected and the organisers were therefore better able to provide feedback to observers on the progress of the fieldwork and to direct them to areas requiring more work. Remarkably, in spite of the increase in the popularity of birdwatching over the last 20 years, the number of observers contributing records was, at around 250, similar in both atlases.

The growth in the total numbers of records in each breeding category over the five years of the fieldwork is shown in Figure 4.1. As to be expected, the initial increase was very rapid but after a few years there was only a small increase each year until in the fifth year when only a few hundred extra records were added. It would appear from these figures that, in Hertfordshire at least, five years' fieldwork was sufficient to ensure a very high level of coverage. Inevitably there are some species which occur sporadically at different sites each year or which tend to occupy ephemeral habitats, for which the atlas maps will over-estimate the distribution in any one year. In addition, any species with a rapidly changing population is likely to give a somewhat misleading distribution map. For example, during the old atlas, the Whitethroat population decreased by a factor of about four between 1968 and 1969 as a result of drought conditions in sub-Saharan Africa (Winstanley *et al* 1974). Thus, in any tetrads surveyed after 1968, there was a much lower chance of finding Whitethroats than in those surveyed before and the distribution map was distorted accordingly. A similar situation has probably arisen in the new atlas with Corn Bunting which is declining so rapidly that by the end of the survey period it had already gone from many areas where it was found at the outset.

The total numbers of records collected in each atlas are shown in Table 4.1. Overall, there were more records in the second atlas (+8.3%) from slightly fewer tetrads and the fraction of records which were of confirmed breeding was slightly higher. In examining any changes for particular species only records of confirmed or probable breeding in the two atlases have been compared and all records of possible breeding have been disregarded. Thus data have only been used where there was clear evidence of the species actually breeding in the tetrad. Overall there were 7.5% more records of confirmed and probable breeding in the second atlas. In assessing the significance of any changes, for each species the ratio of the numbers of occupied tetrads has been

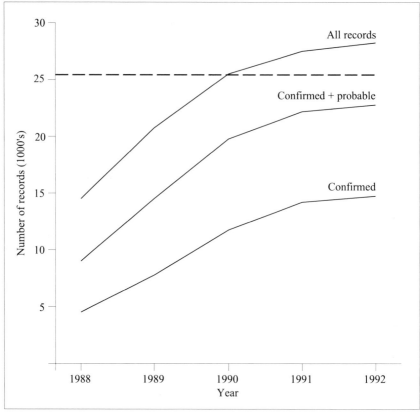

Figure 4.1: The cumulative numbers of records collected in each category of breeding versus the year. The dashed line indicates the total number of records collected from 491 tetrads during the 1967-73 atlas.

compared with the overall change between the two atlases for all species.

Although in this way it has been possible to make allowance for the overall increase in coverage between the two atlases, it is less easy to allow for non-uniform coverage across the county. Some areas, such as the major wetlands, are heavily watched, whilst others hold fewer attractions for birdwatchers and are likely to be visited less often. In the second atlas records were kept of the number of hours fieldwork in each tetrad and, based on the results of the first year's fieldwork, a target of a minimum of ten hours in each tetrad was set. Not all observers were meticulous in recording their time in the field, but for those tetrads where the information is available (439) the target ten hours

	1967-1973 504 tetrads	1988-1992 491 tetrads
Present in breeding season	4776 (18.3%)	5340 (18.9%)
Probably breeding	7809 (29.9%)	8164 (28.8%)
Confirmed breeding	13567 (51.8%)	14814 (52.3%)
Total	26152	28318

Table 4.1: The total numbers of records collected in each atlas.

was achieved in 82% with an overall mean of 15.5 hours per tetrad. This is, of course, only a minimum estimate of the fieldwork effort as many supplementary records were submitted in addition to the data from the timed visits. These figures imply that in excess of 7600 hours fieldwork went into collecting the atlas data.

Hours in the field can only be used as an indication of coverage and other factors such as the individual skills and experience of observers are also important. As a further illustration, in Figures 4.2 and 4.3 the numbers of species recorded in each tetrad in the two atlases, and also the proportion of these records in each of the breeding categories have been compared. Improved coverage should be reflected in higher species counts and a greater proportion of records in the higher breeding categories. It is clear from these figures that there has been a marked improvement in coverage particularly in some parts of the north of the county.

CHANGES IN DISTRIBUTION IN RELATION TO CHANGES IN NUMBERS

Considerable care is needed when interpreting the changes in atlas distribution maps in relation to changes in bird populations. Each atlas record represents the presence of a species within a tetrad and the likelihood of it being recorded by an observer. A single tetrad is a very large area and, for many species, for example Yellowhammer and Greenfinch, it will hold a large number of breeding birds. There could therefore be large fluctuations in numbers without them becoming apparent on a map showing presence or absence at the tetrad scale. Additionally, for the very common species where all or nearly all tetrads are occupied, it is impossible to detect an increase in numbers by means of changes in an atlas distribution. Fortunately, for the less numerous species, the atlas distribution is a very effective way of monitoring change. However, the change in the number of occupied tetrads is not necessarily the same as the change in population, although as will be shown later in this chapter, there is a significant correlation between the two.

CHANGES IN THE DISTRIBUTION OF WETLAND SPECIES

In the new atlas, 39 species were associated with wetlands (Table 4.2) but, of these, 15 occurred only in a small number of tetrads. In Table 4.2, the remaining 24 species have been ranked according to the ratio of the number of tetrads with probable or confirmed breeding in the two atlases. About half of these species have shown an increase in distribution and half a decrease.

The most spectacular increase is that of the Canada Goose with 15 times as many occupied tetrads in the second atlas. Canada Geese now breed throughout the county, even on small ponds. Numbers have increased to such an extent that there is pressure from agricultural and amenity interests to reduce the population, although as yet no effective strategy has been proposed.

Six of the species with an increased distribution are birds of open water, all of which have probably benefited from more disused gravel pits, the maturing of existing pits and, at some sites, specific conservation management.

The species with reduced distributions are, with a few exceptions, those normally associated with wet grasslands, marsh and fen vegetation rather than open water. For instance Sedge Warbler, Reed Bunting, Grasshopper Warbler, Snipe and Barn Owl have all decreased. The decreases of Mute Swan and Sand Martin are probably not related to changes of habitats in Hertfordshire. The Mute Swan, although currently increasing, is only just recovering from the population fall caused by birds ingesting lead fishing weights, the use of which is now widely banned. Although Sand Martins require a particular type of sand face in which to nest, numbers have never recovered

Figure 4.2: Numbers of species recorded per tetrad in 1988-92 (above) and 1967-73 (below).

■ more than 75 species

● 61-75 species

• 46-60 species

· 31-45 species

less than 31 species

Figure 4.3: Proportion of records in each category in 1988-92 (above) and 1967-73 (below).

● Confirmed breeding

▨ Probable breeding

○ Possible breeding

Species	No. of tetrads 1967-73	No. of tetrads 1988-92	Ratio	Change in national population index 1970-90
Canada Goose	8	121	15.13	+
Tufted Duck	31	78	2.52	+
Grey Wagtail	47	85	1.81	?
Yellow Wagtail	47	83	1.77	1.00
Great Crested Grebe	24	41	1.71	+
Kestrel	179	300	1.68	0.76
Coot	97	137	1.41	+
Little Grebe	72	99	1.38	?
Little Ringed Plover	25	33	1.32	+
Mallard	252	333	1.32	1.26
Kingfisher	62	81	1.31	-
Reed Warbler	60	73	1.22	?
Moorhen	345	359	1.04	0.77
Redshank	18	17	0.94	-
Grey Heron	13	11	0.85	1.56
Sedge Warbler	183	150	0.82	0.81
Reed Bunting	266	211	0.79	-
Mute Swan	88	69	0.78	?
Pochard	14	10	0.71	+
Snipe	34	16	0.47	-
Sand Martin	60	22	0.37	-
Water Rail	22	8	0.36	?
Barn Owl	65	23	0.35	-
Grasshopper Warbler	125	41	0.33	-
Black-necked Grebe	0	1		
Greylag Goose	5	8		
Shelduck	0	8		
Mandarin	2	17		
Gadwall	1	15		
Teal	2	1		
Garganey	0	2		
Shoveler	3	10		
Ruddy Duck	1	10		
Ringed Plover	2	12		
Common Sandpiper	3	1		
Common Tern	4	9		
Whinchat	23	2		
Cetti's Warbler	0	2		
Bearded Tit	1	0		

Table 4.2: Changes in the numbers of occupied tetrads between the two atlases for wetland species compared with changes in the national population indices. Where the direction of change is known but not the magnitude this is indicated by a '+' or '-'. A '?' indicates that the national trend is unclear. Occupied tetrads are those with records of either probable or confirmed breeding.

from their collapse thought to be caused by poor conditions in their wintering areas.

Also shown in Table 4.2 are the changes in the national population indices between 1970 and 1990 for those species for which the data are available. With the exception of the National Heronries Census, national monitoring of breeding wetland species was not established until the advent of the BTO Waterways Bird Survey in the mid 1970s and this survey is, in itself, biased towards birds of linear waterways. There are therefore only six species for which changes in national indices can be calculated from 1970 to 1990. For the others an indication of the direction of the recent national trend is given. There is, in general, good agreement between the local and national picture, at least in respect of the direction of the changes if not the magnitude.

Snipe belongs to a group of breeding waders that are in decline in the lowlands nationally due to drainage and agricultural intensification of their wet grassland breeding habitat. The reduction in distribution in Hertfordshire is in line with the national trend although the causes may be subtly different. In Hertfordshire wet grasslands have probably suffered more from the recent drought and over-abstraction of water rather than land drainage *per se*.

The decrease in the number of tetrads occupied by Pochard is only just significant but is intriguing set against a two-fold national increase for the species over the twenty year period (Fox 1991). However even Fox reported a decrease in south-east England.

CHANGES IN THE DISTRIBUTION OF WOODLAND SPECIES

Thirty five breeding species were found to be associated with woodland in Hertfordshire. In Table 4.3, 25 of these species are ranked according to the ratio of the numbers of occupied tetrads in the two atlases. The biggest increase in distribution is for the Sparrowhawk with around 16 times as many tetrads occupied in the new atlas. At the time of the first atlas, Sparrowhawk numbers were at a low ebb as a result of contamination with pesticides accumulated from their songbird prey (Newton 1986). Since the use of the offending chemicals has been banned or greatly restricted, the birds have staged a spectacular recovery and are now relatively common, particularly in west and central Hertfordshire, although still thinly distributed in the north and east.

Hobby, with the second biggest increase, is not strictly a woodland bird, nesting in small copses, woodland edge and hedgerow trees, but hunting over open country. The increase in Hertfordshire has been mirrored elsewhere in southern England with birds expanding from the traditional heathland and downland sites. Fuller *et al* (1985) found birds nesting in significant numbers on farmland and gave evidence that they had been present in their study areas in the late 19th and early 20th centuries. They suggested that this segment of the population had previously been overlooked. Given the continued increase and expansion of range of the species into new counties (Spencer *et al* 1993) this explanation now seems unlikely and a genuine population increase is surely now underway. As yet no explanation for this increase has been suggested.

Of the other woodland species with increased distributions many, such as the woodpeckers and Nuthatch, are birds which favour mature woodland (Smith *et al* 1992). On the other hand many of the declining species are birds of woodland scrub and clearings, such as Nightingale and Tree Pipit. There are likely to be many reasons for these changes but it is possible that changes in woodland management since the 1940s, with the virtual cessation of coppicing, are now starting to affect some of these populations. The lack of coppicing results in few clearings and the over mature coppice stools are now growing through to high forest. Whatever the causes, it is unfortunate that the list of declining woodland species includes some of the most treasured and characteristic birds of Hertfordshire: Wood Warbler, Woodcock, Hawfinch, Tree Pipit,

Nightingale, Redstart and Nightjar.

The majority of the woodland species have been monitored by the BTO national Common Birds Census since the early 1960s. In Figure 4.4 the changes in the national population indices for woodland species are plotted against the changes in the numbers of occupied tetrads in the two atlases. There is a highly significant correlation between the two measures of change with most species lying around the line of equality. There are three clear exceptions to this: Nuthatch, Jackdaw and Redstart, two of which have increased nationally more than the ratio of occupied tetrads would suggest and the third, the Redstart, has increased nationally and decreased in Hertfordshire.

Species	No. of tetrads 1967-73	No. of tetrads 1988-92	Ratio	Change in national population index 1970-90
Sparrowhawk	13	207	15.92	+
Hobby	13	49	3.77	+
Great Spotted Woodpecker	158	318	2.01	2.35
Nuthatch	155	273	1.76	2.98
Green Woodpecker	136	225	1.65	1.00
Long-tailed Tit	264	399	1.51	1.89
Goldcrest	207	308	1.49	1.46
Lesser Spotted Woodpecker	76	112	1.47	1.29
Garden Warbler	239	346	1.45	1.41
Coal Tit	239	300	1.26	1.85
Treecreeper	225	280	1.24	1.56
Mistle Thrush	347	405	1.17	0.77
Marsh Tit	152	156	1.03	0.55
Tawny Owl	268	270	1.01	0.53
Jay	225	211	0.94	1.25
Jackdaw	296	276	0.93	2.53
Willow Tit	227	149	0.66	0.83
Wood Warbler	38	25	0.66	?
Woodcock	80	50	0.63	0.35
Redpoll	146	86	0.59	0.52
Hawfinch	78	43	0.55	?
Tree Pipit	127	52	0.41	0.50
Long-eared Owl	24	9	0.37	?
Nightingale	83	24	0.29	?
Redstart	29	6	0.21	1.42
Chiffchaff	400	462		
Willow Warbler	436	482		
Buzzard	1	0		
Lady Amherst's Pheasant	3	1		
Nightjar	24	2		
Woodlark	7	0		
Firecrest	2	8		
Pied Flycatcher	0	4		
Siskin	2	3		
Crossbill	4	3		

Table 4.3: Changes in the numbers of occupied tetrads between the two atlases for woodland species. For a full explanation, see Table 4.2. The ratios of occupied tetrads for Chiffchaff and Willow Warbler were not calculated because they occurred in too many tetrads.

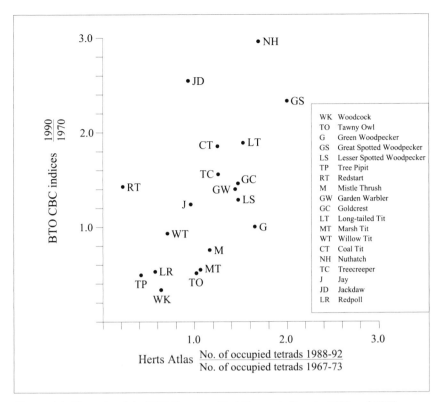

Figure 4.4: The ratio of the BTO Common Bird Census indices in 1990 and 1970 plotted against the ratio of the number of occupied tetrads (confirmed and probable breeding) in the Hertfordshire atlases in 1988-92 and 1967-73 for woodland species.

CHANGES IN THE DISTRIBUTION OF SPECIES OF AGRICULTURAL LAND

The majority of the land of Hertfordshire is devoted to agriculture and, although breeding birds on agricultural land often occur at low densities, their overall numbers are high. Agricultural land also holds certain specialist species which occur in no other habitat. Seventeen species emerged as farmland specialists (Table 4.4), although for some it is arguable in which habitat they should be counted (e.g. Mistle Thrush has been counted as a woodland bird and Kestrel was associated with wetlands). In addition there are a further six species of agricultural land which occur in low numbers of tetrads or are now extinct in Hertfordshire. Of the main species, three have increased their distribution, nine decreased and four occur in too many tetrads to detect an upward change, although they certainly did not decrease.

Given the complexity of agricultural land-use it is not surprising that a very variable group of farmland species has declined. They include seed eaters such as the Tree Sparrow and Corn Bunting as well as Rook, Turtle Dove and Grey Partridge. The detailed habitat associations of these species and their relationships to trends in agricultural land-use are discussed elsewhere in this book. It is interesting to note that, in Hertfordshire at least, a number of species normally thought of as farmland birds, such as Barn Owl, Kestrel and Linnet, were found to be associated with habitats other than farmland.

Many of the farmland species have been covered by national monitoring schemes for the last twenty years and there is a very good correlation between the changes in the numbers of occupied tetrads and the changes in the national population indices over the same period (Figure 4.5).

In all cases the direction of change is the same. The greater spatial resolution of the CBC compared to a tetrad based distribution atlas means that the former method should be more sensitive to change. This seems to be the case for most species. For species which are declining rapidly, the gradual loss of CBC plots and lower breeding densities may reduce the sensitivity of this method. This may explain why the CBC ratios for Tree Sparrow and Grey Partridge are close to the atlas ratios.

CHANGES IN THE DISTRIBUTION OF SPECIES OF BUILT-UP AREAS

Eleven species were associated with built-up areas (Table 4.5) of which three had increased in distribution. Overall this group includes the obvious species of built-up areas, such as Swift and House Martin, as well as others, such as Linnet and Carrion Crow, more likely to be associated with the urban fringe. Collared Dove and Magpie, both of which have increased considerably, are now common birds of suburban gardens.

Species	No. of tetrads 1967-73	No. of tetrads 1988-92	Ratio	Change in national population index 1970-90
Cuckoo	298	401	1.35	1.41
Stock Dove	241	308	1.28	2.51
Red-legged Partridge	241	289	1.20	1.31
Pheasant	375	383	1.02	1.73
Little Owl	189	180	0.95	0.87
Swallow	451	417	0.92	0.67
Lapwing	230	208	0.90	0.44
Quail	24	19	0.79	?
Turtle Dove	364	273	0.75	0.34
Corn Bunting	262	191	0.73	0.31
Rook	318	229	0.72	?
Grey Partridge	291	178	0.61	0.35
Tree Sparrow	372	114	0.31	0.30
Woodpigeon	454	476		
Skylark	452	463		
Whitethroat	413	442		
Yellowhammer	443	454		
Chukar	0	2		
Stone Curlew	10	0		
Stonechat	3	1		
Wheatear	2	0		
Red-backed Shrike	9	0		
Cirl Bunting	4	0		

Table 4.4: Changes in the numbers of occupied tetrads between the two atlases for farmland species. For a full explanation, see Table 4.2.

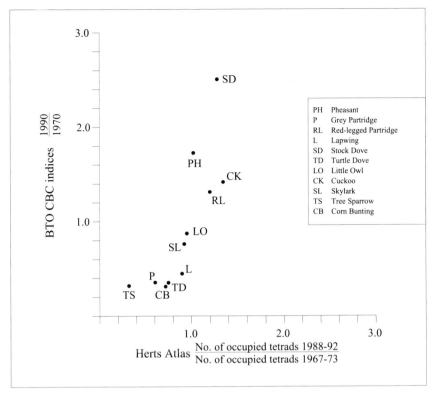

Figure 4.5: The ratio of the BTO Common Bird Census indices in 1990 and 1970 plotted against the ratio of the number of occupied tetrads (confirmed and probable breeding) in the Hertfordshire atlases in 1988-92 and 1967-73 for farmland species.

Species	No. of tetrads 1967-73	No. of tetrads 1988-92	Ratio	Change in national population index 1970-90
Collared Dove	184	431	2.34	+
Magpie	272	436	1.60	1.92
Pied Wagtail	228	300	1.32	1.46
Carrion Crow	375	376	1.00	2.23
House Martin	393	391	0.99	0.82
Linnet	403	369	0.92	0.66
Goldfinch	391	354	0.91	1.82
Swift	225	216	0.91	?
Spotted Flycatcher	334	295	0.88	0.50
Black Redstart	5	1		
Feral Pigeon	-	190		

Table 4.5: Changes in the numbers of occupied tetrads between the two atlases for species of built-up areas. For a full explanation, see Table 4.2.

Feral Pigeon is included in this table although it was only surveyed in the new atlas and not the old.

Bird numbers in urban and suburban areas are not effectively monitored by the national schemes, although most of the species found to be associated with these habitats are also found in woodland or farmland. This may be the reason for the anomalous results for Carrion Crow and Goldfinch, both of which appear to be increasing nationally, whilst decreasing or remaining stable in Hertfordshire.

CHANGES IN DISTRIBUTION OF UBIQUITOUS SPECIES

Ubiquitous species are defined as those for which there are no clear habitat associations. This therefore includes species which occur in virtually all tetrads and those which occur in such a variety of habitats that there are no clear habitat associations with their presence in a tetrad.

The former category includes such widespread species as the Blackbird, Dunnock, Robin and Wren. Four species fall into the latter category: Meadow Pipit, Lesser Whitethroat, Blackcap and Bullfinch. Both Blackcap and Lesser Whitethroat have increased their distributions significantly, whilst Bullfinch and Meadow Pipit have decreased.

v: Habitat preferences

INTRODUCTION

In chapter two the land-use and agricultural statistics for Hertfordshire for the two atlas periods were presented; in this chapter these data are used to look at habitat preferences of some of the bird species and to examine whether these preferences can account for any of the changes in bird distributions between the two atlases.

The details of the methods used to look at habitat associations are given in Appendix 5.1. In essence, the tetrads have been divided into two groups for each species: those with confirmed or probable breeding and those with possible or no breeding. The values of each of the habitat variables have then been compared for the two groups of tetrads. A total of 26 variables have been used in the analysis; 15 relating to land-use, measured from the Ordnance Survey maps, and 11 agricultural variables derived from the MAFF statistics. As described in chapter two, there were very few changes to the land-use variables between the two atlases but, as might be expected, the agricultural variables had changed greatly. Two complete analyses, one for each atlas, were therefore carried out and the results compared.

The results of the analyses are summarised in Appendix 5.2 in which, for each of the species analysed, the direction and strength of the habitat associations are indicated for each atlas.

Although the overall change in the number of occupied tetrads was often small, for most species there was considerable turnover with far more tetrads gaining or losing the species than the net change would suggest. In addition to the simple habitat associations for each species, the data for those tetrads where there had been a change in occupancy between the two atlases has been compared with tetrads where there has been no change.

LIMITATIONS OF THE ANALYSIS

Detailed examination of the results in Appendix 5.2 reveals many interesting habitat associations and changes that have occurred in the last twenty years, but before looking at these in detail it is worthwhile discussing their limitations and their interpretation.

The major limitation is that analyses of this sort are only looking at correlations with species' distributions and are not able to say anything about causation. So, for instance, the presence of a species in a tetrad may be positively associated with, say, the numbers of pigs, yet there may be no clear ecological reason why the two should be linked. In such cases, only detailed studies of the ecology of the species could possibly reveal the causes of the link which may be some other common factor like, for instance, a major owner of pig units managing his woodlands in a particular way. Although this is a particularly trivial and fictitious example, it serves to illustrate the care needed when interpreting the results of correlation analyses. The normal scientific solution to these problems would be to design experiments to test the interpretation of the correlations but this is beyond the scope of this book.

An additional problem is correlations between the habitat variables themselves, of which there are many striking examples in the Hertfordshire data. For instance, many towns and built-up areas are situated next to rivers so there is a positive correlation between rivers and built-up areas. Many wetland species, such as the grebes, are positively associated with both rivers and built-up areas but we would not suggest for one moment that they like towns *per se*. In this simple example it is relatively easy to understand the underlying cause of the observed associations. There are likely, however, to be instances where the true cause is not obvious from the data available.

There are many significant correlations particularly amongst the agricultural variables. Those concerned with tilled land, such as the areas of wheat, barley, field beans and oilseed rape are all highly correlated with each other as are the variables associated with grasslands (permanent grass, clover leys and numbers of cattle). The implication is that the variables essentially describe two types of farming operation: arable and grazing. Given these high levels of correlation, great care is needed in interpreting particular associations. Compared with the agricultural variables, those describing the land use are, in general, not highly correlated with each other except for those describing rivers, streams and open water.

Another statistical limitation of this type of analysis is that, given such a large number of statistical tests (121 species by 26 habitat variables) being carried out, some will be significant simply by chance. Thus with over 3000 tests approximately 150 would be expected to give a statistically significant result by chance alone.

There are instances where species have increased or decreased their distribution without any clear change in their habitat associations or the areas of the habitats themselves. There are many potential reasons for this and great care is needed in their interpretation. Changes in habitat associations do not necessarily imply that the particular habitat has caused the change in distribution. It is quite possible that any causes lie outside the UK and the changes in habitat associations simply reflect the redistribution of birds into sub-optimal or optimal habitats. The most obvious examples would be migrant species such as Whitethroat and Sedge Warbler, adversely affected by conditions in their wintering areas. However, the same thing could happen for resident species whose numbers happen to be determined by, for example, winter habitat. Examples of species in this category probably include many of the farmland buntings.

It is also probable that some of the most important habitat variables are not included in the analysis. So, for instance, many woodland species have increased in numbers and this is probably related to changes in woodland management. The only variables included in the analyses are the areas of different woodland types. Similarly, in agricultural habitats there is no measure of hedgerows and scrub which must be important variables in determining the presence of some species. In sample areas of north Hertfordshire a study in 1985 found a decline in hedgerow length of 17% since 1972 (Joyce 1987) yet there is no measure of this in the analyses because data for the whole of the county are simply not available without a great deal of analytical effort. Similarly the effects of changes in the ways land is managed for particular crops, such as the increased usage of pesticides of all sorts, have not been included.

The final caveat is that a tetrad is a very large area and is certainly larger than the territory size of most species considered here. An analysis of presence and absence on this scale is, therefore, at best only likely to reveal large effects.

In the rest of this chapter, some interesting species or groups of species have been selected to illustrate the sorts of changes that have occurred and their interpretation.

BIRDS OF PREY

The three main birds of prey in Hertfordshire, Sparrowhawk, Kestrel and Hobby, have all increased their distributions over the last twenty years. The Sparrowhawk was the species most adversely affected by the use of persistent organochlorine pesticides in the 1950s and 60s and its population was at a particularly low ebb during the old atlas. It has now staged a spectacular recovery but its habitat associations with all types of woodland have remained unchanged. The Sparrowhawk's recovery in Hertfordshire is probably now virtually complete but whether it can become established in the less wooded areas of the county remains to be seen.

The Kestrel has also increased in Hertfordshire over the last twenty years, a period in which national population indices have fallen. Like the Sparrowhawk, it was adversely affected by organochlorine pesticides but declines were less severe and were noted only in predominantly arable areas. It is probable that in Hertfordshire the numbers have now recovered in such areas. In the old atlas the Kestrel was positively associated with grasslands in the lower areas of the county and strongly negatively with all arable crops. In the new atlas the grassland association remained but there was no longer a negative association with arable. This supports the view that the bird has now spread back into arable areas.

The Hobby is an enigmatic bird which has undoubtedly increased in southern England, including Hertfordshire, over the last two decades. Increasingly it is being found away from what were thought to be its traditional nesting habitats. Although there were only low numbers of occupied tetrads in the old atlas, there was a positive association with wooded tetrads. In the new atlas a wider spectrum of occupied tetrads gave positive associations with woodlands, parklands, wetlands and grasslands.

LAPWING

In the old atlas, tetrads with breeding Lapwings had higher areas of temporary and permanent grasslands, higher numbers of cattle and more barley and oats than those without. This fits with the known habits of the species which nests on grasslands or spring sown arable land and subsequently moves the chicks to grassland. During the years between the atlases the areas of barley, oats and grasslands in Hertfordshire have decreased and there has been a marked shift to autumn rather than spring sowing of barley. In the new atlas the tetrads with Lapwings still had higher areas of grasslands and barley but the associations were less strong. Tetrads with rivers and woodlands were also preferred. It is notable that in neither atlas was there any suggestion of an association with wheat. In the new atlas there was also a weak association with field beans; a crop which has increased in area between the two atlases.

Comparing the habitat variables for those tetrads which retained their Lapwings with those which lost them between the two atlases, there were significant differences for temporary and permanent grasslands; in both cases there were greater areas in those squares which retained their birds.

Taken together, these data support the view that Lapwings have suffered from the loss of grasslands and spring sown arable crops.

SNIPE

The distribution of Snipe has declined significantly between the two atlases, a decline which has also occurred nationally. The habitat associations were similar in both atlases and, as to be expected, are positive for wetlands. The difficulty is that the extent of these habitats has been measured from Ordnance Survey maps and there therefore is no information on their management and wetness; both factors which are important for breeding Snipe (Green 1988). The main change in habitat associations between the two atlases is the loss of the positive association with the length of streams. Snipe are no longer found away from the main river valleys, suggesting that their former sites are no longer suitable, probably the result of drying up because of low rainfall and ground water abstraction.

Stock Dove

At the time of the old atlas, Stock Dove numbers were at a low ebb in the aftermath of the era of the use of organochlorine seed dressings in the 1950s. Those birds which were present showed strong associations with tetrads with greater areas of woodlands, barley, oats, grasslands and higher numbers of cattle. The distribution has now increased significantly so that in the new atlas the habitat associations were less strong. Woodlands were only significant on the basis of total area, although barley and oats remained. There were no significant differences in the habitats of the tetrads which had gained or lost Stock Doves.

The association with barley and oats, which was apparent in both atlases, even though wheat was selected in neither, suggests strongly that the link was via spring cultivations making cereal grains and weed seeds available to the birds at key times of year.

Turtle Dove

Unlike all other species of pigeons and doves, the Turtle Dove has been in decline nationally since the 1970s although the reasons are not clear. Reduction in the availability of weed seeds on arable land and grassland has been suggested along with increased spring hunting pressure in France and deterioration of the habitats in the African winter quarters. In Hertfordshire there has been a marked reduction in distribution between the two atlases with birds less likely to be found in the south and west of the County (Figure 5.1).

The habitat associations show interesting changes. In the old atlas there were associations with woodlands, arable crops and temporary grasslands. In the new atlas the woodland and temporary grassland associations were no longer significant but intriguingly the Turtle Dove was one of the few species to show a positive association with the area of oilseed rape in a tetrad. The tetrads which had retained their Turtle Doves had greater areas of wheat, barley, potatoes and field beans than those which had lost them. They also had smaller areas of temporary and permanent grasslands and numbers of cattle.

The fact that Turtle Doves are no longer associated with tetrads containing grasslands is perhaps linked to changes in grassland management with a shift from hay to silage cropping. Murton *et al* (1964) found that Turtle Doves fed in weedy hay fields in May and June. Nowadays, many of these hay fields have either been lost entirely or are managed for silage.

Nightingale

Sadly, the Nightingale is now much reduced in distribution in Hertfordshire. In the old atlas it was associated with all types of woodland but is now only so with broad-leaved woodlands. Undoubtedly the Nightingale has suffered from a lack of dense scrub in which to nest, either as the result of the cessation of coppicing, the tidying of the landscape or the lack of young plantation woodlands. In other counties it is often found in riverine scrub but this does not appear to be the case in Hertfordshire.

Grasshopper Warbler

There has been a major decline in the Grasshopper Warbler population in Hertfordshire which largely reflects the national picture. Although poor conditions in the African wintering areas have been suggested as the explanation, it is by no means certain that this is the case and habitat changes in the breeding areas may also be implicated. There were large changes in the habitat associations between the two atlases. In the old one

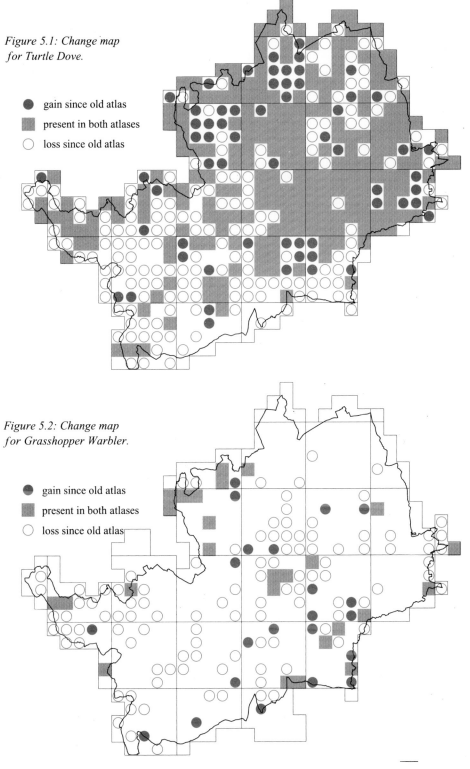

Figure 5.1: Change map for Turtle Dove.

● gain since old atlas
▨ present in both atlases
○ loss since old atlas

Figure 5.2: Change map for Grasshopper Warbler.

● gain since old atlas
▨ present in both atlases
○ loss since old atlas

281

there were positive associations with broad-leaved and mixed woodlands, permanent grassland, and cattle. This presumably reflected the use at the time of young plantations and coppice woodland. In the new atlas these associations had changed completely with birds favouring tetrads with open water and rivers. Thus, in the course of twenty years, the Grasshopper Warbler in Hertfordshire has changed from being a woodland to a wetland species. The change map (Figure 5.2) illustrates the losses from tetrads away from the river valleys and gains for some within them. The fact that no selection for wetlands was found in the first atlas suggests that this is a genuine shift in habitat use rather than simply a reflection of changed population levels. At present it is not clear whether a similar shift has occurred nationally or whether this is a local phenomenon.

ROOK

The distribution of the Rook has decreased significantly between the two atlases. It is a bird that is associated with mixed farming systems, feeding on grasslands, cereals and other tilled fields at different times of year depending on the availability of food. The decrease in the area of grasslands and increased tillage are likely to have adversely affected Rooks in some areas. The habitat associations show the birds to be associated with arable farmland, but not grasslands, in both atlases. Those tetrads in which Rooks were retained between the two atlases had significantly greater areas of wheat, barley and, particularly, oats. Of these, the areas of barley and oats have decreased whilst wheat has increased in Hertfordshire over the last two decades.

TREE SPARROW

In Hertfordshire, the Tree Sparrow is one of the species that has decreased in distribution by the greatest extent over the last twenty years. The habitat associations show that formerly it was found in tetrads with large areas of woodland as well as some of the agricultural crops (wheat, oats, field beans, temporary grassland, and cattle). It was clearly never a bird of out and out arable farmland. In the new atlas the woodland association had gone entirely, reflecting the loss of the species from many areas in the south of the county, but some agricultural associations were just significant (oats, oilseed rape, fallow and temporary grassland). Given that many of these habitats such as oats, fallow and temporary grass have declined in extent between the two atlases, their apparent selection is even more interesting. The Tree Sparrow was also one of the few species to show any association with the area of oilseed rape in a tetrad.

Groups of Tree Sparrows often nest in mature hedgerow trees and the loss of these as a result of Dutch elm disease and general attrition may also be a factor in the bird's decline. Unfortunately, we have no measure of the density of hedgerow trees with which to test this hypothesis. Summers-Smith (1989) has suggested that Tree Sparrow numbers in Britain reflect those on the continent, being supplemented by influxes when continental populations are high. In the 1970s numbers were certainly high in Hertfordshire and this is the period when birds moved into woodland and suburban locations in the south of the county. But, as a seed eating bird, it is also likely that the fortunes of the population are related to agricultural land-use and the habitat associations found here support this to some extent.

CORN BUNTING

Corn Buntings have shown a major decline between the two atlases. In the old atlas they were associated with arable crops, fallow, temporary grasslands, cattle and pigs. By the time of the new atlas the associations with grasslands and fallow had been lost although those with arable crops remained. The Corn Bunting has been reported to prefer areas with barley (O'Connor & Shrubb 1986, Thompson & Gribbin 1986) and the tetrads that retained their birds between the two atlases had greater areas of barley than those which lost them. There was also a significant but less strong association with wheat (i.e. tetrads which retained their Corn Buntings had greater areas of wheat than those which lost them). These results are consistent with the view that Corn Buntings have now retreated to the areas dominated by arable farmland and particularly the lighter soils where barley is widely grown. The ecological reasons for this have still not been determined and to do so will require detailed research into the birds' feeding ecology in the breeding and non-breeding seasons.

SUMMARY

These species accounts have been included as examples of the wealth of information contained in Appendix 5.2. There are many other interesting and illuminating changes in habitat preferences which have occurred between the two atlases. Readers are invited to explore Appendix 5.2 themselves.

VI: Common, rare and future breeding birds in Hertfordshire

Two of the questions most frequently asked of a birdwatcher are what are the most common and most rare birds in their area. In this chapter the most numerous breeding species in Hertfordshire are examined together with the status of some of the rarest. Also, an attempt is made to speculate and indulge in the dangerous practice of predicting some of the future additions to the county's avifauna.

THE MOST NUMEROUS BREEDING SPECIES

Which are the most numerous breeding species in Hertfordshire? In Table 6.1 the 20 most numerous species are listed based on the mean of the estimated breeding population given in Appendix 3.1. The Wren and Blackbird head the list both with over 50,000 pairs. In fact they are almost six times more numerous than the Rook, the 20th species on the list. Woodpigeon at ninth is the highest genuinely wild non-passerine on the list. Pheasant, at number seven, is probably only that high because the population is artificially maintained for shooting. The Willow Warbler is the highest summer visitor at 14th on the list. This species, along with Blackcap and Chiffchaff, are the only migrants represented in the table.

Although sheer numbers are impressive, they may not be the best indicator of a species' impact on the environment. One male Mute Swan represents the equivalent biomass of over 1000 Wrens, the county's most numerous species. In Table 6.2 the top 20 species are again listed but this time ranked by biomass of the breeding population. The mass of the total county breeding population of each species has been calculated

	Species	Pairs	
1	Wren	52,000	
2	Blackbird	51,000	
3	Chaffinch	39,000	
4	Blue Tit	38,000	
5	Robin	37,000	
6	House Sparrow	27,000	
7	Pheasant*	25,000	* number of females
8	Dunnock	21,000	
9=	Great Tit	20,000	
9=	Woodpigeon	20,000	
11	Starling	19,000	
12	Skylark	16,000	
13	Yellowhammer	14,000	
14	Willow Warbler	13,000	
15	Blackcap	12,000	
16	Magpie	11,000	
17	Song Thrush	11,000	
18	Greenfinch	10,000	
19	Chiffchaff	9,000	
20	Rook	9,000	

Table 6.1: The 20 most numerous species breeding in Hertfordshire. Population figures are based on the average estimated population range given in the species texts and appendix 3.1 but quoted to the nearest 1000.

	Species	Total mass of breeding population (kilogrammes)
1	Pheasant	36,700
2	Woodpigeon	21,000
3	Mallard	11,400
4	Blackbird	9,800
5	Rook	8,500
6	Carrion Crow	5,900
7	Magpie	5,200
8	Canada Goose	4,600
9	Mute Swan	3,800
10	Starling	3,100
11	Red-legged Partridge	2,900
12	Moorhen	2,500
13=	Feral Pigeon	1,700
13=	Stock Dove	1,700
13=	Song Thrush	1,700
16	Chaffinch	1,600
17	House Sparrow	1,500
18	Robin	1,400
19	Skylark	1,200
20	Coot	1,100

Table 6.2: The top 20 species breeding in Hertfordshire ranked by biomass of the total breeding population. Figures are rounded to the nearest 100 kilogrammes.

using the average estimated population. The list is considerably different from Table 6.1. The first three places are taken by non-passerines with Blackbird fourth and representing only approximately 27% of the biomass of the top species, Pheasant. When the species were ranked by numbers, there were no wetland species in the top 20, but in Table 6.2 there are five species (Mallard, Canada Goose, Mute Swan, Moorhen and Coot) from this relatively restricted habitat.

It is perhaps a measure of the conspicuousness of bird populations that at the outset of the breeding season the total mass of breeding birds in Hertfordshire is probably less than 150 tonnes – equivalent to the mass of a few oak trees or the load carried by less than a dozen lorries. In comparison the total human population of the county has a mass of probably nearer 50,000 tonnes!

RARE BREEDING SPECIES

There seems little doubt that in times long past, when human population levels and agricultural practices were considerably different from those of today, birds such as Great Bustard *Otis tarda* and Red Kite *Milvus milvus* could have been encountered in the county. Indeed, it does not require a great deal of imagination to place the former species in the prairie-like fields found in the north of the county although the last report of one was around 1808 (Sage 1959). The chances of this happening again are presumably extremely remote. The Red Kite became extinct in England when hygiene practices improved and persecution with the gun became the norm for all raptors. However, this species will be considered again later in this chapter in a more optimistic light with increasing occurrences resulting from the re-introduction programme.

Sage (1959) noted some old breeding records for a number of species, some of which may have bred on a more regular basis in the past, or were of a distinctly one-off nature.

Species	73	74	75	76	77	78	79	80	81	82	83	84	85	86	87	88	89	90	91	92
Black-necked Grebe (R)											–			–		–	■	–		–
Cormorant	–	–		–	–	–	–	–	–	–		–				–	–	–	–	–
Egyptian Goose							–				–	–						–	–	■
Shelduck	–			–	–			–	–	■	–	■	■	■	–	■	■	■	■	■
Mandarin							–				–	–	■	■	■	■	■	■	■	■
Garganey (R)			–				–			–	–	■		■		–	–	–		
Ruddy Duck	–	–	–	–	–	–	–	■	–	■	■	■	■	■	■	■	■	■	■	■
Honey Buzzard (R)			–				–								–					–
Buzzard	–	–		–	–	–	–	–				–			–			–	–	
Golden Pheasant			–	–												–	–	–	–	
Quail (R)								■	■	–	–		–			–	■			
Spotted Crake (R)							–													
Corncrake (R)																				
Stone Curlew (R)	–	■	–	■	■	■	–	■	■		–		–							
Common Sandpiper																	–			
Ring-necked Parakeet			–							–						–				
Nightjar	■	■	■	■	■	■	■	■	■	■	■	■	■	■	■	■	■	■	■	–
Wryneck (R)	■			■	–	–														
Stonechat	■		–			–	–													
Cetti's Warbler (R)					–	–	■	■	■	–	–			–				–		
Savi's Warbler (R)							–							–						
Marsh Warbler (R)						–	–									–				
Firecrest (R)			–				–				–	–	–			■	–	–	–	
Pied Flycatcher						–	–					–	–			■		■		–
Bearded Tit	–	–			–															
Golden Oriole (R)			–			–	–					–	–							–
Red-backed Shrike (R)		■				–	–	–												–
Siskin	–									■			■		–		■			–
Crossbill	■	■		–				–					–				–		–	–

– = Recorded in the breeding season ■ = Probable or confirmed breeding (R) Considered by the national Rare Breeding Birds Panel

Figure 6.1: Records of the rare breeding species of Hertfordshire 1973-92, including occurrences in the breeding season, taken from the Hertfordshire Bird Reports.

These included such species as Bittern *Botaurus stellaris* (1849), Montagu's Harrier *Circus pygargus* (1809), Raven *Corvus corax* (1846), Ring Ouzel *Turdus torquatus* (1864) and Dipper *Cinclus cinclus* (pre First World War).

Gladwin & Sage (1986) list additional species lost and gained by the county. These include, up to the end of the first atlas period in 1973, the following breeding species gained: Canada Goose (1965), Greylag Goose (1963), Egyptian Goose (1938), Mandarin (1972), Ruddy Duck (1965), Black-headed Gull *Larus ridibundus* (1950), Common Tern (1962), Collared Dove (1958) and Bearded Tit (1966). Those considered lost as breeding species include: Black-headed Gull (1964), Whinchat (1972), Wheatear (1967), Bearded Tit (1968), Red-backed Shrike (1968) and Cirl Bunting (1964).

When considering breeding attempts of rarer species there is often some difficulty, because of the general paucity of records, in judging whether they are increasing or decreasing or when exactly a species can be considered to have colonised or finally ceased to breed. These processes are rarely clear-cut and are frequently confused either by initial sporadic attempts or the occurrence of lingering individuals after the last confirmed breeding. To complicate matters there are a number of species, such as

Spotted Crake, which are recognised as genuinely irregular breeders.

It is, therefore, useful to review records from the annual bird reports to register not only breeding records but also the presence of species in appropriate habitat during the breeding season. Figure 6.1 shows this for the 20 years between 1973-92. Whilst this is extremely simplistic and is no doubt biased in later years due to improved observer coverage associated partly with the atlas survey, it is interesting to note how many positive breeding attempts have been accompanied by records of the presence of the species in preceding years.

Table 6.3 lists the rare species which have consolidated their breeding distribution since the last atlas (6), those which have been gained based on records of probable or confirmed breeding in the new atlas (9) and those which have been lost (10). This table is based entirely on atlas data and for this purpose records of probable or confirmed breeding have been taken to imply that birds have bred. There are therefore some species, such as Honey Buzzard, where there is, as yet, no proof of breeding in the county but there is an atlas record of probable breeding because of displaying birds.

Of the species that have consolidated, five are now well established although the Firecrest is still not as numerous as would be expected. Of the ten species recorded as lost, three, Buzzard, Spotted Crake and Bearded Tit, could only be described as sporadic breeding birds in Hertfordshire. The remaining seven have all declined nationally. In fact, Red-backed Shrike is virtually extinct as a British breeding species.

The nine species which have been gained form a diverse group. It contains sporadic breeders such as Black-necked Grebe and Honey Buzzard, as well as wetland species which will surely consolidate their tenure over the next few decades. The Chukar records result entirely from the artificial release of birds.

Some of the species listed as 'gained' or 'consolidated' first bred as isolated attempts before the period under consideration. This includes Egyptian Goose, which bred at Hampermill Lake in 1938, long before it was added to the British List; Mandarin, which first bred in 1972 at Wrotham Park; and Ruddy Duck which bred at Tring Reservoirs in 1965. However, all these species are now consolidating their footholds, with the last two now becoming particularly well established in the county. Of the others, Shelduck is really only breeding regularly in the Lee valley with other pairs possible at Tyttenhanger gravel pits and Stockers Lake, and Firecrest has yet to fulfil its expected potential, not only in Hertfordshire but in the country as a whole.

Lost	Gained	Consolidated
Buzzard	Egyptian Goose	Shoveler
Spotted Crake	Shelduck	Gadwall
Stone Curlew	Wood Duck	Mandarin
Curlew	Black-necked Grebe	Ruddy Duck
Wryneck	Honey Buzzard	Ringed Plover
Woodlark	Garganey	Firecrest
Wheatear	Chukar	
Bearded Tit	Cetti's Warbler	
Red-backed Shrike	Pied Flycatcher	
Cirl Bunting		

Table 6.3: The species which, based on atlas records, have been lost or gained as breeding birds over the last twenty years. Breeding is taken to mean records of probable or confirmed breeding in the relevant atlas period. The species listed as 'consolidated' are those which were breeding in three or fewer tetrads between 1967- 73 but have subsequently increased their distribution.

The last category to be considered in this section on rare breeding species is those that are not included in Table 6.3 but may be possible new additions to the county's breeding list in the future.

Cormorants have increased their inland breeding populations in recent years with some birds, mostly immatures, remaining in Hertfordshire throughout the summer. A rapidly increasing breeding colony is established just outside the county border and nest building has been observed in the Colne valley and at Tring Reservoirs. It may not be long before the first successful breeding occurs within Hertfordshire and it will be interesting to watch the establishment of this species in the future.

Ring-necked Parakeets breed in Berkshire at Wraysbury in the lower Colne valley. The species seems to prefer fairly old trees with suitable holes for nesting. Survival apparently depends on access to garden feeders during hard winter weather. Whilst well established and increasing in the southern and western home counties, it does not show obvious signs of dramatically spreading beyond this base but, given the right combination of habitat and nest sites, it may well breed in Hertfordshire in the future.

Now for some predictions. Red Kite, mentioned earlier in this section, has been seen more frequently in the county in recent years. These are presumably birds associated with the JNCC/RSPB re-introduction scheme in England. This has been extremely successful with the first breeding in the wild in 1992. If this progress is maintained the Red Kite could well be a spectacular addition to the breeding avifauna of Hertfordshire over the next few decades.

With consolidation of breeding colonies in the south-east, it is possible that Marsh Warblers may establish a more permanent foothold in Hertfordshire than the sporadic occurrences to date. A singing male, which had been ringed as a juvenile at an English colony, remained at Rye Meads during the spring of 1993 which bodes well for the future.

Two other species which could find the right conditions in Hertfordshire, and which are expanding their European distributions, are Penduline Tit *Remiz pendulinus* and Scarlet Rosefinch *Carpodacus erythrinus*. The former has yet to be recorded in the county and the latter has occurred only twice. However, if range expansion continues, it is not beyond possibility that both may breed in Hertfordshire in the next 20 years.

THE FUTURE

It is, perhaps, easy to view the Hertfordshire countryside as a static and seldom changing scene. However, as the changes in the agriculture maps show, land usage in a highly populated county is under enormous pressures from a great variety of sources. Whilst the establishment of special areas as reserves for wildlife is an excellent way of preserving the most biologically precious environments, most of the land within the county cannot, nor ever will be, specially protected. Yet it is here, in ordinary farmland and woodland, that the majority of birds live. Once, the future of farming and forestry in Britain looked bleak for wildlife. The chemical control of pests and weeds, plus the elimination of hedgerows to allow the easy working of huge fields all pointed to a loss of the diversity essential to provide a good variety and maintain populations of species. Changes in practices such as from spring to winter sowing of cereals, the favouring of certain crops such as oilseed rape (and latterly linseed) have an effect which is being, or will be, reflected in the birdlife. It will, perhaps, be for the next atlas of breeding birds to analyse the benefits or not of the possible changes in agricultural practices with the reforms to the Common Agricultural Policy. Already people are getting used to the sight of set-aside areas which, with sympathetic management, could develop in only a few years to benefit a wide range of species.

Appendices

Appendix 1.1: List of co-ordinators, observers and artists

LIST OF OBSERVERS WHO CONTRIBUTED RECORDS

P D Adams, N Agar, P Amer, G H Annibal, G Anderson, M Ashworth, L J Atkinson, S Austin, D G Baggott, A Bailiff, H Baker, S Banks, L Barber, J W Barrington, C M Beech, C Beddall, G Bellamy, P Bellchamber, V Benfield, S Bennett, D Best, B Bickerton, J Bishop, A D Bisset, B Borrill, R Boxall, A Boyt, C Brackenbury, J Braggs, N H Brashaw, A K Brew, M C Brew, M J Bridges, British Trust for Ornithology, D Brougham, T Brown, W Burley, I Burrus, C W Burton, P Burton, C I Bushell, D F Calnon, L Carman, N Carter, S P Carter, T E Casson, N Cerri, P J Chadder, P Charlton, G Clayden, D Coates, H Coe, R Cole, A Cook, J Cook, I Cooper, S L Cooper, G W Corfield, P Cosgrove, C Cottrell, V C Cottrell, T J Cox, M Craig, R Craufurd, H Q P Crick, S Cumming, A Curtis, V A Dalkin, G Davies, J Davies, T J Davis, R Dazley, J Dean, T Dean, C W Dee, M Dee, M Dick, R Dimsdale, T Dockerty, C Dowling, J Dowling, B Drayton, R Drew, P Dudgeon, C Dudley, S P Dudley, P A M Dyer, M J Earp, J Edwards, J Eggington, M C Elliott, G Elton, W B Emms, M L Errington, C M Everett, T Evershed, P J Ewins, D Farrow, J Fearnshaw, J D Fearnside, J Ferguson, H D Field, J Fish, A Fisher, E W Fletcher, P Flowerday, P F Foxcroft, A H Gardiner, M Garner, T W Gladwin, J S Godfree, M G Godfree, R Goodacre, A E Goodall, J E Guest, S Harding, A J Harris, M A Harris, W A Hatton, R Hicks, D Hill, D M Hill, P Hiller, T G Holder, M Hornsby, A M Howard, G Howard, A Hughes, T Hukin, C Hull, C A R Hulls, M J L Hurford, M Ilett, J Innes, T J James, A Johnson, D Johnson, I Johnson, I Kelly, M Ketcher, D King, J King, T Kittle, L Knowles, D Lees, A Lewis, B Lewis, P Lewis, S A Lewis, T Lewis, T J Lewis, A J Livett, D McKee, J H Marchant, A Marrett, the late E Maughan, J Melling, D Merrie, N Metcalfe, R Middleton, J Mitchell, A V Moon, D Morphew, D C Mullinger, K A Nash, E Newman, North Herts Birders, M Oakland, S Oxlade, L Oxley, J Palmer, L E Parr, V W Patterson, B Payne, B P Payne, S Pearce, M Peck, A Plumb, A Pratt, D Pratt, C Price, A Proud, J Redwood, B Reed, J M Reed, M Reed, P Rhodes, P Roper, L A Rowe, M D Russell, Rye Meads Ringing Group, J M Saunders, J Sharman, K Sharpe, C R Shawyer, E A M Sly, J M A Sly, C Smart, C Smout, K W Smith, L M Smith, R N Smith, M Sneary, R Spain, B R Squires, I Stewart, the late B Styles, C Swan, H Symington, C E Tack, B Taggart, P Tate, J Taylor, J Temple, J H Terry, P S Thompson, J N Tomkins, D K Toomer, J L Toomer, P Tout, C Townend, B E Trevis, P Trodd, G Tucker, the late W Utley, P Walker, P D Walton, R Waters, C W Watts, D Webb, D J Wedd, D West, G J White, P A Whittington, J Whomes, C Wilkins, P J Wilkinson, M Williams, P Williams, A Wilson, A R Wistow, R J Wistow, R Wooding, J Wright, R Young.

N Borrow: Little Grebe, Great Crested Grebe, Grey Heron, Cuckoo, Long-tailed Tit, Marsh Tit, Willow Tit, Coal Tit, Blue Tit, Great Tit.

A Chick: Red-legged Partridge, Grey Partridge, Quail, Pheasant, Green Woodpecker, Great Spotted Woodpecker, Lesser Spotted Woodpecker, Nuthatch, Treecreeper, Yellowhammer, Reed Bunting, Corn Bunting.

G Clayden: Shelduck, Mandarin, Gadwall, Teal, Mallard, Garganey, Shoveler, Pochard, Tufted Duck, Ruddy Duck, Common Tern, Feral Pigeon, Stock Dove, Woodpigeon, Collared Dove, Turtle Dove, Jay, Magpie, Jackdaw, Rook, Carrion Crow.

H Coe: Mute Swan, Greylag Goose, Canada Goose, Chaffinch, Greenfinch, Goldfinch, Siskin, Linnet, Redpoll, Crossbill, Bullfinch, Hawfinch.

K Colcombe: Grasshopper Warbler, Sedge Warbler, Reed Warbler, Lesser Whitethroat, Whitethroat, Garden Warbler, Blackcap, Wood Warbler, Chiffchaff, Willow Warbler.

J D Fearnside: House Sparrow, Tree Sparrow.

A J Harris: Front cover and spine colour illustrations of Hobby. Water Rail, Moorhen, Coot, Robin, Nightingale, Black Redstart, Redstart, Whinchat, Stonechat, Blackbird, Song Thrush, Mistle Thrush, Starling.

E Leahy: Skylark, Sand Martin, Swallow, House Martin, Tree Pipit, Meadow Pipit, Yellow Wagtail, Grey Wagtail, Pied Wagtail, Wren, Dunnock.

M Pollard: Little Ringed Plover, Ringed Plover, Lapwing, Snipe, Woodcock, Redshank, Common Sandpiper, Goldcrest, Firecrest, Spotted Flycatcher.

J Wilczur: Sparrowhawk, Kestrel, Hobby, Barn Owl, Little Owl, Tawny Owl, Long-eared Owl, Nightjar, Swift, Kingfisher.

Appendix 1.2: Computer methods used

The use of computer technology has provided benefits throughout the production of this atlas. During the fieldwork period the electronic storage of records allowed regular feedback to be supplied to the fieldworkers, allowing more efficient use of their time in targeting habitat suitable for un-recorded species, and identifying tetrads which were in need of further work. It also made it possible to display interim distribution maps at meetings of the Herts Bird Club, which was useful in sustaining the momentum of the project. The effort required to computerise the land-use statistics and the results of the old atlas was more than compensated by the number and level of analyses which could be performed. All the maps in this book have been generated from the computerised data, substantially reducing the amount of work required for their production and eliminating errors which could have arisen during manual transcription. This also allowed late records to be incorporated with ease, and allowed flexibility on the final design. The standard format files could be output directly on a Monotype Prism PS imagesetter, at a resolution of 2400 dpi, which removed the need for intermediate processes and enhanced the final reproduction quality.

The field records were maintained using the Tetrad Recording and Plotting System developed by D J Price for the Devon Birdwatching and Preservation Society for the Devon atlas (Sitters 1988). A second copy of the database was created to store the results of the old atlas. The species status information for each tetrad was extracted from this system using a specially written BASIC program.

The bulk of the statistical analysis and manipulation of the MAFF census results was performed using SAS®, although the SYSTAT™ program was used to test the correlation between land-use and agricultural variables.

To produce the published maps a series of BASIC programs were written. These converted the species distribution, land-use and agricultural data into a series of PostScript® language files. A further BASIC program was written to convert the results of the habitat associations into PostScript files which represented the tables in Appendix 5.2. The county outline and Ordnance Survey grids were translated into PostScript language statements manually. All the PostScript files were proofed on a QMS-PS 810® laser printer.

PostScript® is a registered trademark of Adobe Systems Inc. QMS-PS 810® is a registered trademark of QMS Inc. SAS® is a registered trademark of SAS Institute Inc. SYSTAT™ is a trademark of SYSTAT Inc.

Appendix 2.1: Reconciliation of land-use statistics

In reconciling the MAFF data with the land-use measurements, it has been necessary to deal with a number of anomalies in order to assign all of the 400 hectares in every tetrad to a land-use category.

In the 1988 tetrad-based MAFF statistics, 70 tetrads (14.3%) had in excess of 400 hectares of farmland (ie. more than the entire tetrad). This could be an effect of the process used to perform the conversion from parish-based totals, inaccurate census returns or double counting of land. These anomalies were dealt with by assuming that all land not accounted for by the land-use measurement was in fact farmland and the appropriate MAFF statistics were scaled down to match this. A total of 13,231 hectares was removed from tetrad based statistics by this process, comprising 36.3% of the reported farmland in these 70 tetrads, but only 9.5% of the total farmland in the MAFF data..

In another 82 tetrads (16.7%) the area of farmland was within sensible bounds but still exceeded the amount not accounted for by the land-use measurements. In some cases this is not surprising; parkland had been measured from the maps, but this could also have been included on a MAFF census return if, for example, it was being used as grazing pasture. Wherever possible the excess was removed, initially from parkland, and then from golf courses. This resulted in the removal of 1135 hectares (18.2%) of these land types from the measured totals. In the 64 tetrads where this still failed to eliminate all the excess, the farmland statistics were then scaled down to bring the total to 400 hectares. This resulted in a decrease of only 2210 hectares (1.6%) in the area of farmland as described by the MAFF statistics.

In a far larger proportion of the tetrads (339 – 69.0%) the area of farmland in the MAFF statistics failed to account for all of the 'missing' land. Possible reasons for this are the existence of unregistered agricultural holdings and other undeveloped land not in agricultural use, such as recreational land, common land, nature reserves and private estates. This type of discrepancy has been found in other studies. In 1981 the difference between the area of farmland in the county as recorded by MAFF and that given by the Hertfordshire County Council's Planning Information Service (PLANIS) amounted to 11,400 hectares (Hertfordshire Environmental Forum 1992). For the purposes of this atlas the 35,157 hectares which cannot be accounted for have been assigned to a separate category: other open country.

An identical procedure was used to adjust the 1969 MAFF statistics to produce a dataset representative of the old atlas period.

It is these adjusted farmland statistics, and the revised values for parkland and golf courses which have been used in the subsequent analysis of bird distributions and derivation of bird population estimates.

Appendix 3.1: Population estimates

The individual species accounts contain estimates of the county breeding population. This appendix explains how these have been derived and details the assumptions which have been used. Rather few bird populations in Hertfordshire have actually been counted, so for these estimates it has been necessary to use all available data on breeding densities, some of which are from outside the county.

ASSUMPTIONS USED

1. To overcome the discrepancy between the actual area of land in Hertfordshire and the total area of the 491 tetrads of this atlas, results from 82 tetrads have been ignored. These tetrads are those for which less than 50% of their area is within the county boundary. The area of the remaining 409 tetrads (163,600 hectares) is as close to the true county area (163,415 hectares) as possible using this method.

2. Where possible the breeding densities relate to the actual period of the atlas work. Many of those for woodland and farmland are the result of an analysis of national CBC results (Gates *et al* 1993) or of Hertfordshire CBC and WBS plots.

3. For the more common species use has been made of the results of the land use classification in combination with the species distribution data. The total area of land of each type has been calculated for the occupied tetrads (probable and confirmed breeding) and this multiplied by the appropriate breeding densities. For these purposes it has been assumed that breeding densities in land categorised as golf courses, parkland and other open countryside are the same as on farmland. For the less common species, and those inadequately covered by the CBC or WBS, a variety of methods have been used – these are shown in the following key to Tables 3.1.1 and 3.1.2.

Key to Tables 3.1.1 and 3.1.2.

Method:

CBC	breeding densities from Common Birds Census
HBR	breeding records from Herts Bird Report
Text	derivation explained in text following tables
Survey	single species breeding survey
WBS	breeding densities from Waterways Bird Survey

Breeding density sources:

a	analysis of Hertfordshire farmland CBC results (95% confidence limits)
b	Gates *et al* 1993
c	Holland *et al* 1984
d	analysis of Hertfordshire WBS results (95% confidence limits)

Population estimate units:

f	females
m	males
n	nests
nba	non-breeding adults
p	pairs
t	territories

Species	Method	Breeding densities/source	Population estimate
Little Grebe	WBS	Rivers: 0.17-0.60/km d	
		Open water: 1.9-6.7/km^2 d	
		Streams: 0.13/km	
		Ponds: 0.05/pond	90-200 p
Great Crested Grebe	HBR	1988-91	70-120 p
Grey Heron	Survey	annual BTO	29-71 n
Mute Swan	Survey	1990 WWT/BTO	76 p + 200 nba
Greylag Goose	Survey	1991 WWT	1-5 p + 100 nba
Canada Goose	Survey	1991 WWT	156 p + 909 nba
Shelduck	Survey	1992 WWT	4 p
Mandarin	HBR	1988-91	10-15 p
Gadwall	HBR	1991	24 p
Teal	HBR		0
Mallard	WBS	Rivers: 4.1-7.7/km d	
		Open water: 48-86/km^2 d	
		Ponds: 0.5/pond	4000-6600 p
Garganey	HBR	1988-91	1-5 p
Shoveler	HBR	1991	2 p
Pochard	HBR	1991	9 p
Tufted Duck	HBR	1988-91	
	WBS	Rivers: 0.2-0.4/km	150-300 p
Ruddy Duck	HBR	1991	5 p
Sparrowhawk	Text		300-500 p
Kestrel	Text		300-400 p
Hobby	HBR		20-30 p
Red-legged Partridge	CBC	2.7/km^2	2000-4000 p
Grey Partridge	CBC	2.1/km^2	1000-2000 p
Quail	HBR	1988-91	0-22 p
Pheasant	CBC	5.9/km^2	4000-15,000 m
			25,000 f
Water Rail	HBR	1988-91	1-10 p
Moorhen	WBS	Rivers: 2.5-4.9/km d	
		Open water: 28-55/km^2 d	
		Ponds: 0.5/pond	3200-5200 p
Coot	WBS	Rivers: 1.1-3.7/km d	
		Open water: 12-41/km^2 d	390-1300 p
Little Ringed Plover	HBR	1988-91	15-25 p
Ringed Plover	HBR	1988-91	6-8 p
Lapwing	Survey	1987 BTO/Herts Bird Club	120-360 p
Snipe	HBR	1988-91	10-20 p
Woodcock	HBR	1988-91	50-100 m
Redshank	HBR	1988-91	5-12 p
Common Sandpiper	HBR	1988-91	0
Common Tern	HBR	1991	54 p
Feral Pigeon		20/occupied tetrad	3200 p
Stock Dove	CBC	Farmland: 1.8/km^2 b	
		Woodland: 7.6/km^2 b	2100 t
Woodpigeon	CBC	Farmland: 11.0/km^2 b	
		Woodland: 39.2/km^2 b	
		Built-up: 5.5/km^2	20,000 t
Collared Dove		4-5/occupied tetrad	1400-1800 p
Turtle Dove	CBC	Farmland: 0.6/km^2 b	

Species	Method	Breeding densities/source	Population estimate
		Woodland: 2.7/km^2 b	670 t
Cuckoo		2-5 females/occupied tetrad	680-1700 f
Barn Owl	HBR	T Dockerty (*pers comm*)	10-14 p
Little Owl		1.5/occupied tetrad	240 p
Tawny Owl		Broad-leaved wood: 8.3/km^2	
		Other wood: 5.0/km^2	
		Farmland: 0.5/km^2	1000 p
Long-eared Owl	HBR	C Shawyer (*pers comm*)	0-10 p
Nightjar	Survey	1992 RSPB/BTO	0-1 p
Swift		5-10/occupied tetrad	1100-2200 p
Kingfisher		Rivers: 0.5/km	
		Streams: 0.13/km	100 p
Green Woodpecker		Farmland: 0.4/km^2 b	
		Woodland: 3.7/km^2 b	590 t
Great Spotted		Coniferous wood: 1.0/km^2	
Woodpecker		Other wood: 10.0/km^2	1100 p
Lesser Spotted		Coniferous wood: 1.0/km^2	
Woodpecker		Other wood: 3.3/km^2	170 p

Table 3.1.1: Non passerine population estimates for Hertfordshire.

PASSERINES

Species	Method	Breeding densities (per km^2) Woodland	Farmland & other open countryside	Built-up	Population estimate
Skylark	CBC	1.3 b	7.2-20.2 a	-	8400-23,000 t
Sand Martin	Text				970 n
Swallow	CBC	-	4.2 b	-	4400 t
House Martin	CBC	-	-	3.5 c	5000 p
Tree Pipit	CBC	2.4 b	-	-	100 t
Meadow Pipit	CBC	-	0.5 b	-	260 t
Yellow Wagtail	CBC	-	0.5 b	-	80 t
Grey Wagtail	Text				80-160 p
Pied Wagtail	CBC	-	1.8 b	0.5 b	1400 t
Wren	CBC	134.2 b	11.8-37.0 a	10.5 c	37,000-67,000 t
Dunnock	CBC	26.6 b	7.0-17.6 a	9.0 c	15,000-27,000 t
Robin	CBC	104.4 b	9.8-25.2 a	3.8 c	28,000-46,000 t
Nightingale	HBR				3-12 p
Black Redstart	HBR				0-1 p
Redstart	HBR				0-6 p
Whinchat	HBR				0-2 p
Stonechat	HBR				0-1 p
Blackbird	CBC	66.9 b	19.0-38.4 a	26.8 c	40,000-63,000 t
Song Thrush	CBC	24.6 b	4.9 b	5.0 c	11,000 t
Mistle Thrush	CBC	5.4 b	1.4-3.4 a	1.3 c	2400-4300 t
Grasshopper Warbler	Text				20-50 p
Sedge Warbler	Text				260-580 t
Reed Warbler	Text				120-240 p
Lesser Whitethroat	CBC	1. 8 b	0.7-2.3 a	-	730-2000 t
Whitethroat	CBC	5.4 b	1.3-5.1 a	-	2100-6300 t
Garden Warbler	CBC	8. 1 b	0.3-1.9 a	-	1200-2500 t

Species	Method	Breeding densities (per km^2)			Population estimate
		Woodland	Farmland & other open countryside	Built-up	
Blackcap	CBC	27.5 b	1.5-11.7 a	-	5800-18,000 t
Wood Warbler	HBR				0-9 p
Chiffchaff	CBC	25.7 b	0.9-9.3 a	-	4700-14,000 t
Willow Warbler	CBC	46. 9 b	1.4-8.3 a	-	8500-17,000 t
Goldcrest	CBC	22.0 b	1.4 b	0.5 b	3700 t
Firecrest	HBR				0-10 p
Spotted Flycatcher	CBC	2.6 b	0.7 b	2.0	1100 t
Long-tailed Tit	CBC	7.2 b	1.7 b	-	2600 t
Marsh Tit	CBC	4.0 b	0.4 b	-	450 t
Willow Tit	Text				180-500 p
Coal Tit	CBC	26.7 b	1.0 b	0.7 b	4000 t
Blue Tit	CBC	82.4 b	11.0-32.0 a	10.8 c	25,000-50,000 t
Great Tit	CBC	48.6 b	6.2-14.6 a	2.8 c	15,000-25,000 t
Nuthatch	CBC	7.9 b	0.7 b	0.1 b	1300 t
Treecreeper	CBC	9.2 b	0.9 b	0.1 b	1600 t
Jay	CBC	8.8 b	0.5-2.3 a	-	1100-2000 t
Magpie	CBC	9.3 b	4.2-11.2 a	7.5 c	7700-15,000 t
Jackdaw	CBC	4.9 b	2.2 b	-	2000 t
Rook	Text				7500-10,000 n
Carrion Crow	CBC	7.1 b	4.9 b	-	5200 t
Starling	CBC	12.5 b	4.0-14.4 a	23.3 c	13,000-25,000 t
House Sparrow	CBC	-	-	100.0 c	27,000 p
Tree Sparrow	CBC	1.6 b	0.9 b	-	320 t
Chaffinch	CBC	71.4 b	11.3-31.5 a	12.3 b	27,000-51,000 t
Greenfinch	CBC	5.5 b	3.3 -11.1 a	4.5 c	5800-15,000 t
Goldfinch	CBC	1.2 b	2.1 b	0.4 b	2000 t
Siskin	Text				0-3 p
Linnet	CBC	3.4 b	1.7-6.1 a	0.8 b	2100-6100 t
Redpoll	Text				74-150 p
Crossbill	HBR				0-9 p
Bullfinch	CBC	7.7 b	1.3 b	-	1800 p
Hawfinch	Text				43-130 p
Yellowhammer	CBC	7.6 b	7.1-14.7 a	-	9100-18,000 t
Reed Bunting	Text				1100-1500 t
Corn Bunting	Text				300-730 t

Table 3.1.2: Passerine population estimates for Hertfordshire.

METHODS OF CALCULATING POPULATION ESTIMATES SHOWN AS TEXT IN TABLES 3.1.1 AND
3.1.2

Sparrowhawk

Population estimates were derived by assuming the breeding density in occupied tetrads in Hertfordshire is in the range of 0.3-0.5 pairs/km^2 given by Newton (1986).

Kestrel

Breeding numbers vary annually depending on the availability of prey but Village (1990) gives densities of 0.32 pairs/km^2 for grassland areas and 0.12 pairs/km^2 for arable farmland as reasonable.

Sand Martin

In 1986 the Hertfordshire breeding population comprised a minimum of 355 pairs at eight sites (White 1987). Assuming the same average colony size, and a single colony for each tetrad from which probable or confirmed breeding records were received, gives an estimated total of 970 nests.

Grey Wagtail

The county breeding population estimate of 80-160 pairs is based on one or two pairs per tetrad from which probable or confimed breeding records were received.

Grasshopper Warbler

The breeding population is difficult to establish. An estimated 1.0 to 2.5 pairs per tetrad in which breeding was probable or confirmed implies 40-100 pairs but given the fact that these represent the cumulative breeding attempts over the five years of the atlas the figure should probably be reduced to 20-50 pairs.

Sedge Warbler

Results from Hertfordshire WBS plots during the atlas period give an idea of the breeding density of this species alongside rivers (0.56-1.45 per kilometre) and it has been assumed that similar densities are achieved along the banks of larger water bodies. The degree and significance of farmland breeding is more difficult to establish and has been estimated as 0.25 pairs per tetrad. Appplying these densities to the amounts of those habitats in occupied tetrads gives an estimate of 260-580 territories.

Reed Warbler

The very specific habitat needs of this species during the breeding season should allow its breeding population to be assessed reasonably easily. This has never been done and, based on a density of two to four pairs per occupied tetrad (Sharrock 1976), the best estimate available is 120-240 pairs.

Willow Tit

The county breeding population would be grossly under-estimated if the woodland CBC density of 1.3 pairs per square kilometre were used. Instead we have used an estimate of 1.5-4 pairs per occupied tetrad to give a breeding population of 180-500 pairs.

Rook

During the 1975 BTO national census 8700 Rook nests were counted in Hertfordshire, and a partial survey in 1980 showed a decline of around 14%. Since then numbers have increased in some parts of the county and decreased in others. The current population is thought to number between 7500 and 10,000 nests.

Siskin

With only one confirmed breeding record and two 'probables' during the atlas period, the county population in any one year is probably between nil and three pairs.

Redpoll

The estimated county population is based on one or two pairs per tetrad from which probable and confirmed breeding records were obtained.

––––

Hawfinch

The estimated county breeding population of 43-130 pairs has been derived from an estimate of between one and three pairs in each occupied tetrad.

Reed Bunting

There is a breeding density from Hertfordshire WBS plots of 0.48 to 1.2 pairs per kilometre. To calculate the county population it has been assumed that this applies equally to the banks of open water bodies and an estimate of two pairs per square kilometre of farmland has been used. Applying these densities to the amounts of these habitats in occupied tetrads gives an estimated population of 1100-1500 territories.

Corn Bunting

The results of the 1992 Herts Bird Club Corn Bunting Survey indicate a breeding density of between 0.62 and 1.5 singing males per square kilometre of farmland. Applying this to the total area of farmland in tetrads where the atlas found the species to be probably or definitely breeding gives an estimated population of between 300 and 730 territorial males.

Appendix 3.2: Population trends of Grey Herons and location of heronries in Hertfordshire

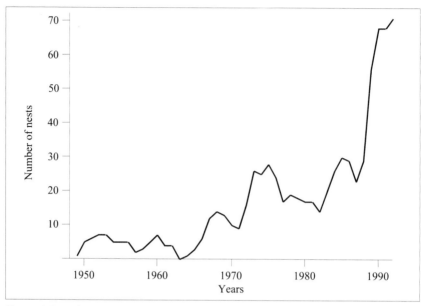

Figure 3.2.1: The number of occupied nests of Grey Heron in Hertfordshire, 1949-92 (Smith 1990).

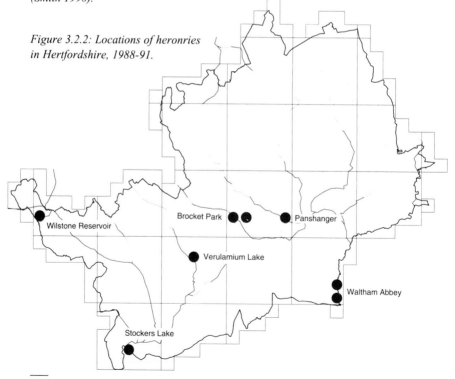

Figure 3.2.2: Locations of heronries in Hertfordshire, 1988-91.

Appendix 5.1: Statistical methods used in the analyses

Most of the statements in this book concerning habitat associations and changes in the numbers of occupied tetrads have been supported by statistical analyses. For simplicity and ease of reading, the details of the methods are not given explicitly in the text. In this appendix the statistical procedures are described.

HABITAT ASSOCIATIONS

The habitat associations in the two atlases have been examined in a number of ways. For each species in each atlas, the simple approach was to divide the tetrads into two groups: those with probable or confirmed breeding records and those with no record or only possible breeding. Mann-Whitney rank tests were then used to compare the median values of each of the land-use and agricultural variables in the two groups of tetrad. A positive association implied that those tetrads with breeding had higher values of the particular variable. A negative association implied the reverse. The results of this analysis are presented in Appendix 5.2 and are referred to throughout the book.

To examine whether changes in the bird distributions between the two atlases could be related in any way to changes in the agricultural variables, two additional analyses were carried out for each species. In the first, two groups of tetrads were selected: those with no breeding record or possible breeding in both atlases and those with no record or possible breeding in the first and probable or confirmed breeding in the second, i.e. the tetrads which had gained the species between the two atlases. Mann-Whitney tests were used to compare the medians of the agricultural variables for these two groups.

The second analysis adopted the same procedure but in this case compared those tetrads which had retained the species with those which had lost it between the two atlases.

CORRELATIONS AMONGST LAND-USE AND AGRICULTURAL VARIABLES

The correlations amongst the land-use and agricultural variables were investigated using Spearman rank correlations. Principal Components Analysis was also used to help simplify the relationships between the land-use and agricultural variables and identify the overall patterns.

CHANGES IN THE NUMBER OF OCCUPIED TETRADS BETWEEN THE TWO ATLASES

The significance of the changes in the numbers of occupied tetrads between the two atlases has been assessed following the procedure described by Buckland *et al* (1990). The ratio of the numbers of tetrads which had gained or lost a particular species between the two atlases was calculated and a binomial test used to assess whether it was significantly different from the 50:50 expected by chance alone.

Appendix 5.2: Habitat associations

This appendix summarises the results of comparisons between the distributions of breeding bird species and land-use or agricultural variables, for the two atlas periods. For each species, the results for the old atlas period are shown above those for the new, with the number of tetrads in which breeding was probable or confirmed. Positive associations (Mann-Whitney rank-sum test) are shown in black and negative associations in red. The following species which had no habitat associations and less than ten tetrads with probable or confirmed breeding have been omitted from the table: Black-necked Grebe, Cormorant, Egyptian Goose, Wood Duck, Honey Buzzard, Buzzard, Golden Pheasant, Spotted Crake, Corncrake, Ring-necked Parakeet, Savi's Warbler, Marsh Warbler, Bearded Tit, Golden Oriole and Red-backed Shrike.

The strength of each association is denoted by the density of the symbol, as follows:

Positive associations: ● $p < 0.001$ ◉ $p < 0.01$ ○ $p < 0.05$
Negative associations: ● $p < 0.001$ ◉ $p < 0.01$ ○ $p < 0.05$

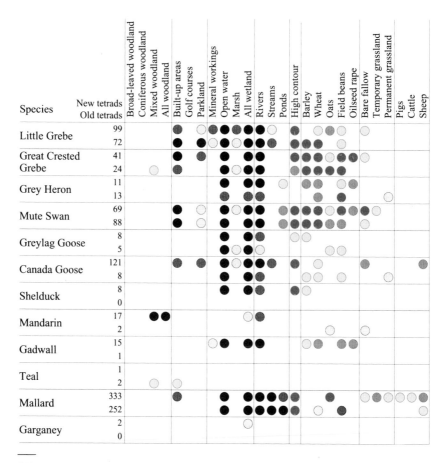

Species	New tetrads / Old tetrads
Little Grebe	99 / 72
Great Crested Grebe	41 / 24
Grey Heron	11 / 13
Mute Swan	69 / 88
Greylag Goose	8 / 5
Canada Goose	121 / 8
Shelduck	8 / 0
Mandarin	17 / 2
Gadwall	15 / 1
Teal	1 / 2
Mallard	333 / 252
Garganey	2 / 0

Species	New tetrads / Old tetrads	Broad-leaved woodland	Coniferous woodland	Mixed woodland	All woodland	Built-up areas	Golf courses	Parkland	Mineral workings	Open water	Marsh	All wetland	Rivers	Streams	Ponds	High contour	Barley	Wheat	Oats	Field beans	Oilseed rape	Bare fallow	Temporary grassland	Permanent grassland	Pigs	Cattle	Sheep
Shoveler	10					●				●		●	●			●	○	○		◐	◐						○
	3									●	●	●													○		
Pochard	10									●		●	●		○		○	○		○	◐						
	14					○				●		●					○	○									
Tufted Duck	78					●		◐	○	●	●	●	●	○	○	●	◐	○			○		○	◐			
	31					●		○		●	●	●		○	◐	●	●	●	○	●			◐				
Ruddy Duck	10									●		●	●				◐	●	○	●	●	○					
	1																										
Sparrowhawk	207	●	○		●											○	○		◐		○						◐
	13	○		●	●																						
Kestrel	300							●		○		●	●			◐	○	◐									
	179			○						◐		●	○			●	◐	●		●			◐			○	
Hobby	49		○	●	◐		●			○		●											○	◐		○	
	13	●	●		●													◐								○	
Chukar	2																○	○									
	0																										
Red-legged Partridge	289	○		○	◐	●				○						●	●	●	○	●	●		◐				
	241	○					○							●		●	●	●	●	◐	◐						
Grey Partridge	178					◐										●	●	●	○								
	291	○	○													●	●	●	●				●			○	
Quail	19					◐	◐							◐	●	●	○										
	24					◐	○							●										○			
Pheasant	383	●	○		●											●	●	●	●	●	●	○	◐	●	●	●	●
	375	●	○	◐	●	◐		○	○				○			●	●	●	●	●	●		●	◐		●	●
Lady Amherst's Pheasant	1																										
	3		○	○												●		○									
Water Rail	8						○			●		●	○				○			○	○						
	22						○			●	○	●	●		○	◐	○		○	●							
Moorhen	359									●	●	●	●	●	●	◐		○									○
	345	○								●	●	●	●	●	●			●					○	○			
Coot	137					●		●	●	●	●	●	●	●		●	◐	●	●	●	●						○
	97					○		●	●	●	●	●	●	●		●	●	●	◐		○		○				
Stone Curlew	0																										
	10					○										◐	●	●	●				○			○	○
Little Ringed Plover	33					●			●	●	○	●	●			●	●	●	○	●	●						○
	25								●	●		●	●			●	●	●		○				●			
Ringed Plover	12						○		●	●		●	●			●	●	●	●	○	○						
	2							○			○	○	○			○											
Lapwing	208	●				◐						○	○				○			○			●	●		○	
	230					○											●		◐			●	●	●		●	○
Snipe	16									○	●	●	◐	●		●											
	34						○			○	◐	●	●	●	●	●											
Woodcock	50	●	○	●	●	◐							○	●												○	
	80	●	●	●	●	○								●		○		○								○	
Curlew	0																							○			
	3																							○			
Redshank	17						○			●	●		●	●		◐	○	○		◐	◐						
	18					●				○	●		●	●	○	●	○	◐	○	○							

Species	New tetrads / Old tetrads
Common Sandpiper	1 / 3
Common Tern	9 / 4
Feral Pigeon	190 / 0
Stock Dove	308 / 241
Woodpigeon	476 / 454
Collared Dove	431 / 184
Turtle Dove	273 / 364
Cuckoo	401 / 298
Barn Owl	23 / 65
Little Owl	180 / 189
Tawny Owl	270 / 268
Long-eared Owl	9 / 24
Nightjar	2 / 24
Swift	216 / 225
Kingfisher	81 / 62
Wryneck	0 / 2
Green Woodpecker	225 / 136
Great Spotted Woodpecker	318 / 158
Lesser Spotted Woodpecker	112 / 76
Woodlark	0 / 7
Skylark	463 / 452
Sand Martin	22 / 60
Swallow	417 / 451
House Martin	391 / 393

Column headings (habitat/land-use categories, read left to right):
Broad-leaved woodland, Coniferous woodland, Mixed woodland, All woodland, Built-up areas, Golf courses, Parkland, Mineral workings, Open water, Marsh, All wetland, Rivers, Streams, Ponds, High contour, Barley, Wheat, Oats, Field beans, Oilseed rape, Bare fallow, Temporary grassland, Permanent grassland, Pigs, Cattle, Sheep

Species	New tetrads / Old tetrads	Broad-leaved woodland	Coniferous woodland	Mixed woodland	All woodland	Built-up areas	Golf courses	Parkland	Mineral workings	Open water	Marsh	All wetland	Rivers	Streams	Ponds	High contour	Barley	Wheat	Oats	Field beans	Oilseed rape	Bare fallow	Temporary grassland	Permanent grassland	Pigs	Cattle	Sheep
Tree Pipit	52	●	●	●	●	●									●		○	○								●	
	127	●	●	●	●		○				○	○	○	●	●		●	●		●			●				
Meadow Pipit	61	●		●							●	●		●								●	○		●		
	69				○		○				●											●	○		●		
Yellow Wagtail	83	●	●		●	●				●		●	●		●	●											
	47	○			○					●		●	●		○	○	○	○	○	●			●			●	○
Grey Wagtail	85					●		●	○	●	○	●	●	●	●	●	●	●	●	●	○						
	47									●		●	●		○	○	○	○	○	○							
Pied Wagtail	300				●	●			●		●	●	●	●	○	●	●	●	●	●			●				●
	228		○		●	●	●		●		●	●	●			●	●		○	○							
Wren	490																										
	460																										
Dunnock	486																										
	455	●			●						●				○	○								○			
Robin	490																										
	472	○		○	○		○										●	●									
Nightingale	24	●		○														○									
	83	●	○	●	●																						
Black Redstart	1																										
	5				○						○																
Redstart	6	○		●	●	●									●												
	29			○	●	○											○	○						○		○	
Whinchat	2				○																						
	23										○	●		○	●	○	○	○					○				
Stonechat	1																										
	3																						○				
Wheatear	0																										
	2																										
Blackbird	491																										
	496																							○			
Song Thrush	490																										
	494				○																						
Mistle Thrush	405	○	●	●	●	●						●	●		●	●		●	●	●	○		●				●
	347	●	●	●	●	○						●	○		●	●		●		●			●	●	●	●	
Cetti's Warbler	2						○		○	○			○														
	0																										
Grasshopper Warbler	41							○		●	○						●		○	○	○						
	125	●		●	●								○					○		○				○		○	
Sedge Warbler	150	○		●	●	●			○	●	●	●	●	●	●								○				
	183				○				○	●	○	●	●	●	●												
Reed Warbler	73			○	●		○		●	●	●	●	●		●	●	●	●	●	●	●	○					
	60				●				●	●	○	●	●		●	●	○		○								
Lesser Whitethroat	334				○																			○			
	208	●		●																				○			
Whitethroat	442				●												●	●	○	●							
	413	●		●														●	○				○	●		○	
Garden Warbler	346	●	●	●	●																						
	239	●	○	●	●								●		○		●		●				●		○		

Column headers (left to right):

Species | New tetrads / Old tetrads | Broad-leaved woodland | Coniferous woodland | Mixed woodland | All woodland | Built-up areas | Golf courses | Parkland | Mineral workings | Open water | Marsh | All wetland | Rivers | Streams | Ponds | High contour | Barley | Wheat | Oats | Field beans | Oilseed rape | Bare fallow | Temporary grassland | Permanent grassland | Pigs | Cattle | Sheep

Species	New tetrads	Old tetrads
Blackcap	481	389
Wood Warbler	25	38
Chiffchaff	462	400
Willow Warbler	482	436
Goldcrest	308	207
Firecrest	8	2
Spotted Flycatcher	295	334
Pied Flycatcher	4	0
Long-tailed Tit	399	264
Marsh Tit	156	152
Willow Tit	149	227
Coal Tit	300	239
Blue Tit	486	465
Great Tit	483	447
Nuthatch	273	155
Treecreeper	280	225
Jay	211	225
Magpie	436	272
Jackdaw	276	296
Rook	229	318
Carrion Crow	376	375
Starling	488	480
House Sparrow	477	478
Tree Sparrow	114	372

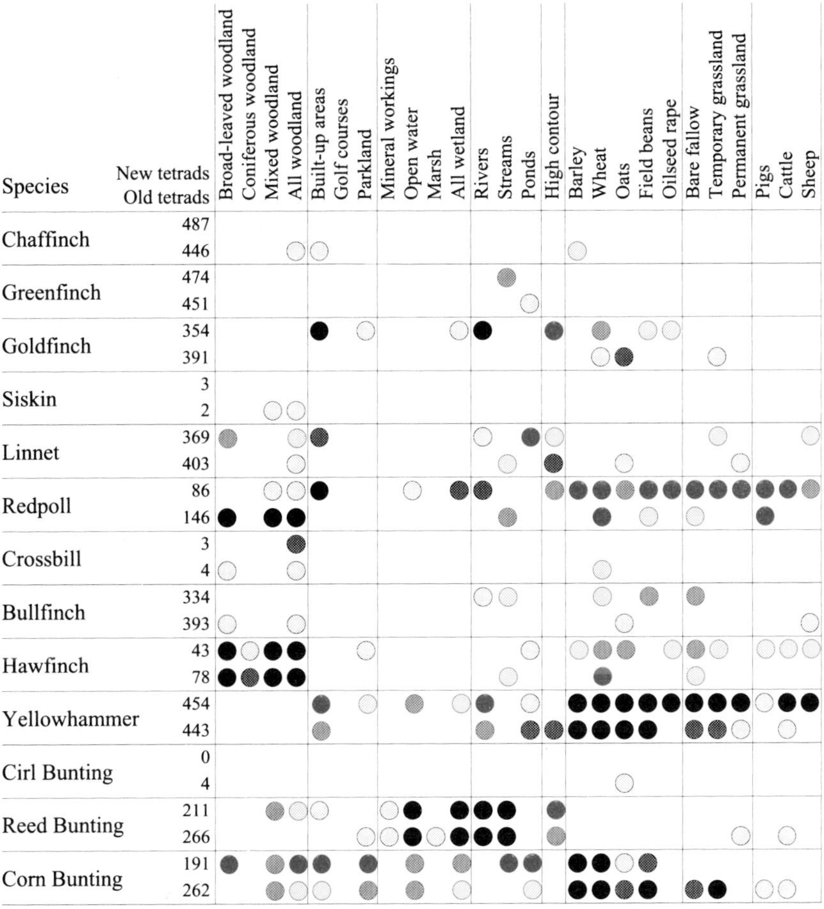

Species	New tetrads	Old tetrads
Chaffinch	487	446
Greenfinch	474	451
Goldfinch	354	391
Siskin	3	2
Linnet	369	403
Redpoll	86	146
Crossbill	3	4
Bullfinch	334	393
Hawfinch	43	78
Yellowhammer	454	443
Cirl Bunting	0	4
Reed Bunting	211	266
Corn Bunting	191	262

Habitat/feature columns (column headers across the top of the chart):

Broad-leaved woodland · Coniferous woodland · Mixed woodland · All woodland · Built-up areas · Golf courses · Parkland · Mineral workings · Open water · Marsh · All wetland · Rivers · Streams · Ponds · High contour · Barley · Wheat · Oats · Field beans · Oilseed rape · Bare fallow · Temporary grassland · Permanent grassland · Pigs · Cattle · Sheep

References

The following texts have been used extensively in the preparation of this book and to aid clarity are not referred to in the text:

CRAMP S & SIMMONS K E L (eds). 1977-82. *The Birds of the Western Palearctic* Volumes I-III. Oxford University Press, Oxford.

CRAMP S (ed). 1985-92. *The Birds of the Western Palearctic* Volumes IV-VI. Oxford University Press, Oxford.

CRAMP S & PERRINS C M (eds). 1993. *The Birds of the Western Palearctic* Volume VII. Oxford University Press, Oxford.

GLADWIN T W & SAGE B L. 1986. *The Birds of Hertfordshire.* Castlemead, Ware.

LACK P C. 1986. *The Atlas of Wintering Birds in Britain and Ireland.* T & A D Poyser, Calton.

MARCHANT J H, HUDSON R, CARTER S P & WHITTINGTON P. 1990. *Population Trends in British Breeding Birds.* British Trust for Ornithology, Tring.

MEAD C J & SMITH K W. 1982. *The Hertfordshire Breeding Bird Atlas.* HBBA, Tring.

SAGE B L. 1959. *A History of the Birds of Hertfordshire.* Barrie & Rockliffe, London.

SHARROCK J T R. 1976. *The Atlas of Breeding Birds in Britain and Ireland.* British Trust for Ornithology, Tring.

In addition the Hertfordshire Bird reports, published as part of the Transactions of the Hertfordshire Natural History Society, have been used extensively.

BAILLIE S R. 1990. Integrated population monitoring of breeding birds in Britain and Ireland. *Ibis* 132:151-166.

BAILLIE S R & PEACH W J. 1992. Population limitations in Palearctic-African migrant passerines. *Ibis* 134 supp 1:120-132.

BATTEN L A, BIBBY C J, CLEMENT P, ELLIOTT G D & PORTER R F (eds). 1990. *Red Data birds in Britain.* T & A D Poyser, London.

BEINTEMA A J, BEINTEMA-HIETBRINK R J & MUSKENS C J D M. 1985. A shift in the timing of breeding in meadow birds. *Ardea* 73:83-89.

BEINTEMA A J, THISSEN J B, TENSON D & VISSER G H. 1991. Feeding ecology of charadriiform chicks in agricultural grassland. *Ardea* 79:31-44.

BIBBY C J. 1989. A survey of breeding Wood Warblers *Phylloscopus sibilatrix*, 1984-85. *Bird Study* 36:56-72.

BIRKHEAD T R. 1991. *The Magpies.* T & A D Poyser, London.

BRENCHLEY A. 1984. The use of birds as indicators of change in agriculture. In JENKINS D (ed), *Agriculture and the Environment, ITE symposium* 13:123-128. Cambridge.

BROOKE M DE-L & DAVIES N B. 1987. Recent changes in host usage by Cuckoos *Cuculus canorus* in Britain. *J Animal Ecology* 56:873-883.

BUCKLAND S T, BELL M V & PICOZZI N. 1990. *The Birds of North-East Scotland.* North-East Scotland Bird Club, Aberdeen.

CAMBELL B & FERGUSON-LEES J. 1972. *A Field Guide to Birds' Nests.* Constable, London.

CROSSMAN A F. 1902. Birds in the *Victoria History of Hertfordshire.*

DALTON S. 1989. Blue Tit nesting in old Blackbird's nest. *British Birds* 82:80.

DAVIES A K. 1985. The British Mandarins – outstripping their ancestors. *BTO News* 136:12.

DAVIES A K. 1988. The distribution and status of the Mandarin Duck *Aix galericulata* in Britain. *Bird Study* 35:203-208.

DAVIES A K & BAGGOTT G K. 1989. Clutch size and nesting sites of the Mandarin Duck *Aix galericulata. Bird Study* 36:32-36.

DAVIES A K & BAGGOTT G K. 1989. Egg-laying, incubation and intraspecific nest parasitism by the Mandarin Duck *Aix galericulata. Bird Study* 36:115-122.

DAVIES A K. 1990. Jackdaw hatching Mandarin eggs. *British Birds* 83: 209.

DAVIES N B. 1987. Studies of West Palearctic birds: 188, Dunnock. *British Birds* 80:604-624.

DAVIS P G. 1982. Nightingales in Britain in 1980. *Bird Study* 29:73-79.

DELANEY S. 1992. *Pilot survey of breeding Shelduck in Great Britain and Northern Ireland 1990-91.* Wildfowl and Wetlands Trust, Slimbridge.

DELANEY S. 1992. Survey of introduced geese in Britain, summer 1991, provisional results. *Report to the Joint Nature Conservation Committee, MAFF & National Trust.* Wildfowl and Wetlands Trust, Slimbridge.

DELANEY S, GREENWOOD J J D & HARLEY J. 1992. National Mute Swan Survey 1990, *Report to the Joint Nature Conservation Committee.* Wildfowl and Wetlands Trust, Slimbridge.

DOCKERTY T L (in prep). An evaluation of Barn Owl re-introductions in Hertfordshire.

ELLIOTT G D & AVERY M I. 1991. A review of reports of Buzzard persecution 1975-89. *Bird Study* 38:52-56.

ELTON G. 1992. Black-necked Grebes at Hilfield Park Reservoir. *Trans Herts NHS* 31:141.

EVANS A D. 1992. Cirl Buntings in Britain in 1989. *Bird Study* 39:17-22.

FEARE C. 1984. *The Starling.* Oxford University Press, Oxford.

FERGUSON-LEES J, WILLIS I & SHARROCK J T R. 1983. *The Shell Guide to the Birds of Britain and Ireland.* Michael Joseph, London.

FLEGG J J M & BENNETT T J. 1974. The birds of oak woodlands. In MORRIS M G & PERRING F H (eds), *The British Oak* 324-340. Faringdon.

FOX A D. 1988. Breeding status of the Gadwall in Britain and Ireland. *British Birds* 81:51-66.

FOX A D. 1991. History of the Pochard breeding in Britain. *British Birds* 84:83-98.

FULLER R J & HENDERSON A C B. 1992. Distribution of breeding songbirds in Bradfield Woods, Suffolk, in relation to vegetation and coppice management. *Bird Study* 39:73-88.

FULLER R J & MORETON B D. 1987. Breeding bird populations of Kentish sweet chestnut *Castanea sativa* coppice in relation to age and structure of the coppice. *J Applied Ecology* 24:13-27.

GALBRAITH H. 1988. The breeding ecology of Lapwings *Vanellus vanellus* on Scottish agricultural land. *J Applied Ecology* 25: 487-504.

GARCIA E F J. 1983. An experimental test of competition for space between Blackcaps *Sylvia atricapilla* and Garden Warblers *Sylvia borin* in the breeding season. *J Animal Ecology* 52:795-805.

GATES S, GIBBONS D W & MARCHANT J H. 1993. Population Estimates for Breeding Birds in Britain and Ireland in GIBBONS D W, REID J B & CHAPMAN R A, *The New Atlas of Breeding Birds in Britain and Ireland:1988-1991.* T & A D Poyser, London.

GILES N. 1992. *Wildlife after gravel: twenty years of practical research by the Game Conservancy and ARC.* Game Conservancy, Fordingbridge.

GLADWIN T W. 1983. Major changes in central Hertfordshire breeding bird populations. *Trans Herts NHS* 29:57-67.

GLEN N W & PERRINS C M. 1988. Co-operative breeding by Long-tailed Tits. *British Birds* 81:630-641.

GOOCH S, BAILLIE S R & BIRKHEAD T R. 1991. Magpies *Pica pica* and songbird populations. Retrospective investigation of trends in population density and breeding success. *J Applied Ecology* 28:1068-1086.

GOODWIN D. 1984. Bird artists, woodpeckers and pigeons. *British Birds* 77:326-327.

GREEN R E. 1985. Estimating the abundance of breeding Snipe. *Bird Study* 32:141-149.

GREEN R E. 1988a. Effects of environmental factors on the timing and success of breeding of Common Snipe *Gallinago gallinago* (Aves: Scolopacidae). *J Applied Ecology* 25:79-93.

GREEN R E. 1988b. Stone Curlew conservation. *RSPB Conservation Review* 2:30-33.

HARDING B D. 1979. *Bedfordshire Bird Atlas.* Bedfordshire NHS.

HARRIS A. 1987. A review of the Common Tern colony at Rye Meads. *Trans Herts NHS* 30:56-59.

HARRISON C. 1975. *A Field Guide to the Nests, Eggs and Nestlings of British and European Birds.* Collins, London.

HARRISSON T H & HOLLOM P A D. 1932. The Great Crested Grebe enquiry, 1931. *British Birds* 26: 62-92, 102-131, 142-155, 174-195.

HASTINGS R. 1988. The Feral Rock Dove. *British Birds* 81:652.

HERTFORDSHIRE ENVIRONMENTAL FORUM. 1992. *A Report on the State of Hertfordshire's Environment.* Hertfordshire Environmental Forum.

HICKLING R (ed). 1983. *Enjoying Ornithology.* T & A D Poyser, Calton.

HIRONS G. 1980. The significance of roding by Woodcocks *Scolopax rusticola*: an alternative explanation based on observations of marked birds. *Ibis* 122:350-354.

HIRONS G. 1982. Conclusion of the studies on Woodcock. *Game Conservancy Annual Review* 13: 35-42.

HOLLAND P, SPENCE I & SUTTON T. 1984. *Breeding Birds in Greater Manchester.* Manchester Orn. Soc, Manchester.

HUDSON A V, STOWE T J & ASPINALL S J. 1990. Status and distribution of Corncrakes in Britain in 1988. *British Birds* 83:173-186.

HUDSON R & MARCHANT J H. 1984. Population estimates of British Breeding Birds. *BTO Research Report* 13.

HUGHES S W M, BACON P & FLEGG J J M. 1979. The 1975 census of the Great Crested Grebe in Britain. *Bird Study* 26:213-226.

JAMES T J. 1981. The distribution and ecology of the Wood Warbler in Hertfordshire. *Trans Herts NHS* 28:24-29.

JOYCE B. 1987. Hedgerow change and management. A study of hedgerow change and management in North Hertfordshire & West Oxfordshire. Unpublished RSPB report.

KELSEY M G, GREEN G H, GARNETT M C & HAYMAN P V. 1989. Marsh Warblers in Britain. *British Birds* 82: 239-256.

LACK P. 1992. *Birds on Lowland Farms.* HMSO, London.

LEADER P & MELLING J. 1989. The breeding population of Tree Sparrows at Rye Meads. *Rye Meads Ringing Group 11th Report*:56-58.

LONDON NATURAL HISTORY SOCIETY. 1992. *London Bird Report for 1991.* LBR 1991:82-83.

MADGE S & BURN H. 1988. *Wildfowl, an identification guide to the ducks, geese and swans of the world.* Helm, London.

MARCHANT J H & HYDE P A. 1980. Population changes for waterways birds 1978-9. *Bird Study* 27:179-182.

MASON C F. 1976. Breeding biology of the *Sylvia* warblers. *Bird Study* 23:213-232.

MCNEIL D A C. 1992. Use of House Martin nests by Blue Tits for breeding. *British Birds* 85:314-315.

MEAD C J. 1984. Sand Martins slump. *BTO News* 133:1.

MIKKOLA H. 1983. *Owls of Europe.* T & A D Poyser, Calton.

MØLLER A P. 1989. Population dynamics of a declining Swallow *Hirundo rustica* population. *J Animal Ecology* 58:1051-1063.

MONTIER D J (ed). 1977. *Atlas of the Breeding Birds of the London Area.* Batsford, London.

MORGAN R A & GLUE D E. 1981. Breeding survey of Black Redstarts in Britain 1977. *Bird Study* 28:163-168.

MOREAU R E. 1951. The British status of the Quail and some problems of its biology. *British Birds* 44:257-276.

MORRIS F O. 1863. *A History of British Birds.* Groomebridge, London.

MOUNTFORT G. 1957. *The Hawfinch.* Collins, London.

MURTON R K, WESTWOOD N J & ISAACSON A J. 1964. The feeding habits of Woodpigeon *Columba palumbus*, Stock Dove *C. oenas* & Turtle Dove *Streptopelia turtur. Ibis* 106:174-188.

NEWTON I. 1972. *Finches.* Collins, London.

NEWTON I & BOGAN J. 1978. The role of different organochlorine compounds in the breeding of British Sparrowhawks. *J Applied Ecology* 15:105-116.

NEWTON I. 1986. *The Sparrowhawk*. T & A D Poyser, Calton.

NEWTON I, WYLLIE I & ASHER A. 1991. Mortality causes in British Barn Owls *Tyto alba*, with a discussion of aldrin-dieldrin poisoning. *Ibis* 133:162-169.

NIGHTINGALE B & ALLSOPP K. 1991. Seasonal reports – winter 1990/91. *British Birds* 84:316-328.

O'BRIEN M & SMITH K W. 1992. Changes in the status of waders breeding on wet lowland grasslands in England and Wales between 1982 and 1989. *Bird Study* 39:165-176.

O'CONNOR R J & PEARMAN D N. 1987. Long term trends in breeding success of some British Birds. *BTO Research report* 23.

O'CONNOR R J & MEAD C J. 1984. The Stock Dove in Britain 1930-80. *British Birds* 77:181-201.

O'CONNOR R J & SHRUBB M. 1986. *Farming and Birds*. Cambridge University Press, Cambridge.

OSBORNE P. 1983. The influence of Dutch elm disease on bird population trends. *Bird Study* 30:27-38.

OWEN M, ATKINSON-WILLES G L & SALMON D G. 1986. *Wildfowl in Great Britain*. Cambridge University Press, Cambridge.

PARR S J. 1985. The breeding ecology and diet of the Hobby *Falco subbuteo* in southern England. *Ibis* 127:60-73.

PARSLOW J L F. 1973. *Breeding birds of Britain and Ireland*. T & A D Poyser, Berkhamsted.

PEACH W J, BAILLIE S R & UNDERHILL L. 1991. Survival of British Sedge Warblers *Acrocephalus schoenobaenus* in relation to West African rainfall. *Ibis* 133:300-305.

PERRINS C M. 1979. *British Tits*. Collins, London.

POTTS G R. 1986. *The Partridge*. Collins, London.

POTTS G R. 1989. The impact of releasing hybrid partridges on wild Red-legged populations. *The Game Conservancy Review*, 1988:81-85.

RAVEN P. 1986. Changes in the breeding bird population of a small clay river following flood alleviation works. *Bird Study* 33:24-35.

SAGE B L & WHITTINGTON P A. 1985. The 1980 sample survey of rookeries. *Bird Study* 32:77-81.

SAWFORD B R. 1981. 1980 Nightingale survey: Hertfordshire results. *Trans Herts NHS* 28:30-32.

SHARROCK J T R. 1984. European News. *British Birds* 77:586-592.

SHARROCK J T R. 1985. European News. *British Birds* 78:638-645.

SHARROCK J T R. 1989. European News. *British Birds* 82:14-25.

SHARROCK J T R and the Rare Breeding Birds Panel. 1982. Rare breeding birds in the United Kingdom in 1980. *British Birds* 75:154-178.

SHAWYER C R. 1987. *The Barn Owl in the British Isles: its past, present and future*. The Hawk and Owl Trust, London.

SHRUBB M. 1990. Effects of agricultural change on nesting Lapwings *Vanellus vanellus* in England and Wales. *Bird Study* 37:115-128.

SHRUBB M & LACK P C. 1991. The numbers and distribution of Lapwings *Vanellus vanellus* nesting in England and Wales in 1987. *Bird Study* 38:20-37.

SIMMS E. 1971. *Woodland Birds*. Collins, London.

SIMMS E. 1985. *The British Warblers*. Collins, London.

SITTERS H P. 1982. The decline of the Cirl Bunting in Britain 1968-80. *British Birds* 75:105-108.

SITTERS H P. 1985. Cirl Buntings in Britain in 1982. *Bird Study* 32:1-10.

SITTERS H P. 1986. Woodlarks in Britain 1968-83. *British Birds* 79:105-116.

SITTERS H P (ed). 1988. *Tetrad Atlas of the Breeding Birds of Devon*. Devon Birdwatching and Preservation Society, Yelverton.

SMALLSHIRE D. 1986. The frequency of hybrid ducks in the Midlands. *British Birds* 79:87-89.

SMITH K W. 1983. The status of the Nightjar in Hertfordshire. *Trans Herts NHS* 29:68-70.

SMITH K W. 1984. Breeding waders in Hertfordshire. *Trans Herts NHS* 29:33-36.

SMITH K W. 1987. Ecology of the Great Spotted Woodpecker. *RSPB Conservation Review* 1:74-77.

SMITH K W. 1988. Breeding Lapwing survey 1987. *Trans Herts NHS* 30:131-133.

SMITH K W, BURGES D J & PARKS R A. 1992. Breeding bird communities of broad-leaved plantation and ancient pasture woodlands in the New Forest. *Bird Study* 39:132-141.

SMITH K W, WALDEN J & WILLIAMS G. 1992. Action for Cirl Buntings. *RSPB Conservation Review* 6:40-44.

SMITH L M. 1990. A century of breeding Grey Herons in Hertfordshire. *Trans Herts NHS* 30:404-407.

SNOW B & SNOW D. 1988. *Birds and Berries.* T & A D Poyser, Calton.

SOOTHILL E & WHITEHEAD P. 1978. *Wildfowl of the world.* Blandford, London.

SPENCER R and the Rare Breeding Birds Panel. 1993. Rare breeding birds in the United Kingdom in 1990. *British Birds* 86:62-90.

STOWE T J. 1987. Management of sessile oakwoods for Pied Flycatchers. *RSPB Conservation Review* 1:78-83.

STROUD D A & GLUE D. 1991. *Britain's Birds in 1989/90: the conservation and monitoring review.* BTO/NCC, Thetford.

STUDDARD P & WILLIAMSON K. 1971. Habitat requirements of the Nightingale. *Bird Study* 18:9-14.

SUMMERS-SMITH J D. 1988. *The Sparrows.* T & A D Poyser, Calton.

SUMMERS-SMITH J D. 1989. A History of the status of the Tree Sparrow *Passer montanus* in the British Isles. *Bird Study* 36:23-31.

TAGGART B. 1991. Mute Swan census 1990. *Trans Herts NHS* 31:146-148.

TAYLOR D W, DAVENPORT D L & FLEGG J J M (ed). 1981. *The Birds of Kent.* The Kent Ornithological Society, Meopham.

TERRY J H. 1986. Corn Buntings in Hertfordshire. *Trans Herts NHS* 29:303-312.

THOM V M. 1986. *Birds in Scotland.* T & A D Poyser, Calton.

THOMAS G J, UNDERWOOD L A & PARTRIDGE J K. 1990. Breeding terns in Britain and Ireland 1980-84. *Seabird* 12:20-31.

THOMPSON D B A & GRIBBIN S. 1986. Ecology of Corn Buntings in north west England. *Bull. Brit. Ecological Society* 17:69-75.

TURNER A K. 1991. Studies of West Palearctic Birds 190: Swallow. *British Birds* 84:555-569.

VILLAGE A. 1990. *The Kestrel.* T & A D Poyser, London.

WILLIAMSON K & BATTEN L A. 1977. Ecological implications of the Common Bird Census. *Pol. Ecol. Stud.* 3:237-244.

WHITE G J. 1987. Breeding Sand Martins in Hertfordshire. *Trans Herts NHS* 30:50-53.

WILSON A D. 1992. Status of Canada and other introduced goose species in Hertfordshire. *Trans Herts NHS* 31:290-297.

WINSTANLEY D, SPENCER R & WILLIAMSON K. 1974. Where have all the Whitethroats gone? *Bird Study* 21:1-14.

Index